Megalithic Science

Douglas C. Heggie

Megalithic Science

ANCIENT MATHEMATICS AND ASTRONOMY
IN NORTH-WEST EUROPE

with 114 illustrations

Thames and Hudson

For Linda

© 1981 Thames and Hudson Ltd, London

First published in the USA in 1981
by Thames and Hudson, Inc.,
500 Fifth Avenue, New York, New York 10110

Library of Congress Catalog Card Number 80—53167

Printed and bound in Hungary

Contents

Preface and acknowledgments

Anyone with a claim to be regarded as a professional scientist risks considerable unpopularity if he comes to the conclusion that the evidence for some well-known theory is not quite as strong as it seems at first sight. Indeed I fear that some readers may look upon this book as an attempt to 'debunk' the theories of megalithic science. In truth, it has been my intention to give an assessment of these theories which I thought I could defend, and if the result seems more cautious than other published accounts, it should also be said that there are many critics whose attitude is much less sympathetic than mine.

Nevertheless, one of the curious features of megalithic science is the fact that different people can come to widely differing conclusions on the basis of the same body of evidence. In many cases, these differences seem to arise because of the widely differing backgrounds of those who have written on the subject. For this reason, I describe in the second chapter my particular attitude to evidence, and to the inferences we may allowably make from it. If a reader finds that he disagrees with much of what is written later in the book, the source of the disagreement may well lie here.

Like all other writers on this subject, in arriving at my opinions I have been influenced by many factors. In particular, since my interest in megalithic science was first aroused by a BBC television programme in 1970, my views have evolved considerably as a result of conversations or correspondence with many people, among whom I would particularly like to mention and thank I. O. Angell, J. W. Barber, H. A. W. Burl, C. J. Butler, P. R. Freeman, E. Hadingham, T. McCreery, E. W. MacKie, G. Moir, J. D. Patrick, C. L. N. Ruggles and A. Thom. They have also frequently sent me drafts, preprints and reprints of articles and papers, which have been very useful. I am also grateful to members of my family and several friends who have accompanied me in the wilds to visit megalithic sites.

It was G. E. Daniel who first made the suggestion that a book on megalithic science might be of interest, and I am very grateful to him and the staff of Thames and Hudson for giving me the initial push in the right direction, and for subsequently keeping me on course.

It is a pleasure also to thank I. O. Angell, J. A. Cooke, G. E. Daniel, M. G. Edmunds, P. R. Freeman, J. G. Morgan and the editors at Thames and Hudson, who between them have read the entire book and made a great many important suggestions. However, no blame of any kind attaches to them for any mistakes which it may contain. Errors are particularly regrettable in anything which claims to be a work of criticism, but I shall be glad to hear about any that readers detect.

Where an illustration has been copied from another publication, a reference to the source will be found in the caption. Other photographs and drawings are my own. For permission to reproduce certain illustrations, I should like to thank several individuals, namely I. O. Angell, M. E. Bailey, J. W. Barber, J. A. Cooke, T. M. Cowan, H. E. Edgerton, R. Freer, D. G. Kendall, E. W. MacKie, J. G. Morgan, R. Müller, H. C. and M. J. O'Kelly, J. D. Patrick, J.-L. Quinio, A. E. Roy, D. A. Tait, A. Thom and J. E. Wood. Many of these have put themselves to much trouble in supplying me with copies of illustrations, for which I am most grateful, and I should also like to thank M. A. Hoskin in this respect.

The following organizations and periodicals have kindly given permission for illustrations to be reproduced: the Ancient Monuments Society, the British Astronomical Association, the Department of the Environment, the Devonshire Association, Doubleday and Co., Glasgow Archaeological Society, the Institute for the Comparative Study of History, Philosophy and the Sciences, the Mathematical Association, *Nature*, Oxford University Press, Pergamon Press, the Royal Anthropological Institute of Great Britain and Ireland, the Royal Society, the Royal Statistical Society, *Science*, Secker and Warburg, Souvenir Press, Springer Verlag, and University of Chicago Press.

My last acknowledgments go to my mother, who has uncomplainingly accepted almost the entire burden of typing and retyping, and to my wife. Writing a book in one's spare time imposes many constraints and she has borne them all cheerfully and patiently.

1 The Stonehenge controversy

> In 1655 there was published by Mr Web a Booke inti-
> tuled Stonehenge-restored (but writt by Mr Inigo Jones)
> which I read with great delight. There is a great deale
> of Learning in it: but having compared his Scheme
> with the Monument, it self, I found he had not dealt
> fairly: but had made a Lesbian's rule, which is con-
> formed to the stone; that is, he framed the monument
> to his own Hypothesis, which is much differing from
> the Thing it self. This gave me an edge to make more
> researches. . . .[1]

The interest of these words lies not so much in the theory that their
writer, John Aubrey, was attacking, but in the strange familiarity they
have for modern ears. Today, about three hundred years later, Stonehenge again lies near the centre of controversy, which this time concerns
its purpose. The origins of this new controversy go back almost to the
time of Aubrey, in fact to a book published in 1740 by Dr William
Stukeley, who noted the fact that 'the principal line of the whole work
[points to] the northeast, where abouts the sun rises, when the days are
longest.'[2] In other words, Stukeley's discovery was that Stonehenge
points to the place where the sun comes over the horizon at the summer
solstice, about 21 June.

    The solstitial orientation of Stonehenge is almost certainly the best-
known single fact about megalithic astronomy, which concerns the idea
that many sites more or less like Stonehenge are deliberately orientated
towards the places where the sun, moon or stars rise or set. Even at
Stonehenge, the facts are not confined to the single orientation which
Stukeley noted, for others were discovered in the ensuing decades.

    One of the most famous authorities to take up these questions was
the astrophysicist Sir Norman Lockyer. He had spent some years in
discussing the orientation of temples in Egypt and Greece, and by the
beginning of the present century, when he was already in his sixties,
he had turned his attention to Stonehenge. Lockyer's view was that
Stonehenge had been a solar temple, and that its astronomical orientation
had served a mainly ritual purpose. This view, which he developed much
further in relation to other megalithic sites in Britain, achieved some
currency, at least among non-archaeologists. However, the history of
Stonehenge astronomy went through its most explosive stage much more

71, 102

recently. Besides making meticulous measurements of its axis, Lockyer had noted a few other features of the monument which lined up with the position of sunrise or sunset at other times of the year, but in the early 1960s the number of astronomically significant lines claimed for Stonehenge leapt to two or three dozen. The theory of astronomical 'alignments' was also complemented by a different sort of theory for the purpose of Stonehenge: it was claimed that the monument may have been used as a device for predicting eclipses of the sun and moon.

These and other claims were made by Gerald S. Hawkins, who again is an astronomer, and they quickly aroused enormous interest. Indeed it seems likely that much of the existing interest in megalithic astronomy was originally inspired by the popular and absorbing book, *Stonehenge Decoded* (1966), which Hawkins wrote (with J. B. White) around the discoveries that he had earlier reported. The tone of the book was confident. 'There can be no doubt that Stonehenge was an observatory,' was how Hawkins came to summarize his conclusion.[3] And the amateur astronomer C. A. Newham, who had independently made quite a few significant discoveries along similar lines, had 'little doubt' about this.[4]

Among scientists, the new theories of megalithic astronomy became a novel and exciting issue for informal debate, as they have remained. One of the reasons for this is that the concepts involved are relatively easy to understand, especially for astronomers, and it is not hard for almost anyone to contribute a useful idea to the debate. Some scientists were sceptical and continue to be. On the other hand, some of those who more or less agreed with Hawkins even elaborated the ideas that he had put forward. The most significant and readable of these scientists was the distinguished and controversial British astronomer Fred Hoyle, whose opinion could hardly be ignored.

Though provocation was presumably not his intention, Hawkins assessed his claims by saying 'I think I have put forward the best theory to account for the otherwise unexplained holes...'[5] The archaeologists responded well to the challenge, but it seems that the tone and manner of Hawkins' claims made some archaeologists less receptive than they might otherwise have been. Professor R. J. C. Atkinson, of University College, Cardiff, considered Hawkins' book 'tendentious, arrogant, slipshod and unconvincing',[6] and expanded his reasons in an article published in the journal *Antiquity*, entitled 'Moonshine on Stonehenge'.[7] Here he criticized the confident nature of the exposition in Hawkins' book, arguing that a general reader would tend to accept Hawkins' conclusions uncritically and in ignorance of their controversial status. As well as concerning himself with other aspects of the style of the book, Atkinson also exposed certain inaccuracies, of which some were archaeological. And although by their training most archaeologists were ill prepared for the claims which megalithic astronomy and other similar theories had made, Atkinson showed himself technically the master of Hawkins in at least one very important matter – the possibility that the alignments might just agree with the astronomically significant positions by accident.

On these turbulent waters another vessel was launched, this time by a retired professor of engineering. In 1967 Alexander Thom published a remarkable book, *Megalithic Sites in Britain*, in which he summarized his own findings on the megalithic sites and their possible astronomical uses. The case he made out was impressive for its sheer weight of evidence, as he had begun his 'long, patient, accurate and modestly pursued work'[8] as far back as the 1930s.[9] Although his evidence, like that of Hawkins, consisted mostly of alignments in megalithic sites, unlike Hawkins it dealt with large numbers of sites, which could be examined statistically. Indeed, as far as astronomy was concerned, Thom made no reference to Stonehenge at all! Nevertheless, he wrote that his findings at these many other sites inclined him to accept the idea that Stonehenge, too, was an observatory for the sun and moon and he even speculated that it might have become the national centre for this activity.[10]

Thom's research had considered the design of megalithic sites as well as their possible astronomical uses, but it was his ideas on megalithic astronomy which developed quite spectacularly in the ensuing decade. These provoked as much disagreement as did Hawkins' earlier claims about Stonehenge.

After ten or more years of the current debate on megalithic science, few clear results have emerged, if one can judge by the reaction which they have provoked. For example Atkinson – who, it will be recalled, had a low opinion of Hawkins' book – has become sufficiently persuaded by the general tenor of Thom's theories to argue that conventional archaeological thinking is in need of drastic revision.[11] However, not all commentators would agree. Indeed, a number of critics who have looked quite closely at some of the issues in megalithic science adopt a view which is at least more cautious and often quite dismissive. Very frequently, it is argued, the research on which the claims of megalithic science are founded has not been done methodically enough, and this makes it difficult to distinguish fact from speculation.[12]

A somewhat oblique comment on the validity of the current research into megalithic science is occasionally voiced by archaeologists who warn of the dangers 'of seeing ourselves in the past'.[13] The argument starts with the premise that scientists admire scientific activity, and are therefore tempted to look for it wherever they can. Of course this argument does not prove that the theories of megalithic science are wrong, though it perhaps helps to explain why few of the researchers in megalithic science are archaeologists by training.

This argument leads us to one consideration which surely does help to explain the confusion that has arisen about the strength of the claims for megalithic science. Scientists as a body have their own ways of assessing theories, even if these exist only at an intuitive level. Archaeologists likewise have their own criteria for judging new ideas. But there is no reason to suppose that the criteria of scientists and archaeologists are identical. Perhaps because the subject is such a small one, no consensus has been reached even within archaeoastronomy itself concerning satisfactory criteria for the evaluation of hypotheses.[14]

In this book we shall be reviewing a wide range of evidence which has been submitted by both sides in the Stonehenge controversy and in the wider problems of megalithic science in general. It would be impossible to offer a comprehensive review and, since it is necessary to be selective, it seems wise to concentrate on the evidence which potentially seems the most informative. But this presupposes the choice of some criteria by which the value of any piece of evidence may be judged. Here is another reason why it is better to discuss ways of assessing the evidence before discussing the evidence itself, and our choice in this important matter will be described shortly. In general, however, it implies that we have to concentrate on studies involving large numbers of sites, rather than on detailed investigations of individual monuments. Thus, while Stonehenge is a convenient and well-known example with which to begin, it is not characteristic of the approach that we shall adopt.

2 The study of megalithic science

The scope of the book

This book is concerned with one aspect of the prehistory of the British Isles and parts of north-west Europe. It focusses on a period characterized by the large stones used in many of its surviving sites, often called the 'megalithic'. This is a term which means more to laymen than to archaeologists, for it embraces a rich diversity of types of monument which may resemble each other only superficially. A glance at the photographs and diagrams in this book will give some idea of their variety,

108 including megalithic tombs such as Newgrange, the great burial chamber and mound in Co. Meath, Ireland; standing stones ('menhirs') such as

100 those at Ballochroy, in Scotland in the county of Argyll;* the great

14 alignments of standing stones near Carnac, in Brittany; and stone circles,

48, 49 which may not be true circles at all, such as Castle Rigg, in Cumberland, England. What evidence there is points to the long period of time over which such monuments were constructed, from roughly 4000 BC for some of the early megalithic tombs to perhaps 1000 BC for the very latest of the stone circles.[1]

In this book, our interest in megalithic sites will begin with a discussion of the ways in which they may have been designed. On the other hand, we shall be ignoring fascinating areas of study dealing with the engineering aspects of the construction of megalithic sites. Though we shall certainly bear in mind the practical limitations imposed by the methods and materials at the disposal of the people who built them, it is almost entirely with the spatial arrangement and design of the monuments that we shall be concerned. In a sense, we seek to draw a broad distinction between 'technology', which we shall ignore, and 'science'.

Given plans of megalithic sites without either scale or compass direction, the *geometry* of their design can be studied, and it has been claimed

---

* British county names in this book are those in use before the 1974 reorganization of county boundaries. The old names are still better known and are of more help in locating sites on the ground. But readers who wish to find out what the modern equivalents are should turn to the index, where new county names are given in parentheses after old ones.

Megalithic sites and other relevant places in England and Wales.

Long Meg
Castle Rigg
Burnmoor
Devil's Arrows
Penmaen-Mawr
Moel ty Ucha
Black Marsh
Kerry Pole
Cefn Gwernffrwd
Prescelly
Mountains
Usk River
Maen Mawr
Rollright
Avebury &
Kennet Avenue
Silbury Hill
Stanton Drew
Sidbury Hill
Woodhenge
Stonehenge
Dorset Cursus
Shovel Down
Stannon
Nine Maidens
Merrivale
The Hurlers
Men-an-Tol
Tregaseal
Merry Maidens

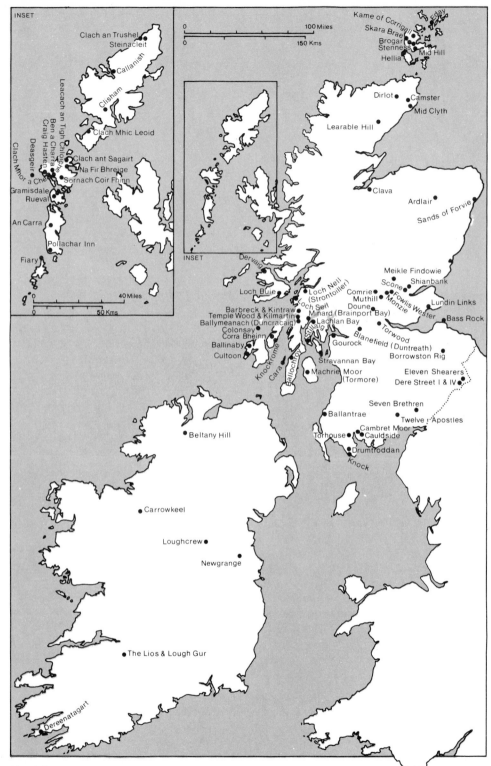

Megalithic sites and other relevant places in Scotland and Ireland.

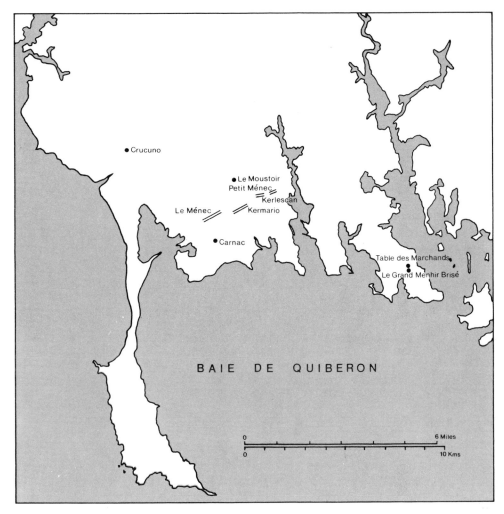

Megalithic sites in the vicinity of Carnac, Brittany.

that certain aspects of their geometry can teach us surprising facts about the mathematical knowledge of the people who built them. If our plans are also provided with scales, we may compare the dimensions of the monuments, and we might find some regularity in these. Indeed it has been suggested, by Thom and others, that particular units of length were used in the design of many sites. This aspect of megalithic science is known as *mensuration*.

While the first half of the book thus concerns the design of megalithic sites, the larger second half deals with a theory of their purpose. If our plans can be orientated to some point on the compass, it becomes possible to test the remarkable theory that the purpose of some of the monuments was *astronomical*, since any directions defined by the monuments can now be related to those in which various astronomical phenomena occur.

This book is devoted to a critical study of some of the claims that have been made regarding each of the three topics we have mentioned: geometry, mensuration and astronomy. It will thus be clear that the raw material for this study is, for each site, a knowledge of the relative positions of its stones and other components. The sort of excavated evidence with which the prehistoric archaeologist is typically concerned – such as pots and pins – is not of immediate interest to us. The archaeological record may yield relevant evidence for our study (where excavation has revealed new megalithic structures previously obscured or in the very important field of dating) and then of course it is of particular value. But mostly we shall be concerned with such evidence as a careful visitor can find without physically disturbing the site.

To say that we largely ignore the excavated evidence is not to say that the evidence we shall examine is somehow inferior or second rate. Like excavated material, it may be damaged and incomplete, and it shares with excavated artifacts the danger of misinterpretation. Perhaps the only sense in which it can be said to be at a disadvantage in comparison with the conventional evidence is that less attention has been given to it.

Sources of evidence

Throughout most of the book we will ignore the vertical structure of megalithic sites. For this reason almost all the information we require can be obtained from accurate plans of the sites, provided that they are also accurately orientated and equipped with accurate scales. The Ordnance Survey has been used frequently in the study of British sites, though it has a number of limitations, as the following example illustrates. If we suppose, on the astronomical theory, that a megalithic site was designed to indicate, say, the place where the sun rises at midsummer, then it is necessary to have a clear view of the horizon to the northeast. However, the view could easily be obscured by a local hillock too small to show up on the Ordnance Survey, and this can only be checked satisfactorily by a visit to the site itself.[2] Also, special care is needed in using the Ordnance Survey to calculate the elevation of the horizon, a measurement which is essential for any accurate discussion of the astronomical theory.[3] Nevertheless, the Ordnance Survey remains a very useful source of approximate information, especially for sites laid out on a large scale.

Smaller sites, particularly stone circles and short alignments of menhirs, require individual treatment. Many plans of these exist scattered throughout the literature, though a satisfactory bibliography of such plans does not seem to be available, and the standards adhered to by different surveyors seem highly variable, even where their methods and conventions are explicitly stated. Nevertheless, old published diagrams and even sketches can indicate which parts of a monument have remained relatively undisturbed in recent decades.

A large number of very fine plans have been published by Thom, whose efforts in this field have earned grateful recognition from archaeologists.[4] Though the plans by Thom and his colleagues may be accurate internally, to a few inches in even some very large sites,[5] it should be observed that the published forms of these surveys are always reductions of the original plans. Such small-scale reproductions, subject to considerable distortion, should be used with care.[6]

Many megalithic sites are so difficult to reach, even without the burden of a theodolite, that the time and effort involved in the thorough survey of just one site can be appreciable, often demanding several visits if the site is complex or the weather unfavourable. Furthermore, skill in the use of a theodolite and other surveying equipment is not acquired overnight. But the amateur should not be deterred from surveying sites for himself, provided that elementary precautions are taken, the methods used are summarized in any published account of the survey, and sufficient checks are performed to allow an estimate of the accuracy of the survey to be made.[7] Later on in this book we shall see something of the accuracy which is required for our purposes, and Thom's pleas for high accuracy[8] are founded on practical experience of inadequate earlier published surveys. It is often extremely useful if a plan shows the shape of each stone, for example at its base.

Many sites are overgrown or at least uncleared, and there is often a temptation to prod for stones concealed under peat or other soil. Apart from the possibility of damage or disturbance to buried artifacts if this is done without professional skill, the prodding may also be confined to parts of the site where concealed stones are expected, thus introducing bias into a survey. Any destructive form of investigation, such as excavation, must be left scrupulously to qualified archaeologists; archaeological evidence is irreplaceable, and its interpretation requires the lengthy training and experience of a professional.

Sources of uncertainty

From what has been said so far, it can be seen that our study of megalithic sites will be based on their surviving remains as represented by surveys. We should therefore enquire what other factors may have affected the survey data, besides the intentions of those who built the sites, for all such influences are potential sources of error.

Arranged in chronological order, the list begins with errors introduced into a site during its construction. Even if we suppose that the attempt was made to erect the site according to some fairly precise geometrical plan, there is a limit to the accuracy with which the stones could have been manoeuvred into position, and, for all we know or are entitled to assume, there may be a limit to the accuracy which was attempted. Then again, if we suppose that certain megalithic alignments had been erected for some astronomical purpose, there is a limit to the accuracy with which the position of any particular astronomical phenomenon can be observed, and some other limit to the accuracy with which this direction can be indicated by an arrangement of stones. These two examples are sufficient to indicate that the sorts of in-built error which we might anticipate may depend very much on the theory under consideration, and so we shall postpone further discussion of this source of error until we come to deal in turn with megalithic mensuration, geometry and astronomy.

Between the date of its construction and that of a survey in modern times, many factors will have altered the features of an archaeological site, some natural and some for which man has been responsible. For example, the action of frost or the growth of vegetation can displace stones entirely, and the effect on the inferred plan of a megalithic site may be considerable.[9] But such processes cannot of themselves account 2, 7, 26, 30 for the curious non-circular shapes of many megalithic rings.[10]

The positions of stones in some megalithic sites have been altered by a wide range of human activities, from carefully recorded and competent reconstruction to wholesale destruction. In important respects the situation has improved since 1906, when Lockyer wrote that 'The disastrous carelessness of the Government in the matter of our national antiquities is, I am locally informed, admirably imitated by the Devonshire County and other lesser councils, and, indeed, by anybody who has a road to mend or a wall to build.'[11] However, Thom occasionally remarks on the changes that have taken place in monuments over the period he has studied them,[12] and the present author has seen a Land-Rover being driven by a local farmer across the stone circle on Borrowston Rig, Berwickshire.

A third source of error arises in the last stage of the process of data collection, from imperfections in the survey. Nowadays this is a less serious source of error than it used to be, thanks to the standards introduced by Thom.

Testing the theories

While uncertainties may thus be associated with the data at our disposal, it is on their interpretation that most suspicion has fallen in the past. Consider, for instance, the hypothetical statement: 'This stone ring is in the form of a circle.' At one level such a statement may be merely a concise description, in the sense that the positions of the stones lie within a small distance of the circumference of some circle. At this level, the statement can be verified simply by confirming that it fits the facts. However, it is a statement that can also be understood at a much deeper level, implying that the ring was originally intended by its designers to be a circle. How do we decide on the truth of the statement at this level?

Clearly it is no longer sufficient merely to establish that the statement fits the facts. Just as it is possible to draw an infinite number of geometrical curves through the corners of a square, so we can draw innumerable curves passing through the positions of the stones of a megalithic ring. For each such curve, the statement that 'this ring is in the form of such-and-such a curve' will fit the facts, but this of itself will not allow us to infer that one particular curve was the design which the builders of the site had in mind.

Let us look briefly at another example, which more easily allows us to see a way out of the problem, and that is megalithic astronomy. This subject takes up most of the second half of this book, but most readers will already be aware of what is meant. Many authors have remarked that certain megaliths point in the directions at which various astronomical phenomena take place. Undoubtedly this statement fits the facts. A number of sites have been studied independently by different people, and there can be no doubt, in these cases at least, that the statement is true.

Now we must ask whether the astronomical significance of the site was what its designers had in mind when they decided on its orientation. As many people have pointed out, megaliths could have been aligned in astronomically significant directions quite by chance. The observation that the astronomical theory fits the facts does not help us choose between the possibility that the alignments are coincidental and the possibility that they are intentional. Indeed, we can be virtually certain that coincidences will occur, but we do not know *a priori* that the megalith-builders were interested in astronomy. Therefore, unless we can do better in discriminating between the two possibilities, we should dismiss any apparently significant alignments as coincidences.

Statements that merely fit the facts are, then, insufficient evidence to justify the study of megalithic astronomy. Can we do any better? The argument that astronomical alignments may be expected by chance is the clue, for it naturally suggests that we should compare the number of alignments we actually observe with the number we should expect by chance. Expressed like this, the further progress of our investigation takes on a statistical appearance, for it is to statistics that we must turn for guidance on a fresh problem which this approach raises: by how much must the number of observed alignments exceed that expected by chance before we are entitled to infer that we have significant evidence for the astronomical theory?

A statistician might answer this question in the following way. Suppose for the moment that the megalithic sites *are* randomly orientated. Then, given certain assumptions, we can calculate the probability that a certain number would happen accidentally to point in astronomically significant directions. In particular, we can calculate the probability for the number which are actually found to do so. (In fact we calculate the probability that *at least* this number will point in astronomically significant directions.) If this probability is sufficiently low, say less than one in a hundred, we have satisfactory grounds for preferring the astronomical explanation.

Note that we test the astronomical hypothesis by a slightly roundabout method: we are really asking whether there is something improbable about the orientations of megalithic sites if we maintain that the hypothesis is wrong. However, expressed like this, the test exemplifies the criterion which we will try to apply to each hypothesis discussed in this book, whether it concerns the geometry of the sites, their astronomical purpose, or a unit of length used in their design. We will not be content if the hypothesis merely fits the facts. On the contrary, *we will demand that there be something about the megalithic sites which we would find very surprising were the hypothesis false.* Only then may we feel justified in accepting it. The application of this criterion is meant to be a unifying theme throughout the book.

It should be pointed out that many writers appeal to statistical considerations like this purely qualitatively, for one often comes across the remark that such-and-such a result could not possibly occur by accident. From an experienced statistician such a statement should be reliable, but the literature on megalithic science abounds with such claims which, on further inspection, turn out to be of no statistical significance whatever. Experience shows that we must resist the temptation to accept such statements if they are unsupported by at least some calculation.

It may seem unfair to insist on a statistical approach when this is not required of most archaeological theories.[13] However, one reason for this is that most theories make only *qualitative* testable predictions, whereas those made by the theories of megalithic science are quantitative. In fact a statistical approach is implicitly used in one very important technique of orthodox archaeology – the method of radiocarbon dating. Archaeologists are well aware that a radiocarbon date of 3100 BC ± 150 for an object means only that the interval from 3250 BC to 2950 BC is *likely* to contain the true date. Furthermore, if a second object is dated at 3050 BC ± 200, no archaeologist would conclude that it was later than the first one, because the difference in dates is not statistically significant. If we are prepared to accept that astronomical alignments are deliberate without testing them statistically, we might as well argue that a date of 3000 BC ± 3000 proves that an object is actually dated to 3000 BC.

The technical problems raised by the statistical approach to megalithic science can be very great, and they have naturally attracted the attention of statisticians to the subject. The problems are made particularly difficult (and, for a statistician, particularly interesting) because the hypothesis itself is generated from more or less the same data on which it is proposed to test the hypothesis. This is in marked contrast to a great many statistical situations, in which a hypothesis, whether it was suggested by a body of data or by some theory, can be tested on as much fresh evidence as the researcher has the patience and other resources to produce. Unfortunately, in archaeological investigations the acquisition of fresh data is often very time-consuming. It may even be impossible, since there is an absolute limit to the number of prehistoric sites which still survive. Naturally, this difficulty is not confined to the questions of megalithic science; it is a fundamental problem in the validation of archaeological theories in general.[14]

While we shall be laying great stress on statistical arguments in this book, there are a few purely qualitative arguments that should be considered in any complete assessment. To some extent we can weigh theories against each other by considering their relative simplicity, their scope and their plausibility. For example, a simple theory which explains a large number of sites is to be preferred to one in which a different explanation has to be devised for each site. The difficulty with such criteria is their subjective nature, and it is compounded by the fact that megalithic science is multidisciplinary. It may well be that most archaeologists, by the broad similarity of their training, will assess the relative simplicity of two rival theories in much the same way, and the same may be true of astronomers discussing an astronomical theory. But it is probably unrealistic to expect archaeologists, statisticians, engineers, astronomers and surveyors to reach similar views on subjective questions, such as the simplicity or plausibility of some hypothesis.

There are some non-statistical criteria, however, which are a good deal less subjective than these. One of the most obvious and general is feasibility. For example, if a theory is concerned with astronomical alignments, it must be possible to suggest some way in which a worker, equipped with the kind of materials and tools thought to have been in use in megalithic times, could have observed the relevant astronomical phenomena and then erected the alignments in the correct directions. Even this is not an entirely satisfactory criterion, however: some people may insist that no apparatus can be considered for whose existence in megalithic times we do not have any evidence; while others might be prepared to allow consideration of an apparatus (perhaps of a perishable type) of which no evidence could have been expected to survive.

The shapes of megalithic sites

Already in this chapter we have used the example of megalithic geometry in discussing the two levels at which the 'scientific' theories of megalithic sites may be employed. In the remaining sections of this chapter we shall review some of the *descriptive* uses of megalithic geometry (cf. p.20); that is, we simply use the words 'circle', 'ellipse' and so on as geometrical language intended to convey briefly some information on the present configuration of the site. Therefore we make no attempt here to extend the investigation to a deductive one, in which we attempt to infer the original plan of the site as intended by its builders. This we defer to chapter 4.

Our reason for separating off the descriptive aspects of megalithic geometry is that they are an important preliminary step towards the subject of the next chapter, the supposed megalithic units of length. A study of the geometry of megalithic rings is needed so that we may estimate their diameters, and then we can use these to test the idea that there was a standard unit of length. However, the geometry of megalithic sites has a second application: in the case of a monument possessing at least one axis of geometrical symmetry, we may test the idea that the axis is orientated in some astronomically significant direction. This is one among many astronomical theories of megalithic sites, and these are the subject of the second half of the book.

Even when we are not concerned with trying to establish the original design of a monument, it is of obvious interest to know how well a proposed design does in fact fit the positions of the stones in the ring. A suitable measure might be, for instance, the mean distance of the stones from the suggested geometrical figure. Associated with each figure there will be a number of parameters (like the radius, if the shape is a circle) which we are free to vary, and it seems natural to choose them in such a way as to optimize the fit of the shape to the site. With one or two simplifications, this is the procedure used by Thom in deducing the dimensions of a site to provide material on which to test the hypothesis of a megalithic unit of length.[15] It must be carefully noted, however, that most of the diagrams of megalithic rings published by Thom show the geometrical figures with parameters chosen to satisfy a different criterion: in general the parameters are selected so that as many dimensions as possible are integral with respect to the unit of length whose existence Thom has inferred from the 'best-fitting' shapes. That is really the subject of the next two chapters, and will not be pursued here.

Shapes for stone rings

It seems to be universally agreed that the simplest shape to fit is the circle.[16] One example of a site to which a circle fits remarkably well is the Ring of Brogar in Orkney, which has been surveyed by Professor Thom and his son, Dr A. S. Thom.[17] Here all but 2 of the 35 measured stones lie within 3 ft (c. 0·9 m) of the circumference of a circle no less

92

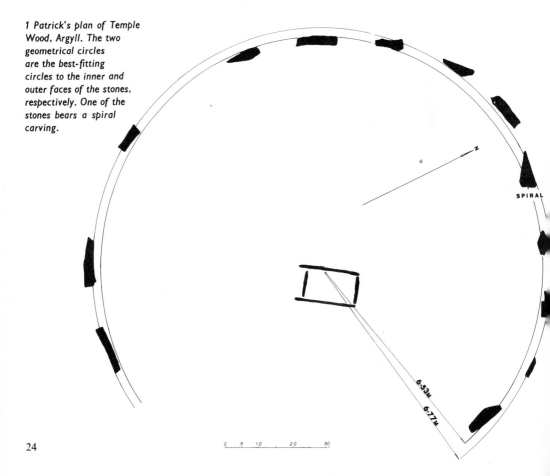

1 Patrick's plan of Temple Wood, Argyll. The two geometrical circles are the best-fitting circles to the inner and outer faces of the stones, respectively. One of the stones bears a spiral carving.

SPIRAL

6·53M

6·77M

0   ·5   1·0   2·0   3·0

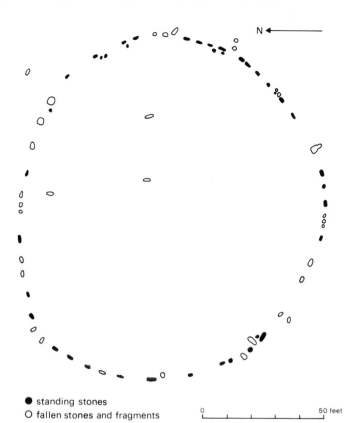

2 Stannon Circle, Cornwall, after Lewis 1895, pl. II. The ring is obviously flattened.

● standing stones
○ fallen stones and fragments

0   50 feet

than 340 ft (*c*. 104 m) in diameter. There is evidence that the site has been partially reconstructed, and the Thoms say that the two 'rogues', respectively 4·6 and 6·0 ft (*c*. 1·4 and 1·8 m) from the circle, seem to be those most seriously affected. Another site which can be described as a circle with fairly comparable relative accuracy is the much smaller ring at Temple Wood, Argyll, which has been studied by a professional surveyor, Jon Patrick.[18] Here only 7 of the 13 surveyed stones lie over 2·76 in. (7 cm) from the best-fitting circle, which has a radius of about 21·7 ft (*c*. 6·6 m).

Even to a perceptive visitor, almost all megalithic rings appear circular. However, inspection of an accurate plan of many sites shows that they are quite definitely not circular. Indeed it has been known for a long time that some rings appear to be flattened circles of some kind,[19] while others appear to be oval.[20] Furthermore, as Thom has stated,[21] these departures from circularity are unlikely to be entirely due to movements of the soil, and it is largely thanks to him that the attempt has been made to systematize these deviations.

Another argument which has some bearing here is the 'structure of the sites, which not infrequently exhibit an 'axis of symmetry'; that is, the half of the site on one side of the axis is in some respects the mirror image of that on the other side. This is not necessarily to say that the stones are neatly paired off on each side of the axis, though they may be, as in the case of the trilithon horseshoe at Stonehenge.[22]

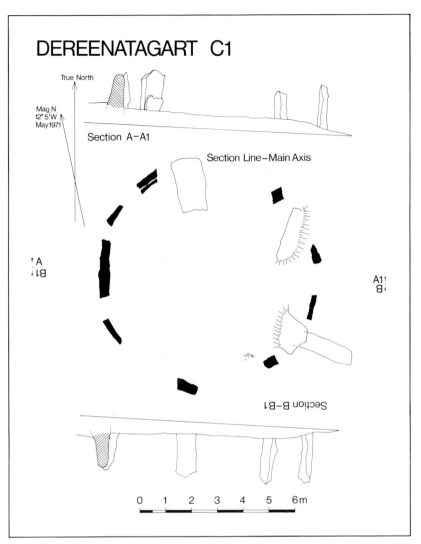

DEREENATAGART C1

True North

Mag.N
12° 5′W
May 1971

Section A−A1

Section Line−Main Axis

↑A
↓B1

A1↑
B↓

Section B−B1

0 1 2 3 4 5 6m

3 Dereenatagart, a recumbent-stone circle in Cork, surveyed by J.W. Barber (Barber 1972). Note the axis (AA_1) passing between the two 'portal' stones and through the recumbent stone. The ring is remarkably symmetric about the axis.

The existence of a structural axis of symmetry has been demonstrated with particular care by the archaeologist John Barber, in a study of an unusually homogeneous group of rings in Co. Cork and Co. Kerry, Ireland.[23] These are 'recumbent-stone circles', so called because one stone in each circle was deliberately set horizontally. Opposite it (at the other end of the axis of symmetry) is generally a pair of upright 'portal' stones, and the heights of the remaining stones are generally graded from the portals to the recumbent.

The evident non-circularity of many sites shows that a useful classification of their shapes will include a variety of forms. Furthermore, although the structural symmetry of many sites may not be directly relevant to their geometry, it at least suggests that one might try symmetric shapes. We shall now discuss some of the sets of shapes which have been proposed to deal with the variety of megalithic rings.

The best-known set of shapes, and the one that has been applied to much the largest number of sites, is Thom's. As well as the circle and the ellipse,[24] it consists of egg-shapes of two kinds and flattened circles of two main kinds.[25] Although the majority of sites are described as circular, by 1955 Thom had found some 12 sites which he described as flattened circles, and 2 egg-shapes. By 1966, such was the pace of his research, 30 flattened circles were known, there were 8 eggs and 20 ellipses.[26] Nevertheless, there is a small group of sites, the most notable being Avebury, for each of which a new shape had to be specially designed.[27]

It is interesting to work out the amount of choice one has in attempting to fit Thom's shapes to a particular site. Suppose that it is possible to decide from inspection of a plan of the site whether it is circular or not.

4

5, 13, 17, 56

26, 27

4 *Four geometrical shapes which, with the circle and the ellipse, form Thom's classification of a great many shapes of megalithic rings. In each case the four points A, B, C, D may be set out according to the stated relationships. Circular arcs are struck from these points, and the Type II egg-shape is completed by two straight line segments.*

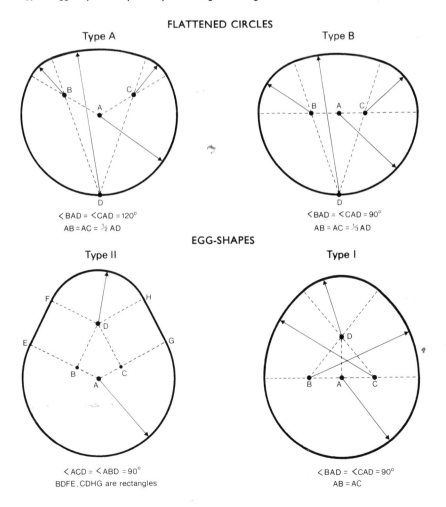

FLATTENED CIRCLES

Type A

$\angle BAD = \angle CAD = 120°$
$AB = AC = \frac{1}{2} AD$

Type B

$\angle BAD = \angle CAD = 90°$
$AB = AC = \frac{1}{3} AD$

EGG-SHAPES

Type II

$\angle ACD = \angle ABD = 90°$
BDFE, CDHG are rectangles

Type I

$\angle BAD = \angle CAD = 90°$
$AB = AC$

5 Torhouse, Wigtown, from the north. According to Thom (1967, 38, where it is referred to as G3/7) this is a flattened circle of Type A. The heights of the stones are graded, the tallest being in the south-east (left in this view). (Cf. Burl 1976, 211.)

If it is not circular, we may be able to decide that the site has either one or two axes of symmetry. When it has two axes, we look to the ellipse, when one axis, by deciding whether the axis is the longest or the shortest diameter of the ring we can determine whether to try an egg-shape or a flattened circle. In the cases of the circle and flattened circles we are free to assign the position of the centre and one dimension (such as the length of a diameter), and, in the case of the flattened circles, an orientation. For the egg-shapes and ellipses we can adjust the centre and orientation, and the shape is then specified by its dimensions; the eggs by no less than three adjustable dimensions and the ellipses by two, such as the lengths of the longest and shortest diameters. Thus these two cases leave much more freedom than one has with the circle and flattened circles. There is a continuous sequence of egg-shapes and ellipses to choose from,[28] which means, for example, that the ratio of the longest and shortest diameters of an ellipse can take any value, but it is remarkable that only two types of flattened shapes are needed to fit almost all known examples.[29]

Few attempts have been made by other workers to apply Thom's classification to new material not already considered by Thom. Circles and ellipses are, of course, not of his invention; we have already mentioned one other attempt to fit a circle, and the literature also contains

examples described by different authors as ellipses.[30] However, Professor R. Müller, an astronomer who has written on megalithic science for many years, has also applied Thom's egg-shapes to three rings near Boitin in Mecklenburg, East Germany.[31]

60

Though Thom's set of shapes has been applied to many more sites than any other set, there are alternative sets to choose from, and we shall mention two.[32] The first is actually closely related to Thom's shapes, and is the work of an American professor of psychology, T. M. Cowan.[33] He showed how Thom's shapes, or shapes very like them, could be fitted into a single sequence. Aesthetically this is an appealing step, since by contrast the geometrical constructions required by Thom for his flattened circles, eggs and ellipses are of three relatively distinct types.

6

A mathematician at the University of London, I. O. Angell, has devised a different set of shapes which also apparently fit a number of megalithic rings about as well as Thom's.[34] As in Cowan's method, something resembling the full variety of Thom's shapes is obtained by a single construction, whereas a different construction is needed for each of the types of shape devised by Thom. Angell's construction resembles the familiar method of drawing an ellipse with two pins or stakes and a closed loop of string,[24] except that three stakes are used. In a later paper[35] the number of stakes was extended to four.

7, 8

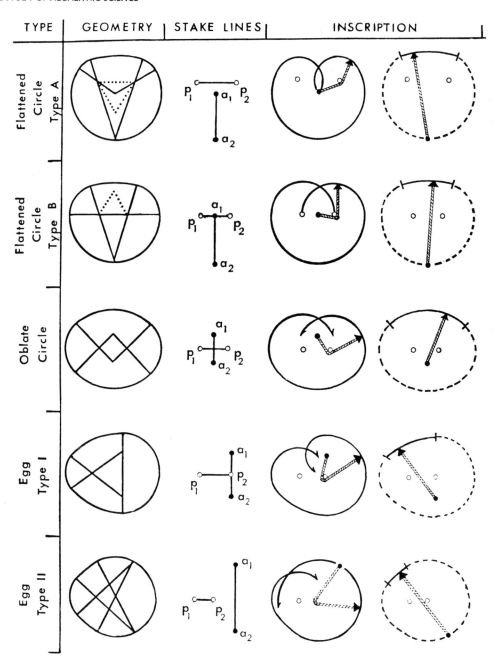

6 Cowan's version of Thom's classification of megalithic rings (after Cowan 1970, fig. 1). The shapes occasionally differ slightly in detail, but they follow an elegant sequence, and all are constructed in much the same way. A rope is anchored at a_1 or a_2 and, as it describes the desired shape, it meets and bends around the other posts p_1 and p_2. (Copyright 1970 by the American Association for the Advancement of Science.)

7 Black Marsh, Shropshire, after Thom 1967, 65, whose construction is a Type A flattened circle. Compare ill. 8.

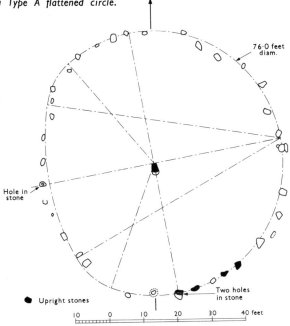

76·0 feet diam.

Hole in stone

Two holes in stone

⬡ Upright stones

10   0   10   20   30   40 feet

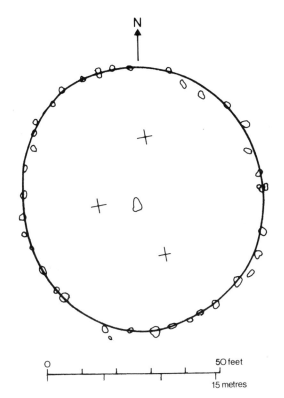

8 Black Marsh, Shropshire, after Angell 1976, fig. 3. His construction uses a loop thrown round three pegs (marked with crosses) and kept taut by the marking peg.

0   50 feet

15 metres

PART II:

THE DESIGN OF MEGALITHIC SITES

3 Megalithic units of length

The quantum hypothesis

In the previous chapter we discussed the geometry of megalithic sites from a purely descriptive point of view. Nowhere did we argue that the shapes considered can give us any information on the geometrical knowledge of the megalith-builders, and we have avoided the difficult problem of trying to establish that any particular geometry was actually used. Now, however, we shall be considering the diameters of megalithic sites, by which we really mean the diameters of geometrical designs which have been fitted to the sites. Is it legitimate to measure the diameter in this way when we do not claim to know the correct geometrical design?

Suppose, for the sake of argument, that the designers of a ring used Cowan's method for an 'oblate circle'. Suppose also that we are trying to fit Thom's shapes to almost all sites, and so we attempt to fit an ellipse. Then by adjusting its dimensions we arrive at estimates of the longest and shortest diameters of the site. Now because Thom's and Cowan's shapes are so very similar, the error in our estimate will be relatively small. Indeed it is only one source of error out of several. Thus we may conclude that we can determine a useful measure of the diameter of a site even if we use a shape which differs slightly from the correct design.

In this chapter we shall be studying some evidence for and against the 'quantum hypothesis', that is, the idea that megalithic sites were set out using one or more basic units of length. A search for the origins of this idea takes us back to Stonehenge, and to the name of William Stukeley, whose astronomical discoveries have already been mentioned. In a book published in 1743 he claimed that a unit of 20.8 in. (c. 0.528 m) had been used in the construction of Stonehenge.[1] Much later, in 1895, the archaeologist A. L. Lewis claimed to have shown that a different unit was used in a few other British sites.[2] Somewhat later still, early in the present century, P. Stephan, who appears to have been a government surveyor, found evidence for a unit of length at a group of rings at Odry, on the River Wda, in Poland.[3] We shall mention this claim again later. However, it is only in comparatively recent years that research into the quantum hypothesis has been pursued at a reasonably scientific and rigorous level. Much of this effort has stemmed from the work of Thom,

6

31

32

and it is with his claims that we shall mostly be concerned. The fundamental unit in his theories is called the 'megalithic yard' (my), and measures about 2.72 ft (*c.* 0.829 m).

Feasibility

In the previous chapter we stated that we would be assessing the theories of megalithic science from two points of view. One of these is statistical, but the second is concerned with practical aspects. We must ensure that the quantum hypothesis does not require the megalith-builders to have been capable of anything of which, with their primitive equipment, they were incapable. Let us see what the quantum hypothesis means in practice.

If we say that some quantum or unit has been used in setting out the linear dimensions of a site, we must consider whether the putative unit was set up afresh at each site, or whether it was derived at each site from some standard. In the latter case, we must enquire how such a standard could have been transmitted both from one place to another and down the years. Let us consider this point first.

Each time a standard unit is copied some error will almost certainly be made, and if such a replica is then itself copied without reference to the original, the difference between the original and the second copy will tend to be larger still. Thus the error will tend to increase the larger the number of copies made. For this reason, Thom noted that the discovery of a highly accurate unit in the design of megalithic sites would imply the existence of a sort of 'headquarters' to construct and verify portable units of a highly standardized length, for use all over the megalithic world.[4] Although the evidence for a highly accurate unit is contentious, as we shall see, this example does show what remarkable implications the possible discoveries in megalithic science could have.

As an alternative to a standardized unit, it could be that, in effect, a fresh unit was chosen for each site. This might be a pace, or a unit related to a man's height.[5] Since such lengths might not be expected to differ very much from place to place, or from one century to another, one might still have the impression that much the same unit was in use at all sites. Clearly, however, it would be wrong to infer any strict social organization as we felt entitled to do when considering a deliberately standardized unit. At the same time one expects that a unit such as a pace would be considerably less accurate than a standardized one, and for this reason the relative accuracy of the megalithic unit of length may be used as a guide to its meaning. Another clue might be the existence of subdivisions of the unit, for it might seem less reasonable to construct such divisions of a rough unit like a pace, than of a carefully standardized unit.

Even when we have speculated about the nature of a possible unit, we must enquire whether there would have been any difficulties in its supposed use. For example, besides the fact that inaccuracies would have arisen when many such units were placed end to end, it must be remembered that the megalithic sites were laid out on ground that was usually rough and sometimes sloping, and even reasonably accurate pacing might be difficult on such a surface. Another point is that the accuracy with which standard units could be used would depend on whether measurements were made with lengths of rope or with rods, for ropes would have been quite inadequate at providing the kind of accuracy with which, according to the Thoms, the famous Carnac alignments were set out.[6]

13, 14

Important as it is to establish what practical obstacles there might be in the way of the quantum hypothesis, all of the above discussion is of little interest unless there is direct evidence for the use of a unit of length in megalithic sites. As the statistician Professor D. G. Kendall has written 'The primary question is not *how* measurements were made, but *whether* they were made.'[7] This is the contentious issue that will take up most of the remainder of this chapter.

Testing the quantum hypothesis

As already mentioned, we shall be taking the diameters of stone rings as our basic data for testing the quantum hypothesis. However, there is plenty of other evidence that many sites were set out with rather striking regularities; thus we may infer that they were planned with some care, and this in turn may predispose us towards the possibility that a unit of length was used. We may think, for example, of the distance between successive stones or stone-holes within those individual circles where we can be reasonably sure that our information is complete. In the excavated part of the Aubrey Circle at Stonehenge, for instance, this distance varies by up to only 9 per cent of its average value.[8] Nevertheless, it seems to be only within individual circles that such features emerge: when the spacing of stones or holes from different circles are treated together no pattern appears to survive.[9] Let us look, then, at the diameters of the stone rings. For the moment we shall ignore the means by which values for the diameters are arrived at, important as this is, and we enquire first how they should be analysed.

71

Suppose for a moment that the sites really were set out with a unit of length. If there had been none of the sources of error described in the previous chapter, an inspection of the diameters would leave no doubt about the existence of the unit, or its value. If the disturbances and the sources of error had been comparatively slight, again an inspection of the data would remove any doubt about its existence, but statistical methods would be useful in estimating its value. Finally there is the possibility of errors so great that even the correctness of the quantum hypothesis is not immediately obvious from the data. Whichever case actually occurs, the quantum hypothesis can only be regarded as established if it can be shown that the diameters of the stone rings take values sufficiently close to multiples of some unit. The whole issue revolves of course on how close the agreement must be, especially in the third case, where visual inspection is insufficient. The criterion we shall adopt is based on our earlier general remarks on the testing of hypotheses in megalithic science. In the present context it can be expressed qualitatively in the following way: we shall require that the agreement between the quantum hypothesis and the measured diameters be so good that we should be very surprised to have such good agreement if we assumed that the quantum hypothesis were incorrect.

Our insistence on a statistical approach – for that is what our demand amounts to – has some disadvantages. Imagine, for instance, that we have a large number of diameters, most of which lie so close to multiples of a certain unit that we are convinced of that unit's reality. If now we add another diameter which has no relation to the unit and if this enlarged body of data is analysed, we shall still find that an overwhelming number of the diameters lie close to multiples of the unit. This simple example shows that, even if we are statistically fairly certain of the existence of a quantum in a body of data, we are not entitled to infer that any particular diameter was laid out with that unit. We might feel certain enough to say that the majority were, but we could not pick out the individual members of this majority.

The same shortcoming of statistical methods actually has an advantage. We may examine a large body of data, convince ourselves of the existence of a unit, and then be told by an archaeologist that one of our sites has recently been proved a fake, or else has been shown to be quite unrelated to all the other sites. Clearly the omission of one site from many will make little difference to the statistical significance of the quantum hypothesis, and indeed if the hypothesis really is correct, the statistical significance of our result should improve. Thus the use of statistical techniques affords some protection against fakes or other casualties.

We have stated that our estimates of the diameters of stone rings are subject to many sources of error. Now we may ask what effect such errors will have on any statistical test we might devise. In almost all cases it will be to conceal the presence of a unit, if one exists. A number of exact circles may, for instance, originally have been set out with diameters equal to various precise multiples of some unit. After 4,000 years and numerous disturbances we measure the sites and deduce their diameters. If the spatial disturbances have been much smaller than the unit, we ought to be able to establish its existence with little difficulty using statistical techniques, whereas if the disturbances have been very great in comparison with the unit, our measured diameters will give the quantum hypothesis little support. Indeed it is quite possible for disturbances to have been so great that no statistical analysis, however clever, can detect the existence of a unit of length. Thus statistical tests tend to err on the side of the sceptic.

There are one or two sources of error which conceivably act in the opposite direction, that is, they could give the spurious impression of a unit in the diameters of rings when in fact none was used. One of these arises because the diameters of most rings are quoted after being rounded to the nearest foot, say, or some other modern unit. Such 'factitious' units are usually easily detected and eliminated.[10]

Another stage at which the data can in principle become dangerously contaminated is in the deduction of the diameter from the plan of the site. What is normally done is to fit some shape, usually one of those described in the previous chapter, to the plan and then to use some dimension of the shape as the diameter. Thus there are three stages to this process: we have to decide which shape to fit, we have to adjust its size and orientation and so on to optimize the fit, and we have to decide which dimension of the resulting shape we shall use as the diameter. It does not seem likely that any undesirable effects will arise from the second and third stages. We may adjust the size and other parameters using either of two methods discussed by Thom;[11] these seem quite objective. Thom's choice of the diameter also seems unexceptionable: it is the shortest diameter for egg-shapes and the longest for flattened circles. This is perfectly reasonable, for these diameters correspond to the longest arcs, which are presumably the best-determined ones in general. For example, in the case of a flattened circle of type A, the longest diameter is twice the radius of an arc which occupies 240° of the perimeter; this normally contains more stones than any other part of the perimeter and so its radius can be more accurately determined than that of any other arc in the perimeter. Where problems can arise, at least in principle, is in the first stage of the process, when we decide which shape to fit.

If we consider a site, perhaps rather ruinous, in which several shapes – for the sake of argument both types of flattened circle – fit reasonably well: which do we choose? Objectively, one would argue that the usual fitting procedure should be applied for both possibilities and that the shape to be used should be the one which then fits best, according to some pre-selected criterion. On the other hand, if one were to choose the one whose dimensions seemed closest to integral values of a supposed unit, the introduction of some bias would be inevitable.[12]

Which method did Thom use in his investigations? One can certainly discount any suggestion that the non-circular geometries were introduced merely with a view to improving the agreement with any particular unit of length; it is quite clear that they were devised to remedy the inadequate fit provided at certain sites by true circles.[13] On the other hand, Thom has gradually arrived at the view that an important guide to the correctness of a proposed shape is that its dimensions should be multiples of certain units. Thus we cannot completely ignore the possibility that diameters derived by Thom in his later work *may* have a slight inbuilt tendency to support the units derived in his earlier work.[14]

Because of such fears, a number of writers have treated Thom's geometry with such suspicion as to reject from consideration all diameters not based on circular geometry.[15] But suspicions engendered by the use of flattened circles and egg-shapes are equally difficult to allay with circles: it is the *choice* offered by the variety of shapes which leads to the possibility of bias, and bias may be present as much in the sites classed as circles as in those considered to be non-circular. Nevertheless, there is no doubt that great care must be taken in the adoption of a set of data, and it can be argued that the oldest sets[16] are the best because of the reduced possibility of bias, however unlikely the presence of bias may be even in the later sets.

Statistical methods

Having obtained a value for the diameter of each of a set of stone rings, how are we to test them for the existence of a unit of length? In 1955 Thom, faced with this problem, had to admit that no rigorous statistical methods existed. Today we are in a stronger position, for several statisticians have been encouraged by Thom's work and other similar problems to devise suitable methods. However, to explain the nature of these methods, and why the problem is such a difficult one, it is instructive to look briefly at the origin of the quantum hypothesis in Thom's work.

What is rather striking about the set of diameters in Thom's paper of 1955, presented as a sort of histogram, is the presence of peaks at about 22, 44, 55 and 66 ft (*c*. 6·7, 13, 17 and 20 m). This observation immediately suggests that many of the diameters lie close to multiples of some unit, and even provides us with an estimate of its size – about 11 ft (*c*. 3·4 m). Thus we might be led to frame a quantum hypothesis that the diameters were intended to be multiples of 11 ft. However, we might equally consider the possibility that some fraction such as one half or one quarter of this was the unit used, and indeed Thom settled for a unit of about $5\frac{1}{2}$ ft (*c*. 1·7 m). Furthermore, he noted that a unit of about 5·435 ft (*c*. 1·657 m) fitted the diameters somewhat better. This he called the 'megalithic fathom'. Since it is likely that it is the radius of a circle which would be measured out, Thom thought that a unit of about 2·72 ft (*c*. 0·829 m) was in use, and this was subsequently called the 'megalithic yard' (my).

Now let us turn to the question of testing this hypothesis. We may recall our criterion that we shall only accept a hypothesis if there is something about the data which would be surprising if the hypothesis were incorrect. In other words, we would like to know whether the peaks in the histogram, at values close to multiples of 5·435 ft, can be reasonably interpreted as a chance effect. We might answer this question as follows.

9 Histogram of the diameters of 46 megalithic rings, after Thom 1955, 282. Peaks occur near values of the diameter which occur frequently. The upper scale is in units of 2 my, and the standard deviation (s.d.) is an estimate of the uncertainty in each diameter.

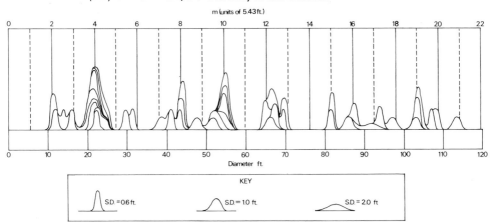

Take each diameter given by Thom and find out the deviation of each from the nearest multiple of 5·435 ft. Obviously this cannot exceed half of the supposed unit. Now we find that, in 42 cases, the deviation is less than one quarter of the unit, i.e. about 1·359 ft, and in the remainder, which number only 10, the deviation exceeds this. Is there anything about this which would be surprising if the diameters had *not* been set out with a unit close to 5·435 ft? If we had the diameters of 52 rings in which we supposed, by hypothesis, no such unit was used, we would expect just as many deviations to exceed one quarter of this value as we would expect to be less than this. We would expect some statistical scatter, also, but no matter how the probabilities are estimated the division into 10 and 42 values found in the study of Thom's data would be highly unlikely.

Now there is an important flaw in this argument. Let us think again of our hypothetical second set of 52 diameters not based on the unit. We repeat that we would expect 26 small deviations and 26 large, with some scatter, when we compare the diameters with multiples of Thom's unit. Clearly, however, these numbers will vary if we try different values of the unit. In particular if, like Thom, we choose a unit which appears to fit the diameters quite well, we must expect that the number of small deviations may exceed 26. For all we know, we may even be quite likely to find some unit yielding as few as 10 large deviations! If this were the case, then we would have to conclude that there was nothing surprising about the unit of 5·435 ft in Thom's data, and we would have no reason for accepting its reality.

The point of this discussion is that the number of small deviations expected in random data depends on whether or not we are given freedom to choose the unit for ourselves. If we do have this freedom then we may expect a larger number of small deviations than in the case where the unit is specified in advance. For this reason, the level at which the number of small deviations begins to be statistically significant depends on whether or not the unit is fixed in advance. Thus a given excess of small deviations is more significant if the unit is fixed than if we are free to choose it.

Let us retrace our steps a little, by considering how we would assess the significance of a particular fixed quantum in a set of data; that is, the supposed unit has not been chosen or adjusted to fit the data, but was obtained from some independent source. This problem has been treated by several statisticians, including S. R. Broadbent.[17] In fact a paper published by Broadbent in 1955 treats several problems of this general class. One of his results, perhaps the most useful, is a test for the acceptability of the quantum hypothesis, or, more correctly, a test for the rejection of the alternative hypothesis that the diameters are distributed rather randomly, with no preference for multiples of the unit. It would be easy to devise a test based on the numbers of large and small deviations which we have considered,[18] but Broadbent based his on a different measure of the deviations known as the 'lumped variance': this is just the average of the squares of the deviations.[19]

A second class of problems discussed by Broadbent in his paper is that of 'estimation': can we find an improved value for the quantum from the data? Broadbent's solution to the problem involves a number of other assumptions, one being that we must know which multiple of the unit each measurement is supposed to be. In Thom's application of these methods[20] he has tended to assume that the multiple to be used is the multiple of the original quantum closest to each diameter, which is a different assumption from Broadbent's. One effect of Thom's assumption is to make the revised estimate of the unit too close to the value originally assumed. Therefore we should not be tempted to take such agreement as evidence for the significance of the unit.

Now let us reconsider the case where the unit is deduced from an inspection of the data. We have already said that we must then be much more cautious in accepting the presence of a quantum, and so if a suggested unit fails Broadbent's lumped variance test it can be rejected completely.[21] What of the case, however, when a unit obtained from the data appears to be significant with respect to this test, which we know to be insufficiently conservative?

Thom tried to resolve this difficulty, in his paper of 1955, by dividing the sites into two groups, Scottish and English. For each group he estimated the best value for the unit and tested this on the other group.[22] It might seem that we are thus testing on the Scottish data a unit derived from the English data, and vice versa. However, we have seen that Thom's method of estimating a unit tends to produce a value very close to the value originally chosen, and this was determined by an inspection of the Scottish and English data taken together. Thus the problem remains: how do we test the significance of a unit which is chosen to fit the data?

General considerations suggest, in the first place, that we should rule out quanta which are either too small or too big;[23] for instance, we consider only units which are no smaller than the size of a typical stone and no larger than the diameter of the smallest circle. Given a unit satisfying these criteria, its significance can be tested by reference either to a second paper of Broadbent[24] or to an investigation by Kendall.[25] The idea behind these tests is basically the one used in our previous discussion of testing significance: one considers artificial bodies of random data, and searches for the best unit in some range, according to some numerical measure of how well a set of data fits the quantum hypothesis, such as Broadbent's lumped variance.[26] From these results one obtains a measure of how well the quantum hypothesis fits random data even when one is free to select the best unit. If the unit derived from the diameters of megalithic rings fits these significantly better, then it is acceptable.

The statistician P. R. Freeman has introduced a test which is different in concept from those of Broadbent and Kendall.[27] It corresponds to the problem of trying to assign a probability to different values of the quantum given our knowledge of the measured diameters, or, rather, to that of trying to determine how our prior expectations are affected by our knowledge of the diameters. Thus Freeman begins by assigning a probability to each value of the unit, based on what we might think if we knew nothing at all about the measured diameters, and then calculates by how much the probability must be enhanced (for a unit which fits the data well) or depressed (if it fits badly). This may seem a strange procedure, but it is a standard statistical approach. Unfortunately, regarded as a means of testing for the existence of a unit of length, Freeman's method is more subjective than Broadbent's or Kendall's, despite certain advantages.[28]

Broadbent's and Kendall's tests are very satisfactory practical solutions to an important and difficult statistical problem, though one should be aware of their limitations. For example, Broadbent's test has been criticized on the grounds that the artificial random samples he used were smaller than the sample of Thom's diameters to which it has been applied.[29] However, Broadbent tried to make his method independent of sample size, and he provided some empirical evidence that he was successful in this. Kendall used a more realistic sample size, and his test is in principle superior to Broadbent's for our purpose because, in generating comparison data at random, he did so with a distribution which closely resembles that of Thom's circles, though without any quantum of course. Broadbent, on the other hand, used a generating method which is less directly related to the problem of the megalithic yard, though it seems that this makes little difference in practice.[30]

In summary, then, two rather different statistical problems occur in the search for the megalithic yard. If we wish to test whether a certain body of data supports the existence of a unit whose value was not influenced by the data in any way, then the lumped variance test of Broadbent's first paper is an appropriate one to use. If the unit has been chosen or adjusted so as to provide a good fit with the data, however, the first test is not sufficiently conservative. Then the second test given by Broadbent, or that devised by Kendall, should be applied.

Statistical tests of Thom's diameters

At the time when Thom published a list of diameters in 1955, Broadbent's investigation into the case of a unit derived from the data was not yet available, and Kendall's method was not to be published for another 19 years. However, when we apply Broadbent's second test to Thom's data of 1955 we do indeed find that his unit of 5·435 ft (c. 1·657 m) is fairly significant, in the sense that, if we had numerous samples of random data and tried to find the best-fitting unit, it would fit as well as Thom's unit in only one sample in about a hundred. In statistical parlance, one might say that the quantum hypothesis with this unit is acceptable at about the 1 per cent level. Kendall's method gives a very similar result – a level of between 1 and 2 per cent.

Thom returned again to the megalithic yard in a paper published in 1962, where he concluded that 'it is certain that the unit of 2·72 ft was used'. Here he was referring to a unit in the radii of the circles, corresponding to a unit of 5·44 ft (c. 1·66 m) in the diameters. The data in this paper mostly refer to sites surveyed since the paper of 1955, and it is obviously of interest to test the significance of the old unit of 5·435 ft on the new data. Since this value cannot have been influenced by the new data, we may use Broadbent's lumped variance test. Omitting sites already discussed in 1955, or those with diameters noted as being particularly uncertain, we obtain a probability level far below 0.1 per cent. This is a highly significant result, for it implies that such good agreement with Thom's unit would occur only once in many thousands of samples of random data.

We have already mentioned the possibility that Thom's earlier data may be more suitable for statistical study than his later work, but most effort has been concentrated on the latter, and it is of interest to mention the results. Using diameters published by Thom in 1967, both Thom himself and Kendall found evidence for a unit close to 5·44 ft, with very low probability levels; much lower, in fact, than those for the 1955 data. [10]

Striking as all these results are, there are several reasons why they may not be as decisive as they seem. One of these is the residual suspicion that, somehow, the choice of geometry open to Thom has allowed the operation of a quite unintentional bias in favour of the megalithic yard. We have tried to minimize this by putting emphasis on the earlier data of 1955, while Kendall's partial solution was to consider the effect of excluding the non-circular shapes in the data of 1967. The fact that the significance of the megalithic yard then deteriorates – though only to a level of 1 per cent, which is still significant – should not be taken as confirmation of our suspicions. A reduction in the amount of available data in any statistical investigation generally makes it more difficult to discriminate between different hypotheses, and tends to reduce the apparent significance of the hypothesis under test. To take an extreme example, no sensible test should be able to distinguish between a random hypothesis and a quantum hypothesis on the basis of just one diameter!

One way of testing the possible geometrical 'origin' of the megalithic yard is to make use of diameters of rings measured by other workers who have not used Thom's special geometries. In his book, *Megalithic Sites in Britain* (1967), Thom did this himself,[31] and found a unit of 2·72 ft (0·829 m), using (presumably) Broadbent's method for estimating a unit. However, we have already argued that some agreement with the original trial value of a supposed unit is not to be taken as support for its reality. On the other hand, we can use Broadbent's lumped variance test since none of these sites had been surveyed by Thom and presumably cannot have influenced his value for the megalithic yard. It turns out that the data do not support Thom's value of the quantum to any significant extent. However, the sample is small, numbering only 23 diameters. Furthermore Thom, in his earliest paper on the megalithic yard, carried out the same test on an overlapping but different sample, and obtained a probability level under 1 per cent.[32]

Later on we shall describe the results of a search for a unit of length in types of megalithic structure other than stone rings, but there is still some further information on megalithic rings which it is interesting to test. These are entirely independent of Thom's data, and so Broadbent's lumped variance test may be used without hesitation when assessing the significance of Thom's unit.

We have already mentioned Stephan's survey and discussion of a
31 group of ten circles at Odry, Poland. Stephan himself thought that their
diameters gave evidence of a unit of 4·616 m (c. 15·14 ft).[33] Although
suitable statistical tests were not then available, Stephan's unit has since
been shown by Müller to be of low significance.[34] Furthermore, as judged
by the lumped variance test, Stephan's measured diameters add no
support to Thom's unit, though as always it may be possible to ascribe
this to the small size of the sample. Müller claims that there is significant
60 evidence for the megalithic yard in a small group of rings at Boitin near
Schwerin in Mecklenburg, East Germany.[35] Another sample in which
one might search for Thom's unit is the group of Irish recumbent-stone
3   circles investigated by the archaeologist J. W. Barber.[36] Although he
used Broadbent's second test, which is generally too conservative when
we are testing a unit which is uninfluenced by the data, it is a fair summary of Barber's study to say that there is little support for a unit bearing
the value discovered by Thom.[37] A study of the seven rings of the Sanctuary, near Avebury in Wiltshire, also fails to provide statistically significant
evidence for the megalithic yard.[38]

Restricting ourselves, then, to the evidence of the diameters of stone
rings, we see that much of the support for Thom's theory comes from his
own measured diameters. One might forecast that this situation is unlikely to change until other investigators summon the energy to survey
comparable numbers of sites with comparable care. At any rate we shall
concentrate henceforth almost entirely on Thom's work, and find out
as much as the data can tell us about the megalithic yard. Before we
enter that discussion, however, one last statistical point remains.

Broadbent's and Kendall's tests are designed to discriminate between
random data and quantal data, and it is obvious enough from their
construction that they do. However, might they not also discriminate
between random data and other types of non-random data? If so, then
once these tests have pronounced that a certain body of data is non-
random, are we entitled to infer that it exhibits a unit or quantum?
Could it not be that the data are really non-random in some other way,
in fact in a way which has little or nothing to do with a quantum but
which has a comparable effect in an application of the statistical tests?
Kendall's answer here was that we can accept the quantum hypothesis
only 'if no other natural alternative hypothesis is available'.[39]

Whether or not it seems 'natural', an alternative hypothesis was proposed by Professor Huber, one of several commentators who contributed
to the lively discussion that followed the presentation of Kendall's paper
at an important meeting held in 1972. Huber pointed out that no less
than 12 out of Thom's 169 circle-diameters lay in a range about 1·5 ft
(c. 0·46 m) wide at about 21 ft (c. 6·4 m). This might suggest the following
type of hypothesis: 'the diameters consist of a mixture of random values
together with a number of diameters lying close to some particular
value.'[40]

Kendall's work showed that this possible alternative explanation
created a significant difficulty, in the sense that sets of fictitious diameters

generated in accordance with Huber's hypothesis would have fooled Kendall's test into wrongly declaring the existence of a unit rather more often than one would like. Thus, although Kendall's test appears to show that there is significant evidence for a unit of length in Thom's diameters, it may only be saying that there is significant evidence for a popular diameter. Nevertheless it turns out that, even when we delete 'Huber's 12', as Kendall called the troublesome diameters, the remaining 157 diameters yielded residual evidence for Thom's megalithic yard.[41]

Huber's hypothesis does not exhaust the range of plausible alternatives. A. H. A. Hogg has suggested that the stone circles consist of a mixture of two populations, one of which is random and the other set out with a unit of length.[42] It is certainly very difficult to distinguish this hypothesis from Thom's by statistical tests presently available. In short, these tests allow us to distinguish between random data and certain types of non-randomness, but they do not directly inform us of the nature of the non-randomness.

Further information on Thom's diameters

One refinement of the statistical methods that we have not yet mentioned is concerned with whether the megalith-builders measured to the centres, or the inner or outer faces of the stones. For example, if a megalithic ring is actually the inner retaining wall or kerb of a ringcairn, it would not surprise us if the measurements were taken from the inner faces of the stones.[43] Thom's diameters are based, so far as the upright stones are concerned, on the centres, and if measurements were originally made in whole numbers of units to the inner faces of the stones, we would find that Thom's diameters were a little larger than multiples of the unit by an amount equal to about the typical thickness of a stone. This amount is usually called β.

Broadbent has given a formula for estimating β,[44] and Thom used it to conclude that, for British sites as a whole, the results are consistent with supposing that $\beta = 0$, i.e. that the centres of the stones were used for measurement.[45] Actually, Broadbent's formula is not applicable for the reason we have mentioned elsewhere, namely that we do not know which multiple of the unit of length each diameter was meant to be. However, the value of β is a matter of interest rather than of importance, and so this and other criticisms need not concern us.

Another way in which our study may be sharpened is by dividing the rings into different groups to see whether the evidence for the megalithic yard is widespread throughout most of the circles, or whether it is more or less confined to one or a small number of groups within them. This can be done by applying Broadbent's second test, or Kendall's test, to each group,[46] though we must always bear in mind that the usual effect of subdividing data is to make any non-randomness look less significant.

One method of division we might consider is by the geometric shape, as classified by Thom. It is of some interest because of the suspicion, which has occasionally been voiced, that freedom of choice between different types may unintentionally have led to a biassing of the deduced diameters in favour of the unit of length. Kendall's investigation in fact shows very clearly that by far the strongest evidence for the megalithic yard resides in the diameters of the non-circular sites.[47] Despite the fact that this group is so small (42 sites in Kendall's sample), by itself it exhibits highly significant evidence for the megalithic yard. However, one cannot entertain the idea that the megalithic yard was used in the non-circular shapes only, since there is also statistically significant evidence for it in the circular sites, when these are considered by themselves. Incidentally, all of 'Huber's 12' are circles.

A second method of dividing the data is by geography. Thom, Kendall, and Freeman all found that evidence for the megalithic yard resided much more clearly in Scottish sites than in a combination of English and Welsh rings, even when one allows roughly for the fact that the samples may be of different sizes.[48] If we recall briefly Huber's alternative explanation of a 'favoured' diameter, it is interesting to note that all but one of the 12 sites with diameters near 21 ft are Scottish; and the exception is in Westmorland. Thus, whatever it is that is non-random about the diameters of stone rings, it is the Scottish sites which are most affected.

Before considering a further subdivision of the data, let us stop to recall what the results on the geographical subdivision imply, even if we ignore for the moment the possibility that Huber's explanation may be correct. We conclude that there is evidence for the megalithic yard in the data for Britain as a whole, and for Scotland by itself. There is insufficient evidence, however, for us to assert with any confidence that it was used in England and Wales, and indeed Kendall was inclined to suspect that evidence for it resided in the Scottish data only. At any rate, we are not entitled to assert that its use was widespread for, as far as England and Wales are concerned, we just cannot tell whether it was used at all. Thus we cannot confirm Thom's early conclusion that the same value of the megalithic yard was used 'from Land's End to John o'Groats'.[49]

It is of obvious interest to subdivide the data on archaeological criteria. P. R. Freeman and the archaeologist A. Burl have considered a rather fine subdivision, in which no subgroup contained more than 10 sites.[50] With such small samples one can be virtually certain that one will never obtain results of statistical significance as judged by, say, Broadbent's second test. Indeed no decisive result emerged from their investigation.

Deviations from the megalithic yard

From the very fact that we have devoted so much attention to the statistical arguments about the megalithic yard it will be clear that the existence of the yard is not immediately evident from cursory inspection of the data. What this means is that the diameters of circles generally deviate quite a lot from the nearest multiple of any unit, even if the unit is chosen so as to fit the diameters as well as possible. In this section we are going to look into these deviations themselves, to see whether a separate study of them leads to any further conclusions about the megalithic yard.

Let us look briefly at the size of these deviations. It is Thom's basic hypothesis that the diameters were intended to be multiples of a unit of 2 megalithic yards (2 my), i.e. about 5·435 ft (c. 1·657 m; see p. 37). Clearly, therefore, the deviations will never exceed half of the unit. For random data the average will be one quarter of the unit, or approximately 1·359 ft (c. 0·414 m). For the real data it is not much less than this, being, for example, 1·11 ft (c. 0·339 m) for a sample of 112 true circles listed by Thom.[51]

Kendall estimated the deviations in a different way, but found very comparable values. He laid considerable stress on the fact that his estimate was comparable with the dimensions of a single stone,[52] and that it varied remarkably little from one selection of data to another. In fact he concluded that, whatever causes might lead to deviations, all were swamped by the effect of the finite sizes of the stones, which lead to errors because we do not know which parts of the stones to measure to. However, we have seen that there is nothing surprising in the fact that the deviations were of this magnitude, and they would even be of this size in completely random data.[53] Thus the effect of the sizes of the stones need not be the dominant cause of the deviations.

Next we must ask if the deviations are due merely to surveying errors, and the fact that the stones never fit perfectly on to the proposed geometrical shape. Burl has compared diameters for the same circles estimated by different surveyors and finds, for a group of five rings on Bodmin Moor, Cornwall, that Thom's diameters lie within 0·7 ft (c. 0·2 m) of those of H. O'N. Hencken, who is the most recent of the other surveyors considered by Burl.[54] This is gratifying confirmation of Thom's own claim that the diameters were known to better than 1 ft (c. 0·3 m).[55]

It is clear that survey errors and so on are a major contributor to the observed deviations. Coupled with the effect of the sizes of the stones, raised by Kendall, one might ask if further explanation of the deviations is necessary. Nevertheless, attempts have been made to explain them by elaborating the quantum hypothesis, and there are many ways in which this might be done. For example, there is Hogg's suggestion that some rings were set out with a unit and others without. Another is that there were slight variations in the value of the megalithic yard from place to place.[56]

Thom himself has offered two sorts of explanation for the deviations. One suggests itself from an inspection of the sizes of the deviations. As we have said, the deviation never exceeds half the unit of 2 my. Furthermore, since the data support the idea of a unit, most of the deviations are less than one quarter of the unit. However, Thom noticed an apparent excess in the number of deviations close to the maximum possible, i.e. half a unit.[57] This suggested to him that some sites may have been set out with half the unit, i.e. the megalithic yard of 2·72 ft (c. 0·829 m), in the diameter. However, the excess of large deviations is of no proven statistical significance. Furthermore, if one tests this new unit of 1 my directly on the diameters using Broadbent's second test or Kendall's test, no result of statistical significance emerges.

Even if we accept the use of the megalithic yard in the diameter, we still naturally find that the actual diameters generally deviate from multiples of the megalithic yard. While accepting the possibility that these might be due to the use of $\frac{1}{2}$ my in some diameters, Thom nevertheless devised a different explanation for these deviations, according to which the diameters were adjusted, away from multiples of the megalithic yard if need be, so that another condition could be met – namely, that the *perimeter* might be a multiple of another unit. This idea raises a new question concerning feasibility: how accurately would it have been possible to measure the length of the perimeter using the equipment available to those who built these monuments? Thom has considered this point and finds in a typical case that the error would be only marginally detectable.[58] Yet, even if we are satisfied that measurement of perimeters would have been possible, is there evidence that this is what was done?

Thom's argument may be summarized as follows.[59] We first notice that the perimeters of many sites appear to favour values close to multiples of $2\frac{1}{2}$ megalithic yards (c. 6·80 ft or 2·07 m). Next, we consider all sites classed as true circles, so that the perimeter is π times the diameter, where $\pi = 3\cdot14$ approximately. Associating each diameter with the nearest multiple of the megalithic yard, we find that there are some which automatically yield perimeters close to a multiple of $2\frac{1}{2}$ my, such as 4 my, and others which do not. Using only the second set, we use Broadbent's lumped variance test to assess the significance of the supposed unit of $2\frac{1}{2}$ my in the perimeters. For this group we find that the unit is indeed statistically significant, though only mildly so, since the probability level, of 6 per cent, is not very low.

However, there are two respects in which this is a misleading estimate of the significance. One, noticed by Thom, has the effect of making the distribution of the perimeters even more significant, namely, that we have tested those circles which should give the worst fit to the unit of $2\frac{1}{2}$ my in the perimeters. On the other hand, the unit of $2\frac{1}{2}$ my was derived in part by inspection of the data, and we have already seen that Broadbent's lumped variance test is insufficiently conservative in such a case.[60] In fact it is easy enough to test for the unit of $2\frac{1}{2}$ my in the perimeters more rigorously, for this is equivalent to a unit of $5/2\pi$ my in the diameters, and in Kendall's results there seems no evidence for such a unit. A similar result is obtained using Broadbent's second test.

Though the statistical evidence is inconclusive, there are two sites where Thom's idea receives some independent support. In the sarsen circle at Stonehenge, the average gap between the thirty stones is close to half their average width, and since the average width is approximately $2\frac{1}{2}$ my, the perimeter is integral in this unit.[61] The sarsen circle is the most carefully constructed of all British megalithic monuments, and so there can be little doubt that a geometry based on these measurements is a close fit to the inner faces of the surviving stones.[62] Regarded as evi-

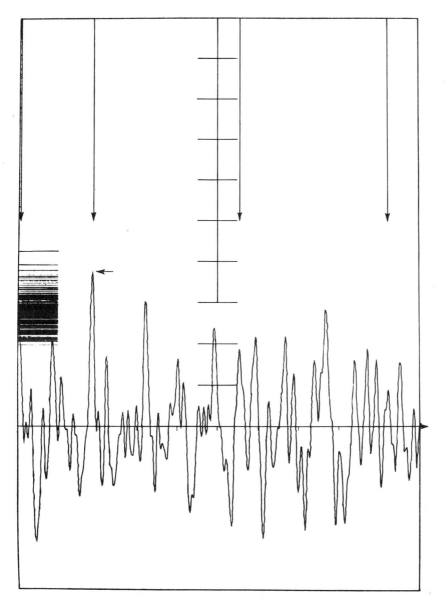

10 Results of Kendall's test applied to the diameters of 109 Scottish circles (Kendall 1974, fig. A.4). The height of the graph above the central horizontal line is a measure of how well the diameters agree with a quantum hypothesis, with a quantum determined by the horizontal coordinate. The four vertical arrows mark places where the quantum considered is 4 my, 2 my, 1 my and $^2/_3$ my, respectively, from left to right. The statistical significance of any peak in the graph can be estimated by comparing its height with those of the horizontal lines at the left of the diagram, which show the heights of the highest peaks obtained in 200 samples of random data. For a peak to be considered significant, it should be higher than almost all the comparison lines. The horizontal arrow indicates the significant peak associated with Thom's megalithic fathom (2 my). If there were a unit of $2\frac{1}{2}$ my in the perimeters, there ought to be another peak almost exactly midway between the two vertical arrows corresponding to 1 my and $^2/_3$ my, but none of the peaks in this range is of any significance.

dence for the megalithic yard, however, the value of these facts is weakened by Thom's observation that there appear to be no other rings where the separation of the stones is integral in megalithic yards or in units of $2\frac{1}{2}$ my.[63]

The other site where there is some evidence for a unit in the perimeters is Woodhenge (Wiltshire). The site consists of six 'nested' rings, and the perimeters of the best fitting egg-shapes lie very close to multiples of a length of about 20 my.[64] However the unit that fits best slightly exceeds 20 my, and the perimeters are not at all significantly grouped near multiples of $2\frac{1}{2}$ my.

The megalithic yard in other structures

So far we have been studying whatever evidence can be found for the quantum hypothesis in the data provided by megalithic rings. However, some interesting evidence on this topic also comes from other types of site, and in any case it is obviously of much interest to study fresh bodies of data as further tests for the significance of the megalithic yard. Generally speaking we shall progress from small structures to large.

Perhaps the smallest with which we shall deal are the so-called cup-and-ring marks – small prehistoric carvings found on rocky outcrops, boulders and standing stones – which Thom has investigated by methods similar to those used in the study of stone rings.[65] Again it was noticed from a plot of the dimensions that there appear to be peaks corresponding to multiples of a basic unit, this time close to 0·82 in. (c. 2·1 cm), which Thom interpreted as 1/40 my. Thom investigated the significance of this unit using Broadbent's lumped variance test. However, we are again presented with the problem of assessing the statistical significance of a unit derived from the data, even though it turns out to be possible to relate it to some other unit, and so a more stringent test is needed. Using Broadbent's second test, we find that the 'megalithic inch' is without significance.

11

11 The diameters of cup-and-ring markings under 12 in. (c. 0.3 m), after Thom 1968, fig. 4. The information is presented as a sort of histogram, the upper scale being in terms of Thom's 'megalithic inch' of approximately 0.82 in. (c. 2.1 cm).

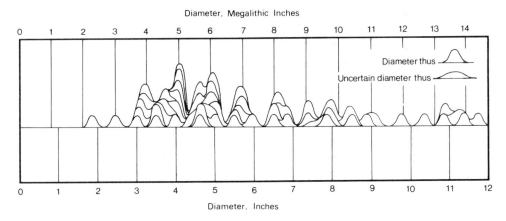

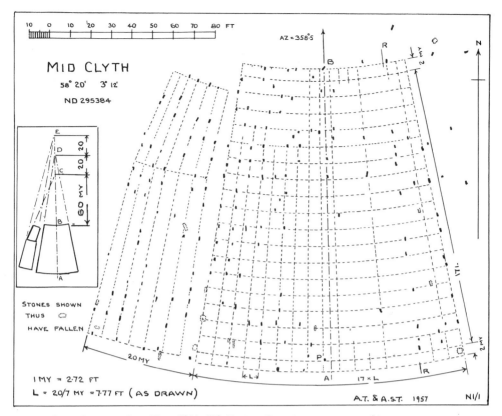

A.T. & A.S.T. 1957

12 Mid Clyth, Caithness, from Thom 1964, 529. Various dimensions are expressed in terms of the megalithic yard, and the inset shows the relationship between the main fan and the smaller ones to the west.

More on the scale of the megalithic yard again, we might investigate the distance between individual stones in megalithic sites. Thom has studied this recently, and his new conclusions confirm the ones he reached in 1962 on the basis of a much smaller amount of data.[66] There is marginally significant evidence for the use of the megalithic yard, but the probability level for $\frac{1}{2}$ my is about 3 per cent; in other words, the distances are clumped towards multiples of $\frac{1}{2}$ my to an extent which would be exceeded in only about one in thirty samples of random data. This probability level was determined by Broadbent's lumped variance test. However, the significance is probably poorer than this, since Thom noticed that $\frac{1}{2}$ my fitted the data better than the megalithic yard itself; thus the unit tested was to some extent influenced by the data.

One site omitted from this study, but already considered by Thom in 1964, is the fine fan-shaped array of stones at Mid Clyth, Caithness. The geometrical pattern which Thom arrived at for this site is a grid which rather resembles the lines of latitude and longitude on a map. Here we are concerned with the lines of latitude, and Thom assessed the significance of these by using methods similar to those used in studying diameters of stone rings for the presence of a unit of length. One first of all chooses an arbitrary line of latitude, and then one measures the distances, in the direction of the near-vertical 'lines of longitude', of all stones from this line of latitude. If these distances lie close to multiples of some unit in a statistically significant sense, then it may be inferred that the stones lie significantly close to evenly spaced 'lines of latitude'. Using the test in Broadbent's second paper, Thom found overwhelming support for a unit of 7·743 ft (c. 2·360 m), at a probability level which must be very much less than 1 per cent. It is a pity that this is not the megalithic yard, although it happens to be close to 20/7 my.

No other investigation we have yet discussed has given evidence for any unit as strong as this, and so it is worth assessing further. An important point is that we are not quite in the situation envisaged by Broadbent: we have freedom to select not just the size of the unit, but also the position of the arbitrary line of latitude as well. Thus even Broadbent's second test is insufficiently conservative. But Thom's result for Mid Clyth is statistically so significant that one might reasonably doubt whether the needed modification to Broadbent's test would greatly affect his conclusion. The issue is, however, also relevant to our discussion of the Carnac alignments.

On a much larger scale than the Caithness fans, but susceptible to much the same kind of analysis, are the famous alignments near Carnac, *13, 14* Brittany. One of the more complete is that known as Le Ménec, which

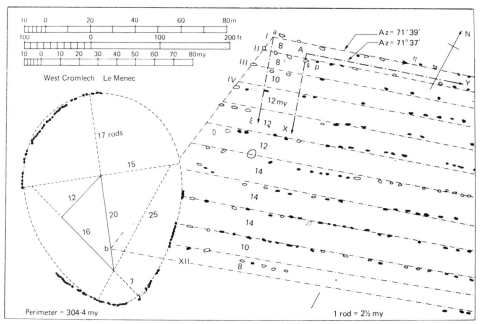

13 The west end of Le Ménec alignments, Brittany, after Thom and Thom 1972, fig. 1. According to their analysis, the stones lie at distances significantly close to integral multiples of 2½ my from the sloping line cutting across the ends of the alignments. Also the rows themselves are separated by distances integral in the megalithic yard. Note the Type I egg-shape proposed for the geometry of the enclosure.

14 Part of Le Ménec, Brittany, from the south-west. The two stones in the foreground are the third and fourth stones from the west end of row IX (see ill. 13); the grading of the stones in this part of the row is very striking. (Photo M. Jos Le Doaré, Châteulin, Finistère.)

consists of a dozen roughly parallel alignments extending for about 3000 ft (c. 1 km), and Professor Thom and his son Dr A. S. Thom have investigated these for the presence of units of length related to the megalithic yard.[67] We shall now describe some of their results; but it must be noted that many of the stones at Carnac are known to have been disturbed, and until a re-analysis is undertaken using only the undisturbed stones, these results must be regarded as provisional.[68]

The task which the Thoms set themselves was to decide whether the stones on each row were separated from each other by multiples of some unit related to the megalithic yard. It turned out that the megalithic yard itself showed 'relatively poor results', and most of their discussion is centred on a unit of $2\frac{1}{2}$ my. Often referred to as the 'megalithic rod' (mr), it is the unit which we mentioned in the context of perimeters in the previous section.

On the hypothesis which the Thoms were examining, each stone should lie close to one of a set of imaginary points (called 'nodes') which lie evenly spaced at an interval of $2\frac{1}{2}$ my along each row. It follows that, if we could measure the distance of every stone on a given row from one such node, then the resulting distances should be close to multiples of $2\frac{1}{2}$ my. Therefore the Thoms' first task was to find a point on each row from which the distances to all the stones on that row lay as close as possible to multiples of $2\frac{1}{2}$ my. This they did using methods adapted from Broadbent's paper of 1955.

The points thus found must themselves be nodes, if the Thoms' hypothesis is correct, and so the Thoms could now calculate where all the nodes on all 12 rows ought to lie. They then found that it turned out

13 to be possible to draw a line at the western end of the alignments in such a way as to pass through one node on each row. Such a line they termed a 'nodal line', and it has the property that the distance of every stone from this line ought to be a multiple of $2\frac{1}{2}$ my, or 1 mr.

To assess the statistical significance of the megalithic rod at Le Ménec, the Thoms combined information from all the rows and applied Broadbent's lumped variance test. The result was a probability level of about 1 per cent, which means that random samples would produce comparable or better agreement with the megalithic rod only once in about a hundred occasions. However, this is an insufficiently conservative estimate. One difficulty is the familiar one that the value of the unit was not stated without some reference to the data themselves. Also, freedom to choose the positions from which one measures the distances of the stones can lead to spurious levels of statistical significance. [69] Thus Broadbent's first test is an unreliable measure of significance here. One might be tempted to use the test in Broadbent's second paper, but it may well be far too conservative, since there is no evidence that the Thoms investigated any more than three possible units,[70] let alone a whole continuum of units, as envisaged by Broadbent when devising his test. One need not therefore accept the conclusion of J. D. Patrick and the astronomer C. J. Butler that the evidence for Thom's unit at Le Ménec is not significant.[71] No existing statistical test can be relied on to yield a sound estimate of significance in a situation such as this.

15 Evidence for a unit of length at Kermario, according to Thom and Thom 1974, 43. For each section of the alignments a little box is plotted to show how far the positions of the stones in that section lie to the east of where they would be expected to be on the assumption that the alignments were set out with a unit of $2\frac{1}{2}$ my (taken as 6.800 ft, or c. 2.073 m).

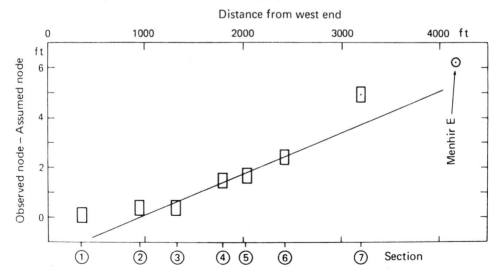

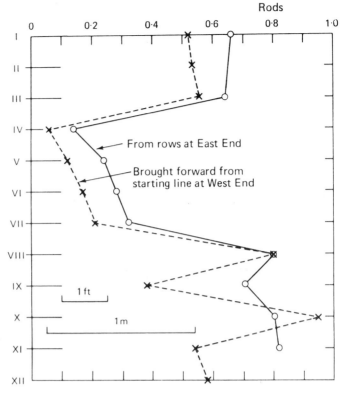

Position of nodes relative to cross line EF at East End.

From rows at East End

Brought forward from starting line at West End

16 Evidence for a unit of length at Le Ménec, according to Thom and Thom 1972, fig. 7. Each row is represented by a roman numeral (cf. ill. 13). The solid line indicates the positions of the nodes at the east end of the rows, and the dashed line shows where they would be expected to lie if the rows had been measured out with a unit of 1 megalithic rod (2½ my). The impressive agreement can be improved further by changing the assumed value of the megalithic yard by only 0.025 per cent.

In the same way, the problem of the applicability of Broadbent's tests also bedevils any assessment of the evidence for units of 2 and 2½ my in the extensive Kermario alignments, about 1 km east of Le Ménec.[72]

In the case of the Kermario alignments, considerable effort was expended by the Thoms in choosing the point on each alignment from which the distances to the stones were measured. This thorough discussion revealed a number of curious results which may have an important bearing on the significance of the unit of length. The Thoms first divided the alignments longitudinally on geometrical grounds into several sections. Then they found, separately for certain of these sections, the 'best' points on the rows from which distances should be measured, that is, points such that the distances to the stones in that section lay as close as possible to multiples of the appropriate unit of length. (In fact the situation was a little more complicated, for the Thoms dealt simultaneously with all the rows in each section by finding the best straight line cutting the rows at right angles, in close analogy with the line of latitude at Mid Clyth.) The result which the Thoms found is that the nodes for all the sections (except the first) lie slightly to the east of where one would expect them to be if one moved an integral number of megalithic rods from the nodes in the first (westernmost) section. Furthermore, the discrepancy, though small, increases fairly steadily as one moves eastwards along the sections. This is a surprising result and demands expla-

15

nation. So far the only one available is the Thoms', which is that a unit of length was indeed used in the design of the alignments, and that the slight but increasing discrepancy towards the east is due to our use of slightly too small an estimate for the megalithic rod.

An equally remarkable result of the same general kind was found for the alignments at Le Ménec. As we have already mentioned, the Thoms found that the nodes at the western end of the alignments lie on a line making a certain angle with the rows. Starting from this line and working eastwards by multiples of the megalithic rod, they calculated where the nodes ought to lie for the eastern half of the alignments. Next, using only the positions of the stones in the eastern section, they determined where the nodes for the eastern half actually do lie. What the Thoms found was that the nodes thus determined generally lay remarkably close to those found by calculation from the west end. Again this is a surprising result which calls for an explanation, and the only one that has been offered is the Thoms'.

It may be as well here to summarize the evidence from the Carnac alignments. The statistical significance of the quantum hypothesis at Le Ménec is quite marginal, and so there is no satisfactory direct evidence that a unit of length related to the megalithic yard was in use. However, intercomparison of different sections of both Le Ménec and Kermario alignments has yielded results of considerable significance. From these results it seems hard to conclude other than that the alignments were set out with great accuracy and care, whether or not the Thoms' explanation is the only one that can be devised.

Let us now turn to a somewhat comparable analysis by J. E. Wood of the Merrivale stone rows on Dartmoor, Devon.[73] There are two main rows, respectively 596 ft (181·7 m) and 865 ft (263·7 m) long. At certain points on these rows are stones which are taller than the others, and Wood measured the distances between these, and between these and a cairn on the second row. When he compared the distances he found that pairs of nearly equal distances appeared, and one triple. For example, two stones in the first row were separated by 43·3 ft (13·2 m), and a different pair in the second row were separated by 41·7 ft (12·7 m). The largest difference noted in any pair or the triple was 7·9 ft (2·4 m).

Wood went on to suggest that these repeated distances were multiples of three basic lengths, which can also be found in other measurements at this fairly complex site. However, let us go back one stage and estimate the significance of the first result, about the pairs of nearly equal distances. We shall do so very crudely, but it would be imprudent to pursue the matter further if we could not provide some assurance that this first result was of significance. In the first row there are 5 tall stones, which yield 10 distances less than 596 ft (181·7 m). The second row has 10 positions yielding 45 distances less than 865 ft (263·7 m). The probability that any particular one of these lies within 7·9 ft (2·4 m) of at least one of the first set of distances is roughly $(10 \times 2 \times 2·4)/263·7$, or about 0·18. Thus out of 45 distances we may expect about $0·18 \times 45$, or about 8, to do so. In fact the number which does so is 9.[74] Now it would be wrong to compare one number with the other in a formal statistical manner, because we have not taken care to use the correct distribution of distances between pairs of points. However, it should give us the feeling that there may be no result of any significance in these nearly equal pairs of distances, and so we need not pursue Wood's analysis any further.

From distances between stones it is a natural step to the study of distances between neighbouring sites. In his paper of 1964 Thom investigated a possible unit with a value equal to 5 my, but again we are in a position where Broadbent's lumped variance test is not really a satisfactory means of assessing significance, since the unit was at least partly suggested by an inspection of the data. It indicates a result which is significant at a probability level of about 1 per cent. Broadbent's second test yielded a result of no statistical significance, but a re-examination of virtually the same sample by Freeman showed that units of 13·63 ft and 68·79 ft (c. 4·154 m and 20·97 m respectively) were somewhat significant, at about the 5 per cent probability level.[75] If the first of these is regarded as 5 my, the corresponding value of the yard is 2·726 ft (c. 0·8309 m), which is very close to Thom's value. Actually the significance of the unit of approximately 5 my may be greater than these results suggest. It would generally not be possible to set up a group consisting of more than three sites in such a way that *all* distances would be multiples of one unit;[76] therefore if we test all lengths together we should expect the effect of any unit to be somewhat diluted.

Other ancient units of length

Assuming there was a standard unit such as the megalithic yard, did it arise in north-west Europe or was it imported? Did it fall out of use at the time when the construction of megalithic sites ceased, or did it survive in the design of the new structures which took their place? The archaeologist E. W. MacKie has laid great stress on the search for evidence that units like the megalithic yard were used elsewhere and at other times.[77] Indeed, he has suggested that the origins of the unit may be sought in the Middle East or Asia. For example, there is excavated evidence that a unit of length, now known as the 'Indus inch', was in use at Mohenjo-Daro, a city in the Indus Valley occupied in the 3rd millennium BC, and the megalithic yard is just 0·36 in. (c. 0·0091 m) short of 25 of these. Now the Indus inch measures 1·32 in. (c. 0·0335 m) and so it is not surprising that the megalithic yard should lie close to *some* multiple. However, there is some reason for paying special attention to a multiple of 25, since this is very close to the 'gaz', a traditional unit used in North-West India.

MacKie has also succeeded in tracing what he believes to be descendants of the megalithic yard. For example, he considers that there is evidence for the use of a unit close to the yard in the dimensions of brochs, the strong round towers which were built in Scotland near the end of the 1st millennium BC. MacKie and the physicist G. I. Crawford have applied Broadbent's lumped variance test to data from 32 brochs, and

25

found that the evidence for the megalithic fathom (5·435 ft or *c*. 1·657 m) in the diameters is statistically significant at a probability level of about 1 per cent.[78]

It is doubtful if such arguments have won more than a few converts to the megalithic yard, since many archaeologists find it hard to believe that there was a unit used throughout megalithic times, let alone later and in other parts of the world. The fact that the megalithic yard can be linked with a unit of length thought to have been in use in Precolumbian America[79] does not inspire much confidence in such comparisons. However, there is a piece of excavated evidence in favour of the megalithic yard, in the form of a graduated hazel rod which was found in a Danish burial mound dated to late in the 2nd millennium BC.[80] It can be interpreted as a measuring rod, and its length is only a few per cent less than the megalithic yard.

The accuracy of the megalithic yard

We have already stressed the fact that the diameters of stone rings, as measured by Thom, are not *precise* multiples of the megalithic yard or any other comparable unit, and we noted a number of possible explanations for these deviations. There is a further possible source of deviations, which we shall now turn to: can we say anything about the accuracy with which the supposed megalithic unit was used? It is clearly going to be very difficult to disentangle this class of deviations from the others, and as much as we can expect is to set an upper limit to the error with which the megalithic yard was used.

Much controversy has been generated by Thom's claims that the value of the yard was held accurate to something around 0·003 ft (*c*. 0·9 mm).[81] In fact Thom used a formula in Broadbent's first paper for this purpose, but one can give two reasons why it is an overestimate of the precision of the yard. The first is the by now familiar one that Broadbent's formula requires one to know to which multiple of the unit each measured diameter corresponds, whereas we do not.[82] The second point is more subtle, being a question of how Broadbent's result is to be interpreted, and it is best explained by an analogy.

Suppose we wish to find the average height of the inhabitants of a large town. By measuring sufficiently many inhabitants we can determine the average with very high accuracy, to within 1 in. (*c*. 2·5 cm), say. However, this does not mean that the heights of all the inhabitants lie within 1 in. of the average. In the same way the number 0·003 ft derived by Thom, even supposing Broadbent's formula is applicable, may be much smaller than variations in the length of the unit used in the construction of megalithic sites.[83]

Kendall has adopted a different and very appealing approach to estimating the accuracy with which the megalithic yard was used.[84] What he did was to generate on his computer a large number of fictitious diameters by adding together numbers which he obtained by subjecting Thom's unit to variations of about 4 per cent. In other words, he simulated the sorts of diameters which one would have obtained had Thom's unit been used with errors typically of this relative size. Kendall then subjected this fictitious data to statistical test, and found that the diameters lay much closer to multiples of the unit than do Thom's diameters. The lesson of this valuable exercise is quite clear: the statistical data on diameters is quite consistent with the use of a unit subject to substantial variations certainly exceeding 4 per cent, i.e. about 0·1 ft (*c.* 3 cm). Note that this greatly exceeds Thom's estimate of the accuracy of the megalithic yard.

We have already mentioned that the accuracy with which the unit was used could be an important clue to its meaning. As Kendall pointed out, his result implies that even pacing would have been too accurate. Of course, it is possible that pacing was used, but that the remainder of the deviations are due to causes other than variations of the unit.

The Thoms have given another method of estimating an accurate value of the megalithic yard, which we can exemplify by considering their treatment of the Ring of Brogar, Orkney.[85] The diameter of this circle they determined as being $340·02 \pm 0·60$ ft (*c.* $103·64 \pm 0·18$ m), the uncertainty being estimated from the extent to which the positions of the stones deviated on either side of the best fitting circle. They noted that this lies close to 125 my, and then, assuming implicitly that this distance was actually intended to be 125 units, they arrived at an estimate equivalent to $2·720 \pm 0·005$ ft (*c.* $0·8291 \pm 0·002$ m) for the megalithic yard. One difficulty here, of course, is knowing just which multiple of the yard, if any, the diameter was meant to be; we can be no more sure of this value of the yard than we are of this multiple. Furthermore, even if we accept this multiple, we are still in a situation where the accuracy with which we can estimate the average value of the megalithic yard need have nothing to do with the accuracy with which it was used. Finally, it should be said that a result like this from an individual site has no proven statistical significance, in the sense in which we have used this concept so far. We have chosen Brogar for the simplicity of its geometry, but the aforementioned difficulties apply in their essentials to similar attempts to produce refined values of the megalithic yard or rod from individual rings, such as Avebury or Stonehenge.[86]

Finally we turn to limits imposed on the accuracy of the megalithic yard by the evidence of the stone rows of Carnac. In discussing them one should stress again the remarkable discovery at Le Ménec, namely, that if we find the nodes for the stones at the west end of the rows, and extrapolate to the east end, the resulting positions are surprisingly close to the nodes found by studying the stones at the east end. The unit the Thoms discussed was the megalithic rod, of $2\frac{1}{2}$ my, and the alignments are about 450 mr long. If the random variations in the individual units amounted to 1 per cent, the discrepancy at the east end would reach about 0·2 mr, which is about as large as the Thoms' result allows. Substantially greater variations would destroy the agreement which the Thoms discovered. The evidence at Kermario *suggests* maximum possible variations of much the same order.

92

27

16

15

57

The meaning of the megalithic yard

In this chapter we have examined much of the evidence which has been presented in recent years for and against the hypothesis that megalithic sites in north-west Europe were set out using one or more units of length, especially those related to Thom's megalithic yard of 2·72 ft (0·829 m). While studying this evidence we have tried to apply statistical tests to show where, if at all, there is something about the evidence that would be surprising if the quantum hypothesis were false. For this reason we have laid no stress on the study of the individual sites, such as Brogar and Avebury, which have furnished Thom with what he considers to be the best estimates of the value of the megalithic yard. When we look at statistical studies of large bodies of data, such as Thom's diameters of stone rings, or the very interesting relationship between the positions of stones at either end of the Carnac alignments, or the arrangement of Woodhenge, a reasonably persuasive result emerges.

On the other hand, we have found little evidence for a *highly accurate* unit. It is true that we might be able to estimate, say, the average unit with some precision, but there is apparently nothing to suggest that any unit was used with an accuracy better than about 1 per cent, as we estimated from the Carnac alignments. Thus there seems little justification for the claim that a *highly accurate* unit was in use throughout the area we have discussed. However, if a unit were subject to enormous variations of, say, 50 per cent, it is unlikely that the statistical study of the diameters of megalithic rings would yield evidence such as we have seen. Thus we are led to ask what kind of unit could have variations of several per cent about its average value. M. Hammerton's answer seems the best – a unit related to some measure of the human body.[87] Whether this was a pace as Porteous has proposed[88] cannot easily be decided; it might, for instance, have been a length derived from a man's height.[89] Kendall's work showed that pacing was too accurate for the sorts of deviations from multiples of the unit which we find today in the diameters. Naturally, however, there are numerous possible reasons why the present-day deviations may be considerably larger than those present originally, and so pacing is not ruled out on these grounds. On the other hand, pacing may not have been accurate enough for the evidence we have seen at Carnac. Kendall quoted evidence that pacing can be kept accurate to several per cent after training,[90] whereas the evidence at Le Ménec and Kermario seems inconsistent with accuracies poorer than about a per cent or so. Thom has stoutly resisted the idea of pacing, partly because of the evidence at Carnac.[91]

The evidence for the supposed widespread geographical uniformity of the megalithic yard also hinges on Carnac. As far as work on diameters of stone rings is concerned, it seems possible that the evidence resides entirely in Scottish sites. Outside Scotland, it is only at a very few individual sites, such as Woodhenge and Carnac (but not Avebury and Stonehenge), that we have any evidence which seems difficult to explain if we deny the hypothesis that a unit of length was used. Even here it is

15, 16

16
15

only a presumption, however reasonable, that the units were consciously related to the megalithic yard. The evidence for the use of a unit in cup-and-ring marks seems poor.

Our very cautious conclusion on the supposed accuracy and wide geographical distribution of the megalithic yard goes some way towards resolving an important difficulty. If it is suggested that the unit was deliberately standardized throughout Britain and beyond, then archaeologists are faced with an idea that conflicts with their customary view of the societies that produced the megalithic monuments, namely, that they were divided into rather separate local groups.[92] If indeed the evidence for the widespread use of a highly accurate unit is not as compelling as Thom and others would maintain, then this apparent paradox loses much of its force.

By laying stress on the statistical study of the megalithic yard we may have avoided some pitfalls. We have certainly tried to avoid inferences based on aspects of the data which could equally well be attributed to mere chance. The price paid for this attempted rigour is the rather elusive quality of the statistician's megalithic yard. For instance, we have already seen that it is very difficult to distinguish the hypothesis that *all* the circles were set out with the megalithic yard from the alternative that only *some* were. Thus it is impossible to point to this or that particular ring and claim confidently that it was set out with a unit of length. Nevertheless, the statistical approach offers a basis on which we may distinguish what we ought to believe about the megalithic yard from what we need not believe.

4 Megalithic geometry

Having assessed at some length much of the statistical evidence for and against the megalithic unit of length, we are ready to take up once again the question of megalithic geometry, but this time for its own sake. In recent years the evidence presented for megalithic geometry has to some extent been intertwined with that for the megalithic yard. In fact it has been argued implicitly that a geometrical design which contains lengths which are integral in the megalithic yard is more likely to be valid than one without. Therefore it is helpful to have assessed the evidence for the megalithic yard before investigating the suggested geometries. But we shall not take up the question of the *validity* of the geometry until later in the chapter. For the time being we shall attempt to summarize some of the geometries suggested for megalithic sites, looking at these in a little more detail than was justified in chapter 2.

Stone rings

In attempting to provide a geometric construction for a megalithic site, Thom usually tries to ensure that it satisfies certain 'megalithic criteria'. For example, he attempts to ensure that the diameter of each site lies close to a multiple of the megalithic yard or of a simple subdivision of it. Because, however, the shapes are mostly constructed from circular arcs of different radii, in general he imposes the condition that as many as possible of the radii must be integral multiples of the basic unit. Since the constructions of the egg-shapes are based on right-angled triangles, this implies that the triangles may be Pythagorean; that is, their sides are integral in the basic unit and so satisfy the famous Pythagorean relation $a^2 + b^2 = c^2$ with whole numbers a, b, c. Such triangles, or approximations to them, also underlie Thom's designs for elliptical rings. Finally we recall Thom's claim that the perimeters were close to multiples of $2\frac{1}{2}$ my (c. 6·80 ft or 2·07 m), and this is adopted as a further criterion.

Note that we are now concerned with an approach to geometry which is different from the one described earlier. In chapters 2 and 3 we described research in which Thom tried by statistical means to find the best-fitting shape of a particular type for each site. In general the resulting diameters are not exact multiples of the megalithic yard or any related unit, as we saw in the previous chapter. Nevertheless, it would be Thom's contention that the diameters were generally intended to be multiples, and that the deviations are due to various accidental causes, except where the desire for an integral diameter was overridden by the supposed requirement that the perimeter be integral in units of $2\frac{1}{2}$ my. What we are concerned with now is the geometrical intention of the designers of a monument, as proposed by Thom, and this is almost always slightly different from the design that fits the stones best. For example, the ring on Borrowston Rig (Berwickshire) and the middle circle of The Hurlers (Cornwall) are, *106* according to Thom, supposed to have diameters of 50 my (*c.* 136·0 ft or *c.* 41·45 m), and the circular parts of the patterns do superpose very closely.[1] However, the best-fitting diameters are, respectively, 136·0 and 136·7 ft;[2] the second diameter thus differs from the one which, according to Thom, was intended by the builders.

The megalithic criteria apply to most of the types of shape discussed by Thom, but we shall illustrate their application with regard to only one – the ellipse. For the ellipse it turns out that, if it is based on a Pytha- *111* gorean triangle, then all the main lengths will be integral: the largest and smallest diameters, and the distance between the foci, which are two important points that may be used in the construction of an ellipse. However, there is no mathematical reason why the perimeter shall then be integral. Thom mentions Penmaenmawr (Caernarvonshire) as a good example, where the three relevant lengths are given as 31, $29\frac{1}{2}$ and $9\frac{1}{2}$ my, respectively. Now $31^2 = 961$ and $29\frac{1}{2}^2 + 9\frac{1}{2}^2 = 960\frac{1}{2}$, and so the basic triangle is very close to being Pythagorean in units of $\frac{1}{4}$ my.[3] Also the perimeter is 95·06 my – very close to a multiple of $2\frac{1}{2}$ my. On the other hand at Sands of Forvie, Aberdeenshire, the triangle is not Pythagorean or even nearly so. Accepting the major axis and focal distance as $16\frac{1}{2}$ and 6 my respectively, the third side is 15·37 my,[4] which is not close to a mul- tiple of any of Thom's units, unless we include $\frac{1}{8}$ my. A noteworthy pro- perty of megalithic ellipses is that several have an eccentricity near 0·5.[5]   *17, 18*

It turns out that not all ring-shaped sites can be approximated satis- factorily by one of the basic sequence of shapes favoured by Thom. *26* Among these are some of the grandest of megalithic sites, including Avebury and Stonehenge. For example, the Y and Z holes at Stonehenge *71* are interpreted as lying on an incomplete spiral of circular arcs.[6] In ge- neral terms the special shapes devised by Thom for the construction of these monuments are based on the by now familiar megalithic criteria of integral lengths and perimeters. However, the complex design for Avebury is unusual in the corpus of Thom's shapes in that the arcs of *27* which the design is composed meet at slight corners, instead of joining smoothly.[7] This feature is repeated in only a few other sites, including the design of one of the Kerlescan enclosures in Brittany.[8] Another special *19, 20* shape of some interest, because it is applied to one of the oldest monu- ments which Thom has considered, is that of the mound of Newgrange, which consists of a combined egg-shape and ellipse.[9]

Much the same threads run through Thom's discussion of the geo- metry of cup-and-ring marks. Here the unit is the 'megalithic inch'.

17 Meikle Findowie, Perthshire. Described as a 'definite' ellipse (Thom 1967, 72), its major and minor axes are 9½ and 8.08 my. The distance between the foci is 5 my and so the eccentricity is 0.53. Its perimeter is 27.66 my.

18 Eccentricities of ellipses listed by Thom (1967, 72). Although there is a concentration around a value of 0.5, there is also a wide spread of values. Furthermore if the eccentricity is under 0.2, the greatest and least diameters differ by less than about 2 per cent, and such a ring might frequently be classified as circular. This perhaps accounts for the absence of small values. It can be shown that an ellipse with an eccentricity of 0.5 could not be based on an exact Pythagorean triangle.

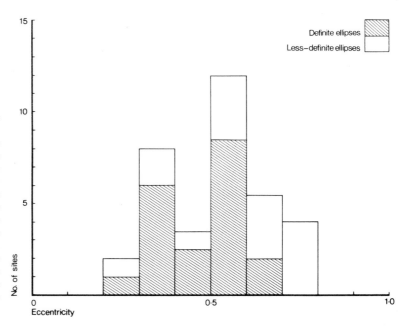

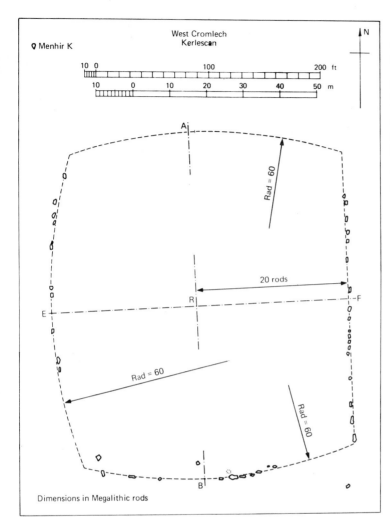

19 The Thoms' plan of the west enclosure at Kerlescan, Brittany (Thom and Thom 1973b, 171). Note the 'corners', a somewhat unusual feature in the geometries proposed by Thom. Three of the sides are circular arcs with radii equal to 60 mr. The calculated perimeter of the figure is 150.11 mr, which is close to an integer, as normally required by Thom.

20 Megalithic 'parallelograms' in Exmoor, near the border of Devon and Somerset, after Chanter and Worth 1906, pl. IV. The orientation of the stones leaves little doubt that they are associated. Horizon altitudes and dimensions are noted. The work of Chanter and Worth includes examples of other equally curious and unusual arrangements.

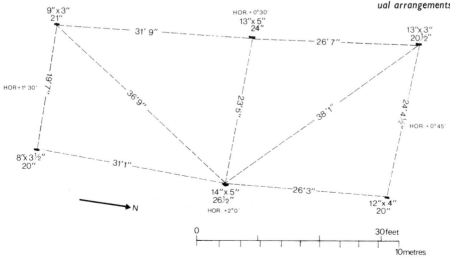

63

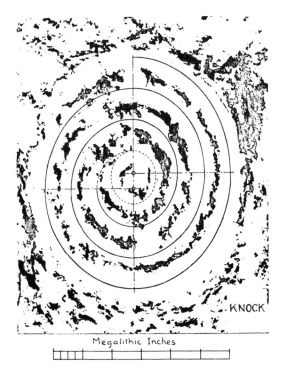

Megalithic Inches

21 The ring marks at Knock, Whithorn, after Thom 1969, 84. Thom's design consists of a sequence of half-ellipses. Of the triangles on which the elliptical arcs are based, one is exactly Pythagorean, and the remainder approximately so. A rubbing by Hadingham (1975, 148) looks definitely more circular.

We have seen that this unit is of poor statistical significance, but Thom adopts the same megalithic criteria.[10] Also, similar basic shapes appear, including circles, and ellipses and egg-shapes based on exact or near-Pythagorean triangles. Again there are some special shapes. For example there are spirals composed of semi-circular arcs analogous to the design of the Y and Z holes, or of elliptical ones, all obeying certain integral criteria, and some based on Pythagorean triangles. According to E. Hadingham, however, in his book *Circles and Standing Stones* (1975), the true geometry was often affected by the very practical necessity of avoiding irregularities in the surface of the rock.[11]

Stone rows

When we turn from megalithic rings to stone rows, we find that we have already dealt with much of their geometry by studying the evidence they give for the use of a unit of length. Let us consider first the fan-shaped arrays of stones which are found in Caithness and in Brittany. We have already mentioned Mid Clyth, where the evidence for certain features of Thom's proposed design is so strikingly good. For example, there seems little doubt that the stones were deliberately placed on evenly-spaced 'lines of latitude'. However, Mid Clyth is untypically well preserved. At Dirlot, Caithness, the stones appear to fit the suggested design quite well in terms of the lines of longitude,[12] though one can make little sense of their relation with the suggested lines of latitude.

The Carnac alignments are on an altogether bigger scale than the stone fans. Also there is more to their geometry, according to the Thoms, than is suggested by our discussion of these monuments in connection with the megalithic yard. We may recall the theory put forward by the Thoms that the positions of the stones were intended to lie on 'nodes' separated by a certain amount ($2\frac{1}{2}$ my at Le Ménec), so that the distance of each stone from a particular node on the same row should be a multiple of this unit. Now at the west end of Le Ménec the Thoms found that one node on each of the 12 rows lay close to a certain transverse line, which they termed a 'nodal line', cutting across the rows.[13] Except for other lines parallel to this, there appeared in fact to be only *one* such line with this remarkable property. At the east end of Le Ménec no nodal line could be found, except for the northern rows. However, in this case the nodal line lay at right angles to the direction of the rows, in contrast with the situation at the west end. Also, there is a bend near the middle of the rows.

22 *The stone fan at Dirlot, Caithness, from Thom 1971, 96. A few of the 'lines of longitude' are quite well defined by the surviving stones, but the evidence for the 'lines of latitude' looks poor. Dotted lines are contours.*

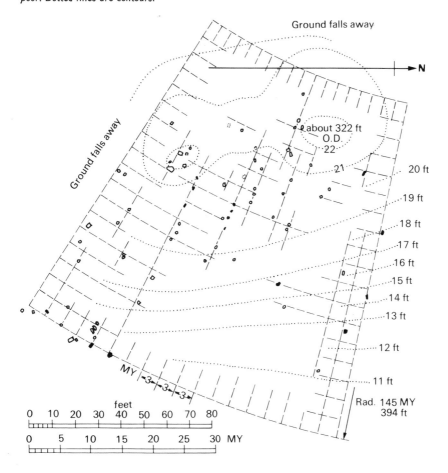

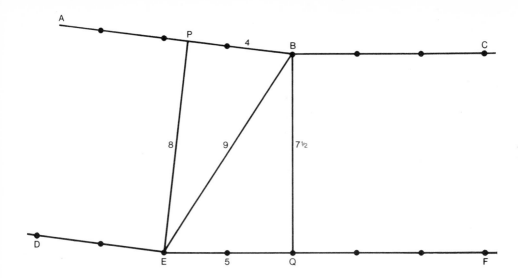

23 The Thoms' geometrical interpretation of the bend in Le Ménec (Thom and Thom 1972, 21). AB and DE represent the two northernmost rows to the west of the bend, and BC, EF are the same rows to the east. Lengths are given in megalithic yards. The triangles are very nearly Pythagorean, and therefore very nearly right-angled at P and Q. The nodes in DE (marked by dots) lag 4 my behind those in AB, and so BE is parallel to a line joining nodes. But the nodes are separated by 2½ my, and since EQ is twice this, the line BQ should be parallel to a line joining nodes on the east of the bend. In fact, independent statistical examination of the stones on the east of the bend gave a result consistent with this construction.

24 The 'quadratic relation' at Le Ménec. For each of the twelve rows, the distance from the most northerly row is measured at the west end (x_w) and at the centre of the alignments (just to the west of the bend). For each row, their difference is plotted against x_w as a dot. The continuous curve represents a mathematical quadratic relation.

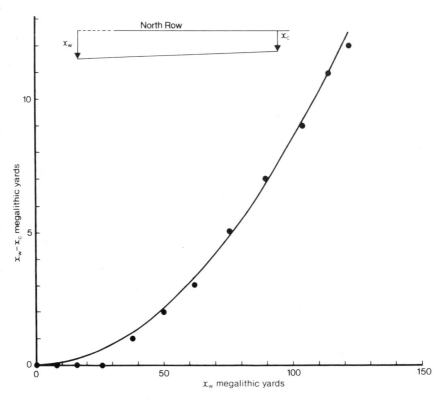

The Thoms suggested that near-Pythagorean triangles were at the basis of these results, together with the fact that the rows appeared to be separated by distances which were multiples of the megalithic yard or $\frac{1}{2}$ my. At the left of the bend the space between the first two rows was 8 my, and the sides of the left-hand triangle are, respectively, at right angles to the rows, along the rows, and parallel to the line of nodes. The adjoining triangle shares the same hypotenuse and gives a change in the direction of the rows, their separation, and the position of the nodal line, all consistent with what is actually found to the right of the bend. Writing of similar relationships in the Kermario alignments, the Thoms considered it 'inconceivable' that they could have come about by accident.[14]

Another remarkable fact about Le Ménec concerns the convergence of the rows from west to east.[15] The Thoms first found the straight lines which best fitted the western sections of the rows, consistent with the megalithic criterion that the rows should be separated at each end by integral multiples of the megalithic yard. They then obtained the distance of each row from the most northerly row, at both the west and east ends of this section. It turned out that the difference between these distances was approximately proportional to the square of either distance. This seems a significant result, in the sense that it does not seem accidental.

The validity of the geometrical theories

So far we have confined our discussion of megalithic geometry to a descriptive account of some of the discoveries which have been claimed. The essential limitation, however, is that we have merely described a number of geometrical figures to which, more or less, the positions of the stones conform: as yet we are far from being in the position where we can assert with any certainty that the proposed geometry must have been the one used by the constructors of the monuments. That the monuments were often set out with care is not in question – that is evident enough, and might even predispose us to the view that their design embodies geometrical principles of some kind, just as modern buildings do. The problem is to uncover the geometry, and to show that there are sound reasons for accepting the proposed geometry rather than any other.

To tackle this question, we recall from chapter 2 our criteria for investigating problems of this type. We reject theories which merely fit the facts – and that, more or less, is the position so far in this chapter with regard to the geometry of megalithic sites. To be acceptable, we demand first that the theory be feasible, which in this case means that one must be able to suggest a practical way in which the geometry could have been set out on the ground. Equally important, however, is our demand that there should be features of the sites which would be surprising were the proposed geometry wrong. This was the criterion which, in the previous chapter, led us into statistical arguments of some intricacy, and we shall see later that statistical methods are also useful in assessing some of the basic evidence on megalithic astronomy. However, the statistical study of megalithic geometry is essentially more difficult than that of other aspects of megalithic science, and most of the time we must proceed without the protection of satisfactory statistical methods.

One way around this problem is to appeal to what the Thoms call a 'philosophical' assessment.[16] We find that many sites can be fitted by shapes whose geometries are based almost entirely on a few simple types, together with the 'megalithic criteria' which have already been described. These principles appear to be geographically widespread, applying to sites all over Britain and also in Brittany. Thus the strength of the theory is claimed to lie in its comprehensiveness and essential simplicity.

25 *Geometry of Torwood broch, Stirling, according to E.W. MacKie. The surviving wall is shaded, and crosses mark points measured on the inner wall near the base. These are fitted quite well by a combination* *of a semi-ellipse and two circular arcs, whose dimensions satisfy the integral criteria in megalithic yards. A semi-circle of radius 6½ my fits the upper half about as well.*

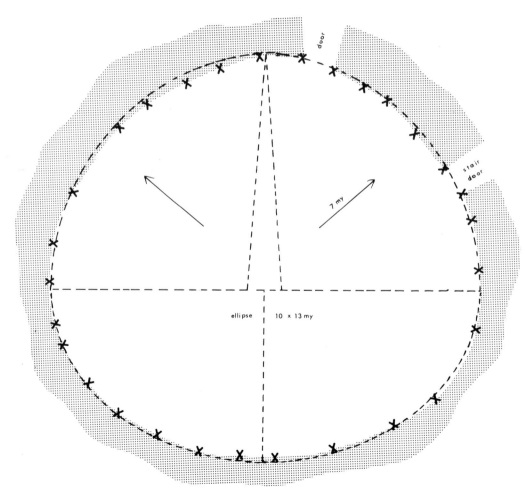

Despite its apparent attractiveness, this argument has a mixed appeal. There are many theories with these qualities which are rightly relegated to the realms of speculation; any archaeologist can think of theories which can claim simplicity and comprehensiveness but which are generally regarded as fantasy. Another point to be made about this is that we cannot be sure that all megalithic sites have much in common, and so it could even be considered as a flaw of the geometrical theory that the one thing they do share is the logic of their design. This problem is all the more acute if one contends that certain principles of megalithic geometry also underlie the design of Scottish brochs, as MacKie has done,[17] since these were built perhaps two millennia or more after the megalithic rings. These are debatable points, but suffice to indicate that a geometrical theory must be something other than comprehensive and simple to be acceptable.

The feasibility of megalithic geometry

We begin our investigation of megalithic geometry with practical considerations. For example, would there have been any problems in constructing sites in accordance with Thom's ideas, and are these surmountable? Even before a site is constructed, however, it must be designed, and one must mention the problem of designing shapes which simultaneously satisfy some or all of the various criteria adopted by Thom. The very fact that he has devised many such designs is proof enough that the creation of such geometries is a feasible task, though it is not necessarily an easy one.

The plan for a site having been designed along Thom's lines, it would not be difficult, using primitive equipment, such as pegs and ropes, to mark it out on the ground, at least as far as smaller sites are concerned.[18] The circles, flattened circles and egg shapes are all composed of circular arcs (which can be marked out using a length of rope fixed at one end) and straight segments. The marking out of some of the shapes requires the setting out of angles of 120° and 90°, but practical constructions for these angles can be suggested readily. Some extra geometrical procedures are needed for the special shapes devised by Thom for a few individual sites, such as the bisection of an angle for the design of Kerry Pole, Montgomery,[19] but these introduce no essential difficulty. Likewise it is easy to set out an ellipse and, with scarcely more elaboration, the shapes suggested by Cowan.

Matters change when we consider very large sites, such as Avebury. If we suppose, following Thom, that its perimeter consists of circular arcs, the aforementioned methods of setting out the site would be rather impractical because of such problems as rope-stretch. Much more satisfactory methods could be devised in which constant reference to the centre of the arc is not needed.[20] On the other hand there is some evidence that the stones of Avebury were erected after the bank and ditch had been constructed, and these would have been a serious obstacle if Thom's accurate design was to have been laid out subsequently.[21]

Even for a small site, however, problems of construction are not over when the design is plotted on the ground, for the stones still have to be placed in position. If the centre of each stone had been placed on the proposed design, the excavation of the stone hole must have involved the destruction and loss of the marked position. For this reason, Stephan thought that the stones would have been placed with their inner faces touching the proposed design.[22] Yet Atkinson pointed out that, at Stonehenge at least, the preparation of the hole for each stone would have destroyed an area of ground larger than the sectional area of the stone itself. He therefore thought that the stones would have been adjusted so that their inner faces touched a string stretched across the prepared holes. In other words we should think rather in terms of polygonal shapes, with one face for each stone, than of curved shapes.[23] As well as considering how stones could have been placed *on* a proposed design, we should also enquire how they could have been spaced *along* it, because some theories suppose that it was necessary to space out a particular number of stones or stone-holes evenly along the perimeter of the design. Hoyle has suggested a way in which this could have been done, for example with the Aubrey Holes at Stonehenge.[24]

71

When we consider practical aspects of setting out stone rows, fresh problems arise. One of the most curious occurs at Mid Clyth, where the centres from which the lines are supposed to radiate are invisible from the rows themselves, because the ground falls away just beyond the convergent north end of the rows.[25]

12

The motivation for megalithic geometry

Can we suggest why it might be that the constructors of the stone rings wished to use certain geometrical designs? The absence of any such suggestion would prove nothing, of course, and even if we can find one it may not be possible to establish its truth with any certainty. However, one fact which makes this question particularly intriguing is that the distortions from circularity are rarely apparent to a visitor on the ground, and can usually only be discerned in a good plan.[26]

Considering first the theories of Thom, can we (or he) explain why there is such an emphasis on integral dimensions? One of Thom's proposals is that integral dimensions were used for the purpose of recording mathematical results known to the people who designed the rings. After all, if they lacked any more conventional writing material, this may have been one way they could record such information[27] (although common sense might suggest there would have been less strenuous means of storing such knowledge). One piece of mathematical knowledge that may have been so stored is Pythagoras' Theorem. It is not necessary to imagine that the megalithic geometers were aware of this result in the form in which it is known to us, for they may have known only that triangles with certain integral sides contained one right angle. Another possibility is that stone rings were designed with approximately integral perimeter and diameter in order to provide rational approximations to π, the ratio of the circumference of a circle to its diameter.[28]

Next one might ask why it was necessary to go to the trouble of designing distorted, non-circular rings. It has been suggested that it was done in order that the integral properties could be satisfied more easily.[29] Alternatively, its purpose was possibly the design of sites in which the ratio of perimeter to diameter (i.e. the *largest* diameter in the case of a non-circular site) should be as close to 3 as possible.[30] However, the evidence seems to contradict this particular idea: for 15 egg-shaped rings listed by Thom,[31] one finds that the average ratio is 2.94 ± 0.026, which differs significantly from 3. Also J. E. Wood has argued against the idea in his book, *Sun, Moon and Standing Stones* (1978), on the grounds that it would generally have been easy to improve upon the relatively poor approximations to 3 which Thom's designs represent.[32]

Thom and others have suggested quite a different set of reasons for certain types of megalithic geometry – astronomical ones. These are really the province of the following chapters, but it will do no harm to sketch a few of the suggestions here. The simplest is that some element of the geometry of a site may be orientated on the point of rising or setting of a conspicuous astronomical object – the sun, the moon or a bright star. One example is Woodhenge, whose geometrical axis points to the rising position of the sun at midsummer.[33] A more elaborate one is Castle Rigg, Cumberland, which Thom rates as the 'most spectacular success' in combining astronomy and geometry.[34]

In 1967 Thom suggested that the fan at Mid Clyth in Caithness might have been designed as a series of stellar orientations,[35] but by 1971 he had devised a different theory for the geometry of this site, though still an astronomical one. The suggestion then was that the rows were designed for the purpose of facilitating certain calculations concerning the motion of the moon.[36] Later the Thoms devised suggestions along the same lines for the rows at Le Ménec and Kermario,[37] and these even incorporated an explanation for the curious bends in the rows at Le Ménec. They pointed out how much of the geometry was explicable by their hypothesis, and they preferred these suggestions to the idea that the rows were set out only to demonstrate the properties of the near-Pythagorean triangles which, it is claimed, underlie the bends in the rows. Few would doubt the inadequacy of the latter suggestion.

This by no means exhausts the suggested astronomical explanations for the peculiar geometry of some megalithic sites. Hoyle thought that the distorted stone rings, rather than being mere geometrical curiosities, perhaps embodied a knowledge of the irregular rate at which the sun appears to perform its annual orbit around the earth.[38] In the nineteenth century, some writers held the view that certain rings represented the orbit itself.[39] Curiously, this idea reappears in Hoyle's own discussion of Stonehenge, as we shall see later. Recently it has been suggested that flattened circles represent the shape of the moon just before it is full,[40] and I. O. Angell has shown how shapes such as those of some megalithic rings can be constructed by measuring the shadow cast by a vertical stick throughout the year.[41]

48, 49

12

23

None of these suggestions need impress us that an interest by the megaiith-builders in geometry is any more plausible. First we should have to be convinced that they were interested in the appropriate branches of astronomy, and that is a topic we shall not take up until later. There is a sense, however, in which the proliferation of explanations for the stone rings may make at least one or other of them less plausible. According to Thom, for instance, the astronomical, geometrical and metrical properties of such a site as Castle Rigg are not alternatives; he claims that it embodies all three types of property simultaneously. If, then, we considered that the construction of an astronomically meaningful monument, by itself, or of a geometrically significant one, was an implausible undertaking, then we should be less disposed to take seriously any suggestion that a monument was actually erected which had both properties. An example is Stonehenge, where Hawkins was indeed reluctant to entertain the idea of a deliberate combination of mensuration, geometry and astronomy.[42]

Finally we should perhaps bear in mind the possibility that the peculiar geometries of some sites result simply from poor attempts to construct circles, and so the geometries really had no motivation. Burl has suggested that this explanation could account for some features in the strange geometry of Avebury.[43] There the stone circle is surrounded by a ditch, and if different sections of this were dug simultaneously by different gangs of workmen, corners might result where neighbouring sections met. These might then produce corners in the shape of the megalithic ring, since the stones stand near the inner edge of the ditch.

27

An instructive site where comparable ideas may be applicable is the Lios, Limerick.[44] Excavation revealed a central post-hole which could have been used as the basis for the roughly circular geometry. However, the circle appears not to have been marked all the way round, in what is to us the obvious manner. Instead, ten points on the perimeter were marked by twelve upright stones set into the ground, and then the spaces between these were filled, slightly irregularly, by somewhat smaller stones resting on the ground and against the outer bank. The result is a monument whose shape vaguely resembles one or two of the more complicated shapes devised by Thom.

Another rather prosaic possible explanation for the geometry, this time of flattened circles, is that there may simply not have been enough level ground for a true circle. Indeed at some sites the flattened side does appear to occur where the ground falls away.[45]

Goodness of fit

It would be a mistake to think that much can be gained by plausibility arguments. The claims made for deliberate megalithic geometry could not be dismissed merely because we were unable to understand why the megalith-builders might have been so concerned with it. Nor, of course, could we regard the case for megalithic geometry as proven if all we could do was to demonstrate that a practical interest in geometry is very understandable. We must now study the evidence itself, to see whether it demonstrates beyond reasonable doubt that the geometrical shapes proposed for various sites were in fact those used by their original designers.

The first test which any geometrical theory must pass is that of goodness of fit, that is, the stones must conform reasonably closely to the shape proposed. There are various ways in which the fit can be measured. Thus one can measure the mean of the squares of the distances by which the stones deviate from the proposed shape, or else the maximum deviation. Alternatively, one can count the number of stones which lie on or touch the proposed design. This is a more rapid method, though the extent to which it genuinely measures goodness of fit depends on the width of the stones.

Thom himself gives few quantitative estimates of how well his proposed designs agree with the positions of the stones. Qualitatively, the agreement is generally satisfactory, and sometimes very striking. On the other hand, Hogg has expressed surprise at how widely some of the small stones of the Caithness fans depart from the proposed grids.[46] Also, *12* Barber has concluded, from an inspection of plans of about twenty sites, that on average about a quarter of the stones do not touch the outline proposed by Thom.[47] However, it can be plausibly argued in some cases that the stones were not intended to lie *on* some geometrical shape but to lie with one face touching it, as we have seen, and then if a site had been subject to slight disturbance it is to be expected that many of the stones would no longer even touch the geometrical shape. Of course, sufficiently larger disturbances to any site will have the same effect.

The importance of testing goodness of fit derives from the fact that it has been used by itself to establish the correctness of the geometry in certain cases. For example, when discussing the site Moel ty Ucha, *26* Merioneth, Thom states that 'we can see how perfectly the construction fits the stones' and elsewhere that 'the agreement is much too close to be accidental.'[48] A similar inference has been made about the proposed geometry of Avebury.[49] *27*

On the other hand there is a limit to the extent to which one should lay stress on goodness of fit. For one thing, even if most of the stones conform to a proposed geometry, it will almost always be possible to propose some other shape which fits the stones as well or even better. For example, consider the smaller fan-shaped stone rows near Carnac.[50] It has been shown that a much more satisfactory fit with the positions of the stones in one of these can be obtained by relaxing the constraint that the geometry should be fan-shaped, as it is at Mid Clyth. A geometry consisting of a few straight lines fits much better in this case than a fan-shaped one.[51] Thus, if goodness of fit by itself were a sufficient reason for accepting a geometry, one would undoubtedly reject the fan-shaped geometry. If another example is needed, consider Angell's constructions for stone rings.[52] These appear to fit the positions of the stones about as well as Thom's, judged qualitatively, in cases for which results have *7, 8, 28, 29* been published.

26 Moel ty Ucha, Merioneth, after Thom 1967, 85. This is an example where the geometry was specially devised for the one site. The design passes within the outline of almost all the stones, though the sizes and shapes are quite irregular. A number of azimuths and outlying features are indicated.

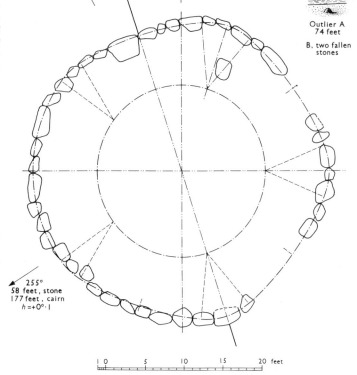

15°·6 h = −0°·2

Outlier A
74 feet

B, two fallen
stones

B   N   A 17°·3

255°
58 feet, stone
177 feet, cairn
h = +0°·1

27 Goodness of fit of Thom's proposed geometry for Avebury, Wiltshire (Thom, Thom and Foord 1976, 189). Note how well the positions of the stones agree with the suggested arcs, which are part of the coherent geometry for the whole site. However the trend of the deviations from the arc FG strongly suggests that the theoretical radius of curvature is too small. Also, possibly stone 39 belongs to an extension of arc GH.

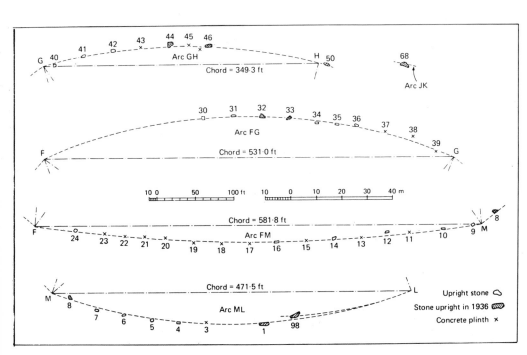

G 40   41   42   43   44 45 46   H 50   68
                    Arc GH   Arc JK
              Chord = 349·3 ft

        30   31   32   33   34 35 36   37   38
                    Arc FG   39
              Chord = 531·0 ft   G
F

10 0   50   100 ft   10 0 10 20 30 40 m

              Chord = 581·8 ft
F   Arc FM   8
  24 23 22 21 20   9 M
          19 18 17 16 15 14 13 12 11 10

              Chord = 471·5 ft   L
M   Arc ML
  8   Upright stone ⌒
    7   6   Stone upright in 1936 ▨
        5   4   3   98   Concrete plinth ×
                    1

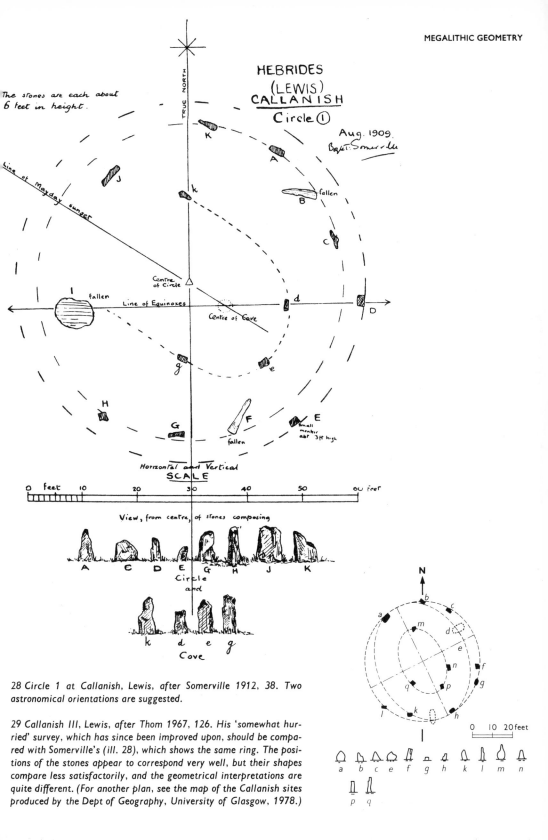

The stones are each about 6 feet in height.

HEBRIDES
(LEWIS)
CALLANISH
Circle ①

Aug. 1909
Boyle Somerville

Line of Mayday sunset

TRUE NORTH

K

A

k

B   fallen

C

Centre
of Circle

d

Line of Equinoxes

D

fallen

Centre of Cove

g

e

H

G

F

E

fallen   small
menhir
abt 3 ft high

Horizontal and Vertical
SCALE

| 0 feet | 10 | 20 | 30 | 40 | 50 | 60 feet |

View, from centre, of stones composing

A   C   D   E   G   H   J   K
Circle
and

k   d   e   g
Cove

28 Circle 1 at Callanish, Lewis, after Somerville 1912, 38. Two astronomical orientations are suggested.

29 Callanish III, Lewis, after Thom 1967, 126. His 'somewhat hurried' survey, which has since been improved upon, should be compared with Somerville's (ill. 28), which shows the same ring. The positions of the stones appear to correspond very well, but their shapes compare less satisfactorily, and the geometrical interpretations are quite different. (For another plan, see the map of the Callanish sites produced by the Dept of Geography, University of Glasgow, 1978.)

N

a   b   c
m   d
e
n   f
q   p   g
l   k   h

0   10   20 feet

a   b   c   e   f   g   h   k   l   m   n

p   q

It could be argued that, if we find at least one geometrical shape which fits the stones very well, we have done enough, since such a design cannot be substantially different from that used by the designers. On the other hand, it could still be that the underlying geometrical principles (such as the use of Pythagoras' Theorem) were quite different, even if the shapes were nearly the same, and it is often the former to which most interest attaches.

It is difficult, therefore, to decide on the essential correctness of a proposed geometry on grounds of goodness of fit. If for a site one has rival geometries which fit the site equally well, one might think it natural to choose the simplest, but there is unlikely to be agreement about what is meant by 'simple'. Are Thom's shapes more or less simple than Cowan's or Angell's? This point was raised some time ago by J. M. Hammersley, who expressed the opinion that there was no satisfactory method of incorporating the concept of simplicity in any quantitative way into this sort of investigation.[53]

Recently, however, J. D. Patrick and C. S. Wallace, of Monash University, Australia, have made good progress in this respect.[54] Making use of concepts from information theory, they devise for each rival geometry a quantity called the 'information measure', which quantifies in a rational way both the extent to which a theory fits the actual shape of the megalithic rings and its complexity. The more complicated a geometry is, or the poorer its fit to the positions of the stones, the larger is its information measure, and the best geometry can be found by looking for the one with the smallest information measure. This investigation is certainly one of the most interesting developments in the study of megalithic geometry in recent years, though the results so far have not been very decisive. The reason for this is that the method has been applied mostly to Irish sites which Thom himself has not studied extensively. Therefore, although Patrick and Wallace found that Thom's shapes fared worse on the whole than those with which they were compared, this tells us little about the validity of Thom's theories when applied to sites in other parts of the British Isles.

There is another reason why goodness of fit by itself is an inadequate test of megalithic geometry. Even if we knew the correct geometry of a site we would not expect the present positions of the stones to conform to it.[55] Quite apart from the errors which the constructors might have made in marking on the ground the design they had in mind, they may have made further errors in attempting to place the stones along the design, and we have already listed several disturbing effects on the positions of the stones which can further increase the departure of their present measured positions from the intended shape. Some of these sources of error can be avoided if our investigations are based on the positions of stone-holes revealed in excavations, as in MacKie's study of an apparent megalithic ellipse at Cultoon, Islay.[56] However, this does not remove all sources of error, and so there is a limit to the extent to which we may expect the positions of the stones or stone-holes to agree with the true, intended geometry. This fact has an important consequence, for it is therefore not necessarily true to say that, the better a shape fits a site, the greater are its chances of being correct (if such a statement has any meaning).

Stones with geometrical significance

In effect the geometrical theories make a number of predictions concerning the manner in which the circles were laid out. For stone rings almost all the designs suggested consist of circular arcs which, for smaller rings at least, are likely to have been described by the obvious method of attaching a rope of the requisite length to the centre of the arc. If the geometrical theories were incorrect it would be very surprising if stones or traces of isolated posts were found, by excavation if need be, at the centres indicated by the geometry, as is the case with the Lios. It turns out, in fact, that the centres of stone rings are not now marked on the surface very often. Even when there is a central stone, Thom considers that in no case does it occupy one of the geometrical centres exactly;[57] the centre is always very slightly to one side, as at Cambret Moor, Kirkcudbright.   66

The centre is by no means the only position with geometrical significance, if certain of the theories we have discussed are correct. A very remarkable example is afforded by the ellipse on Machrie Moor, Arran.   30
Note in the diagram how the symmetry of the stones very closely matches that of the proposed ellipse, with the exception of the gap at 12. The alternation of small and large stones is also noteworthy, as is the fact that the long axes of the smaller slabs are placed along the line of the elliptic outline, rather than at right angles to a line joining the stone to the centre of the ellipse. (For the stone at 6 the two directions coincide, of course.) While this is one of the strongest cases for a particular geometry that we have seen, it is quite possible that Cowan's suggested alternative to the ellipse (called the 'oblate circle' in ill. 6) would share these attractive properties.

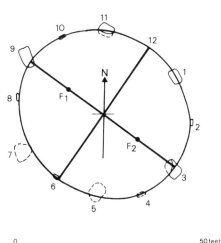

30 The ellipse on Machrie Moor, Arran, after Roy et al. 1963, 64. Note the alternation of large and small stones and their relation to the axes of the suggested elliptical construction. F_1 and F_2 are the foci.

The ellipse on Machrie Moor is one example where the stones them-selves appear to be specially related to the geometry, and there are broadly similar examples to be found in the work of Thom, as in the case of Castle Rigg.[58] This is classified as a flattened circle, and there are stones on the circumference of the large arc at intervals of 60° on either side of the main axis of symmetry. There are other sites where stones are separated by 45°.[59] Certainly the chance of these properties occurring accidentally is small, although they were presumably not predicted in advance of an inspection of the survey and so, like the significance of a unit of length discovered by examination of the same data, their signi-ficance must be treated with caution. In the case of Castle Rigg, Thom himself recognized how difficult it is to show that the property was deliberate. However, one other curiosity of Castle Rigg deserves to be mentioned. The flattened circle consists of arcs of different radii, and the points where different arcs meet are marked by stones.

48, 49

Interesting as such evidence is, none of it is really of the decisive nature that we are seeking. There is a clear difference between, on the one hand, deciding on a geometry for a site and then noticing that some of the stones lie on parts of the geometry with special significance, and, on the other, suggesting that the geometry requires a marking post to have been fixed at one or more points and then finding, by excavation or otherwise, traces of this kind of activity. Then again, when we see cases in which several of the geometrical points are marked, as at Castle Rigg, we must also consider the numerous cases in which the stones do not seem to be specially disposed in relation to the geometry.

Integral dimensions

Let us move on to a discussion of Thom's claim that megalithic rings were designed so that as many dimensions as possible should be integral in the megalithic yard, or else in a unit closely related to it, such as the megalithic rod (of $2\frac{1}{2}$ my) for the perimeters. Thom has claimed in speci-fic cases that such results cannot be accidental,[60] and constitute substan-tial support for the suggested geometry. How can we assess this claim? Expressed in slightly different words, Thom's finding is that a satisfac-tory fit with the shapes of many megalithic sites can be obtained with geometry in which many of the dimensions are integral. Should we be surprised by the fact that this is possible, bearing in mind that the fit is never quite perfect, and that the position, size and orientation of the geometry can usually be adjusted within limits without causing a noti-ceable deterioration in the fit? If it is surprising, it would be unreason-able not to give serious attention to Thom's claims. On the other hand, one might consider the idea that one generally had enough freedom to adjust the dimensions so that they could be made integral, without ruining the agreement of the geometry with the positions of the stones. If this turns out to be the case, then clearly the fact that designs with integral dimensions are possible would not be surprising, and would not constitute extra evidence in favour of the proposed geometries.

Consider first sites described as perfect circles. We know that the diameters tend to cluster around multiples of 2 my, and Thom considers that some diameters were intended as multiples of 1 my or possibly even of $\frac{1}{2}$ my. Clearly, then, the diameter of the best-fitting circle (which will never be exactly integral) need only be adjusted by at most $\frac{1}{4}$ my, or about 20 cm, in order to produce a shape with an integral diameter. This is a change of at most about 10 cm in the radius. Since it is unlikely that such a change would produce a noticeable effect on the extent to which the circle fitted the stones, unless these were small, regular, exceptionally carefully erected and relatively undisturbed, we should not regard the possibility of integral diameters as surprising.

The megalithic criteria also state that the perimeter shall be integral in megalithic rods, and it is impossible for this to be satisfied exactly if we also demand that the diameter shall be integral in $\frac{1}{2}$ my. The problem is that we have only one adjustable quantity – the diameter – and two conditions to satisfy. However, if more than one circle with integral diameter gives a satisfactory fit to the positions of the stones, it is possible that the perimeter property will be approximately satisfied by at least one of these. Furthermore, since the integral properties are never all satisfied exactly, it could be that choosing between as few as two circles would be enough to produce one which satisfied them well enough. In this case it should not surprise us if a circle can be found which approximately fits the stones, whose diameter is integral in $\frac{1}{2}$ my, and whose perimeter is approximately integral in megalithic rods.

This discussion demonstrates one way in which we can assess the importance of the claims for integral dimensions. If each ring is such that circles of several different integral diameters fit the positions of the stones about equally well, we should not be surprised if it is possible to find one which also satisfies the perimeter property approximately. The fact that such circles can be found should not be regarded as significant evidence that the proposed geometrical criteria are correct. If, however, each ring is such that only one circle with an integral diameter fits satisfactorily, it would be surprising if this circle also approximately satisfied the perimeter property, and this would constitute significant evidence in favour of these geometrical criteria.

Unfortunately there is not enough suitable information to enable us to assess circular megalithic rings in this way. However, it is helpful to have established the principles behind the method in this simple case, because it is possible to apply the same method to other more elaborate shapes for which more information is available. Furthermore, it is mainly in the context of elliptical and egg-shapes that the importance of the megalithic criteria has been emphasized.

The size of an ellipse is determined by two adjustable quantities, for which we can take the longest diameter and the focal distance. On the other hand, one also has more criteria to satisfy, in that the longest and shortest diameters, the perimeter, and the distance between the foci of the ellipse, must be integral in the appropriate units, or at least approximately so. Nevertheless, one can assess the evidence in much the same way as for the circle. If it is possible to adjust the longest diameter and the focal distance slightly without significantly affecting the fit with the positions of the stones, we should not be too surprised if it is possible to fit them with an ellipse for which these dimensions are exactly integral. There is no reason to suppose that the other two dimensions will be approximately integral. If, however, one can find several different ellipses, each with two integral dimensions and each providing a satisfactory fit with the positions of the stones, there is a chance that at least one of these will satisfy the remaining integral conditions approximately. A somewhat similar discussion can be given for egg-shaped rings.

Let us suppose for a moment that it is the freedom to choose between several different elliptical or egg-shapes which accounts for the fact that Thom's shapes satisfy the integral criteria approximately. Clearly the more freedom of choice we have, on this theory, the more accurately should it be possible to satisfy the criteria. Now Thom has quantified the extent to which the perimeters of a number of egg-shaped and elliptical designs lie close to multiples of the megalithic rod,[61] and it is possible to calculate how much choice we would need to obtain this measure of agreement. It turns out that, if each site can be adequately fitted by as few as three shapes, and for each site we choose the one which satisfies the perimeter condition best, then the resulting shapes will satisfy the condition about as well as Thom's shapes do.[62]

This cannot be our final conclusion, since we have not yet accounted for the fact that the remaining integral criteria are also satisfied. For example, we must ensure that the smallest diameter of each ellipse is approximately integral in the appropriate unit, and to do so we would require still greater freedom of choice. However, the extent to which the smallest diameters in Thom's list[63] actually do so is not quite as good as the extent to which the perimeters fit the integrality criterion. Hence no very great increase in the freedom of choice is needed. Furthermore, for ellipses of low eccentricity, quite large changes in the interfocal distance lead to quite small changes in the smallest diameter, and this means that a large freedom of choice may be obtained without ruining the fit with the positions of the stones.[64]

We can summarize the implications of these remarks as follows. In the first place, we have Thom's result that elliptical and egg-shaped designs can be found for many rings, each design satisfying approximately the integral criteria, but now we have two possible explanations. One is Thom's, that these are the designs with which the rings were set out. The second is that a certain amount of freedom is available in choosing the dimensions for each site, and one can then exploit that freedom to satisfy approximately the integral criteria. Two of the criteria can be satisfied exactly, but if there are several such designs which fit the positions of the stones reasonably well, one may have enough choice to be able to select one which, on average, satisfies the remaining integral criteria as well as the ones selected by Thom.

Obviously the second explanation could be ruled out if we knew that Thom had arrived at his values for the dimensions of the ellipses and egg-shapes by some process which led to a unique answer. Unfortunately, the method by which he obtained the listed dimensions is not stated in his book, and if the method involved some trial and error, the second explanation becomes a real possibility. Though the Thoms have recently stated that the dimensions were not adjusted in any way to make the perimeters satisfy the integral criterion,[65] other evidence suggests that there is some freedom in the choice of the dimensions. In two cases Thom himself mentions that alternative dimensions can be found,[66] and the case of the Tormore ellipse, on Machrie Moor, Arran, is also instructive. Its longest and shortest diameters were stated by its surveyors[67] to be 47·8 ft and 41·6 ft, respectively, i.e. approximately 17·57 my and 15·29 my. The dimensions chosen by the Thoms[68] were 18 my and 15½ my. Notice that dimensions of 17½ and 15½ my would have given closer agreement with the surveyed dimensions. However, they would have resulted in a perimeter that would not have satisfied the integral criterion as well as the perimeter of the ellipse chosen by the Thoms. These examples show that there is some freedom in choosing the dimensions of ellipses and egg-shapes, and therefore one cannot dismiss the possibility that it is this which has resulted in shapes which have nearly integral perimeters. Thus the integral dimensions in the designs proposed by Thom need not have been intended by the megalith-builders.

30

We have concentrated on a discussion of ellipses and egg-shapes taken as a whole, but there are one or two individual sites with other shapes which are sufficiently complex to make separate discussion possible. One example which Thom considers to be particularly remarkable is Avebury.[69] The geometrical design proposed for this ring is, as usual, composed of circular arcs of different integral radii. What is remarkable about it is that, not only is the entire perimeter integral, but so are most of the component arcs. That they are integral to a statistically significant extent is hardly in question. What is important to decide is whether this significance should be attributed to the intentions of the designers of Avebury, or whether it is the result of a certain amount of trial and error in fitting the design to Avebury. Unfortunately, Thom gives no details of the manner in which the design was arrived at, and so this question must remain unresolved. However, it has been shown that the centres of the arcs in the design can be moved over quite a wide area without any deterioration in the goodness of fit, provided that the radii of the arcs are suitably adjusted.[70] This gives a great deal of freedom which could be exploited to satisfy various integrality conditions.

27

If the case for integral dimensions in the ellipses and egg-shapes suggested by Thom seems indecisive, some important conclusions follow. The first is that the supposed evidence for integral dimensions does not lend any additional support to the reality of the megalithic yard,[71] or to the correctness of the proposed geometries. The second consequence is that the evidence for Pythagorean triangles is also unsatisfactory. It is well to stress the weakness of the evidence for Pythagorean triangles, since some writers have been tempted to hail their supposed existence as evidence for an astonishing level of geometrical knowledge among the megalith-builders.

A consequence of this is that one should be extremely cautious about accepting the existence of Pythagorean triangles in other situations. If it is true that the evidence for those in megalithic ellipses and egg-shapes is unsatisfactory, then claims for their presence in the design of the Carnac alignments or the Station Stone rectangle at Stonehenge[72] require much stronger individual justification than they have at present.

23
71

Conclusions

The deduction of the geometrical design with which a megalithic site was set out is clearly a problem of great difficulty. In Thom's words, when he wrote of Castle Rigg, 'no method of rigid proof can be produced to show that this construction was actually used by the erectors.'[73] This is true, though we would have been content with much less. Had it been possible to show, for example, that the near-integral right-angled triangles in megalithic ellipses were unlikely to have come about by trial and error, then we should have treated this as significant evidence for the proposed megalithic geometry. In this sense the geometrical hypotheses we have been discussing are potentially provable, and our survey of megalithic geometry need not have been as inconclusive as it has turned out to be. For example, we have seen insufficient evidence to justify the statement that we can be 'perfectly certain' of the geometry of part of Avebury.[74] Likewise, the conclusion that 'π was doubtless known to the Stone Age geometers'[75] seems quite unwarranted.

It cannot be seriously doubted that Thom's classification of the shapes of different sites is a useful one. The fact that the larger, presumably older rings tend to be true or flattened circles, while the smaller, later sites include a larger proportion of ellipses and egg-shapes[76] implies that Thom's scheme has a genuine significance. The same is implied by the distinctive geographical distribution of certain geometrical types. However, it might well be that similar correlations would be exhibited if other types of shape were fitted to the sites, and so these results need not distinguish Thom's geometrical theories uniquely.

Interesting as the study of megalithic geometry is for its own sake, it also has implications which are potentially of importance. For example, Thom has described as 'inescapable' the conclusion that the designers of the stone rings must have been responsible for the cup-and-ring marks, since both types of design were, he maintains, governed by the same principles.[77] Such a result would be of obvious importance to the archaeologist if well founded. However, it is just here that doubts arise. We have seen that Thom's integral criteria for megalithic ellipses may not be an original feature of the designs, and the same could equally well be true of the cup-and-ring marks. It is quite possible that the geometrical connection between megalithic rings and cup-and-ring marks lies in the way they have been interpreted, rather than in the way they were designed.

5 The astronomical hypothesis

History of the subject

The fact that astronomical theories of megalithic sites have been mentioned in the foregoing chapters shows that they are not completely independent of the theories of geometry and mensuration. Nevertheless, the two latter topics are much more closely intertwined than is either with megalithic astronomy. It is true that some authors have suggested detailed links between the geometry of individual sites and their supposed astronomical functions, but the most significant evidence is not of this type. On the contrary, it consists of the discussion of large numbers of sites in a quasi-statistical fashion, so that the geometrical details of individual sites are smothered out and leave – if the astronomical theories are correct – a relatively sharp picture of the astronomical features which they share in common.

The notion that megalithic sites in general are associated somehow with the sun appears to have existed for a very long time, but Stonehenge was the most prominent single site in the early history of the subject. It remains today the one whose supposed astronomical functions are most widely known – if somewhat vaguely and uncritically for the most part. How far the evidence at Stonehenge justifies such ideas we shall see as we review this and many other sites in later chapters. Nevertheless it is here, with Stukeley's discovery (published in 1740) that the axis of Stonehenge points to the midsummer rising position of the sun, that the study of the subject begins.[1]

Seven years later, a somewhat different theory was published by J. Wood, an architect, who thought that Stonehenge was a sort of calendar:[2] one of its circles contains 30 stones, about the number of days in a month. This suggestion is a forerunner of some of the ideas which came to be widely discussed in the 1960s. Eclipses were loosely connected with Stonehenge by H. Wansey in 1796, and this is another thread that still runs through contemporary research.[3]

Even by the close of the eighteenth century, such ideas seem to have been widely canvassed and applied to other sites. By 1772 Sir Joseph Banks regarded the stones near Stenness in Orkney as 'temples of [the] Sun and Moon', and the idea that circles such as Callanish in Lewis were 'rude astronomical observatories', serving a comparatively practical purpose, was expressed as early as 1808 by J. Headrick.[4] Astronomical

71

107

48, 49

alignments, such as the axial orientation of Stonehenge, were already playing a significant role in these ideas. In 1849, J. Otley considered the Keswick Circle (i.e. Castle Rigg) to exhibit solar orientations,[5] and subsequently the notion that orientations might occur at many sites was expressed by A. L. Lewis. Lewis thought that orientations of stellar significance were also involved, and in addition he pointed out the possible astronomical significance of natural features on the horizon,[6] thus foreshadowing a topic which was to be discussed quite intensively some 75 years later. Nor was work such as this by any means confined to Britain, since pioneering investigations were being conducted in France by Gaillard at about this time.[7]

One thing most of these suggestions lacked was precision, but the late nineteenth and early twentieth centuries saw this rectified. The outstanding figure in this development was Lockyer.[8] As well as Stonehenge, Lockyer also studied many other sites as a 'holiday task'.[9] His work at these sites was not always as precise as at Stonehenge, but the astronomical theories were considerably elaborated by Lockyer's study of them. In this he was influenced by the results of his earlier researches in Egypt, where he had come to the conclusion that several of the most famous temples were orientated to the rising and setting positions of certain bright stars.[10]

Lockyer's work was very influential, especially on the continent.[11] In the British Isles, his lead was followed by B. Somerville, who became interested in Lockyer's theories in about 1908.[12] He was responsible for one of the first discoveries of an orientation to the moon, at Callanish.[13]

Despite Lockyer's expressed diffidence – in the preface to his book he stated, 'Further observations are required in order that the hypothesis. . . may be rejected or confirmed' – he had no doubt about the essential correctness of the astronomical theories. Unfortunately, what he never really concerned himself with, except in a brief, qualitative fashion, was the problem of showing that the supposed alignments could not reasonably be attributed to chance. After all, many lines are defined by a site if it is not too simple, and there are a considerable number of astronomical phenomena with which each might be associated. One might therefore expect some alignments to occur quite by accident.

It is only comparatively recently that the problem of the significance of the alignments has been tackled. Since the task is one of showing that more lines can be associated with astronomical phenomena than one could expect by chance, the first requisite is information on a relatively large number of sites. This is now available thanks to the work of Professor Thom (whose interest in the subject, one may note in passing, was first aroused by the work of Somerville at Callanish).[14] Indeed, among British workers it is Thom who must be credited with first taking seriously the question of significance.[15] Furthermore, following the point of view outlined in chapter 2, it is to this type of investigation – which we may loosely refer to as 'statistical' – that we shall devote most of our attention.

In spite of the fact that the statistical approach represented a revolutionary improvement in the means of assessing the astronomical theory, quantitative non-statistical research, more or less in the tradition of Lockyer, has continued in recent times. For example, despite some statistical considerations, G. S. Hawkins' famous work on Stonehenge by and large maintained this tradition, and it in turn attracted the interest of Sir Fred Hoyle. No assessment of megalithic astronomy would be complete without some mention of these researches.

The nature of megalithic astronomy

One thing these introductory remarks suggest is that the astronomical theory of megalithic sites is really a group of theories. Even a single monument such as Stonehenge has been interpreted in several different ways astronomically; the astronomical objects supposed to have been observed include the sun, the moon and the bright stars; and the supposed purpose of megalithic astronomy has ranged from eclipse-prediction to time-keeping. The megalithic sites for which an astronomical interpretation has been offered are equally diverse, ranging from passage graves through megalithic rings to alignments of menhirs. In the next chapter we shall take up the question of the types of megalithic structures thought to have served an astronomical purpose, and there we shall discuss the feasibility of megalithic astronomy. In this chapter we shall look at this question from the astronomical viewpoint: what reasonable limitations does astronomy itself place upon the scope of our investigations? What astronomical phenomena might have been observed by prehistoric people?

Notice that the subject of this chapter and the next is only indirectly related to the question of whether there is any evidence for megalithic astronomy. However, it is only after we have reviewed the necessary astronomical background that we shall be properly prepared to tackle this central issue of the remainder of the book.

In this chapter we shall also discuss the possible aims and purposes of megalithic astronomy. For the most part it is appropriate to deal with them separately for the sun, the moon and the stars when we consider these in turn. However, a number of general remarks are best placed here.

Much discussion has centred on what the purpose of megalithic astronomy might have been. Was it strictly practical, as in the construction of a calendar for agricultural purposes? Was it done for religious reasons, or perhaps political ones, to strengthen the grip of some ruling élite by the prediction of spectacular phenomena, such as eclipses? Was it done, finally, for curiosity? All these possibilities have been raised before, and even if we have evidence for megalithic astronomy it may remain a matter of conjecture why megalithic man was interested in it.

It is quite possible that clues to the answers to these questions will be found in considerations which have little to do with the astronomical study of megalithic sites. The locations of the sites may furnish one clue, their architecture another. Archaeological evidence on the type of society which produced the megaliths is also surely important. In some respects, for example, the calendrical theory makes most sense in the context of an arable economy.[16]

For the moment, however, we shall simply describe some of the purely astronomical aspects of megalithic astronomy. For this purpose one or two preliminary definitions are necessary. We shall later be concerned with megalithic sites which in some way point to or indicate a place on the horizon. There are many ways in which this can happen, as we shall see in the next chapter; one example is the axis of Stonehenge. Any such indication will be referred to as an 'orientation' or 'line'. For example, we might speak of a 'lunar line' when we mean an orientation or indication to the place on the horizon where the moon rises or sets at some particular point on its orbit. We reserve the word 'alignment' for a particular type of megalithic site which consists of a row of menhirs.[17]

71

Azimuthal orientations

Occasionally, it has been claimed that some sites are orientated to particular points of the compass, especially to the north or south. Such orientations may be referred to as 'azimuthal' orientations, since 'azimuth' (A) is merely a precise way of referring to a compass direction. Thus north corresponds to an azimuth of 0°, east to 90°, south to 180°, and west to 270°.[18] No conspicuous astronomical objects rise or set either due north or due south, and so these are rather different from the orientations normally considered in megalithic astronomy, such as the orientation of Stonehenge to the place where the sun rises at midsummer.

31

The problem with accurate orientations to the north or south is in knowing how they could have been set up, since our Pole Star was too far away from due north in megalithic times. Somerville, who discovered the possibility of such an orientation at Callanish, suggested two possible ways in which it might have been done.[19] The first is that one could set up temporary orientations for the Pole Star when at its positions furthest east and furthest west of the pole, and then divide the angle between these. The second method relies on finding the direction of due south from the altitude of the sun, and is probably inferior to the first method.

107

The purpose of such orientations could have been practical.[20] It would have been possible to tell the time of midday by observing when the sun crosses the orientation, and time at night could have been determined by the transit of stars across it.

The sun

Azimuthal orientations are the simplest to describe, since virtually no astronomy is required. It is a different matter when we come to solar or lunar orientations. Since the details of the motion of the sun and moon are quite intricate, they can be a little difficult to grasp. Therefore it may be helpful to have complementary treatments of this subject, and it will be found that the framework of the following descriptions is rather different from that normally adopted.[21] In fact the framework used here

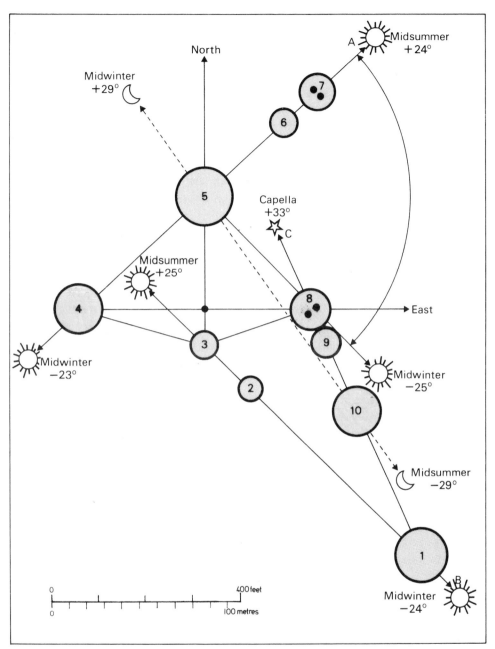

31 A group of circles at Odry, near Czersk, Poland (schematic, after Müller 1970, 86; cf. larger-scale survey Stephan 1916, pl. XXXV). The line 3—5 is directed approximately south-north, though it has not been shown that this is unlikely to be accidental. Orientations for the sun, the moon, and the star Capella are also noted. (For the moon, the terms 'midwinter' and 'midsummer' refer to the time of year at which the full moon has the stated declinations at a major standstill.) Note that pairs of stones stand near the centres of circles 7 and 8; these form foresights for sunrise at the two solstices when viewed from circle 5. Several other circles have a single central stone (not shown). The arc shows the range of sunrise directions throughout the year.

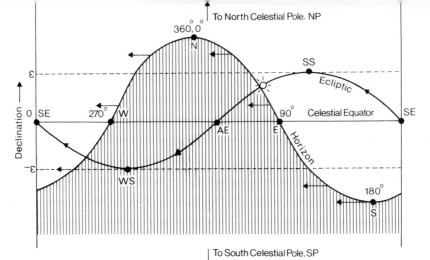

To North Celestial Pole, NP

To South Celestial Pole, SP

32 Schematic Mercator map of the sky. Any point in the sky lying vertically above an observer on the earth's equator lies on the celestial equator. The annual path of the sun is called the ecliptic. This crosses the equator at two points which the sun reaches at the times of the autumnal equinox (AE) and the spring equinox (SE). (By convention, the vertical margins of the map, both of which define the same line in the sky, pass through the position of the sun at the spring equinox.) The sun traverses the ecliptic in the direction of the arrowheads. It reaches its maximum declination, denoted by ε, at the summer solstice (SS), and its minimum declination, $-\varepsilon$, six months later at the winter solstice (WS). Only half of the sky at any time lies above the horizon. In the figure, one can think of the shaded area below the horizon as an opaque mask. As the earth rotates, causing objects to rise in the east, the mask moves to the left, coming on at the right-hand side of the diagram as it disappears at the left. Points corresponding to the north, east, south and west points of the horizon are denoted by N, E, S and W, respectively. The corresponding figures are the azimuths associated with these points. The configuration corresponds to sunrise at a date about halfway between the summer solstice and the autumnal equinox.

is very convenient for descriptions of astronomical phenomena. On the other hand, it is not the framework which would suggest itself most readily to a naked-eye megalithic observer, who would presumably adopt a framework based on the horizon.[22]

32, 33

Let us think of the stars drawn on a chart just as the earth's surface may be represented by a Mercator projection. Dividing the map horizontally is the 'celestial equator', on which lies any star which, at some time during the course of each day, appears overhead to an observer on the earth's equator. By analogy with a Mercator map of the earth, the north and south 'celestial poles' lie off the map; they are the two points in the sky which appear vertically overhead as seen from the earth's poles.

Only about half the sky is visible above the horizon at any one time. If we sketch the horizon at some instant for an observer in northern temperate latitudes it is a curve approximately divided by the celestial equator. By the earth's rotation the horizon moves to the left, completing one sweep of the Mercator chart per day. As it moves off the left-hand side it continually reappears on the right. The upper and lower extremes of the horizon curve are, respectively, the north and south points, and the celestial equator cuts it approximately at the two other main points of the compass: the east point, where the equator is rising, and the west point, where it is setting. Note that the maximum distance of the horizon from the celestial equator (at the north and south points) decreases with increasing latitude of the observer.

On the Mercator chart we can plot the position of the sun. Its path, known as the 'ecliptic', is traversed in one year. Note that the ecliptic and the equator cross at the right-hand edge of the map; this is just an astronomers' convention. The sun is here at the time of the spring equinox. As summer approaches the sun moves to the left and it is clear that it spends a shorter period of time below the horizon. The highest part of its orbit is reached at the summer solstice. Thereafter it crosses the equator again at the autumnal equinox, passes the winter solstice three months later, and finally crosses the equator at the vernal equinox of the following year. 32

If we wish to find graphically the point on the horizon where the sun rises or sets, we may insert the sun's position at the date in question on the ecliptic, and then draw a horizontal line through it. Where this line intersects the horizon curve gives the required points. It is easy to see now that the sun rises and sets furthest to the north at the summer solstice and furthest to the south at the winter solstice. In fact, the places where the sun rises or sets at the solstices are usually regarded as the primary targets towards which some megalithic sites may be orientated.

To determine the positions of these points it is necessary to know the height of the summer solstice position of the sun above the celestial equator (which astronomers call ε). In general, what determines the point on the horizon at which any object rises or sets is its distance from the equator. Astronomers call this the 'declination' of the object, and denote it by δ. Thus ε is the value of δ for the sun at the summer solstice. Note that the declination of a point on the sky is analogous to the latitude of a point on the earth's surface. Like latitude, it is an angle. Indeed astronomers generally use angles to measure distances across the sky.

For measuring the position of any point on the horizon we use the azimuth which we defined on p. 86. Thus there is a relation, which can be found mathematically, between the azimuth of a point on the horizon and the declination of any object which rises or sets there.[23] Therefore, if we know the azimuth of the direction indicated by a megalithic orientation, and some other data, we can determine the declination of any object which rises or sets in that direction.

The quantity ε, normally known as the obliquity, varies slowly over the centuries.[24] If a megalithic orientation of low accuracy is being discussed, this does not matter. However, if it is possible to determine the direction defined by a solar orientation to a few minutes of arc or better,[25] it is necessary to define with some precision at which date in the past it is proposed that the orientation was in use. In assessing the significance of such an orientation it is relevant to enquire whether the date of the site has been *chosen* so that the solstitial declination at that date is in agreement with the declination indicated by the orientation.

Even if we consider the solstice at a certain date in the past, the astronomical hypothesis does not give the unique declination ε. Unless the precision of the orientation is no better than about 1° (about twice the apparent diameter of the sun or moon) it is necessary to specify whether the centre of the solar disc or the lower or upper limb (edge) is indicated.

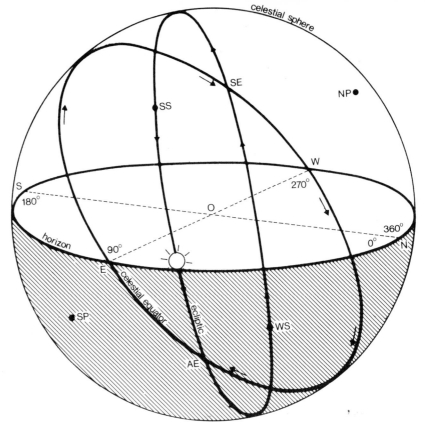

33 The observer's conception of the sky. To the observer, O, situated on level ground, the stars appear as if on the inside of a great sphere (the 'celestial sphere'), which we view here from the outside. The symbols have the same meanings as in ill. 32, and the configuration is meant to be the same. The essential difference is that here we think of the horizon as fixed while the sky rotates about an axis joining the two poles (NP and SP). In ill. 32 we think of the sky as being fixed, while the horizon moves across it. Any point on the celestial sphere can be defined by its elevation above the horizon and its azimuth.

The declination of the centre differs from that of either limb by about 15′, and the precise declination of the 'lower' limb depends on whether the sun rises (or sets) parallel to the slope of a hill, or past a fairly level horizon.[26] For very precise orientations it is even necessary to take into account small changes in the apparent diameter of the sun, which are caused by the annual variation in our distance from the sun.

On practical grounds it is probably easier to set up an accurate orientation for the sun or moon at the instant when one limb or the other crosses the horizon, rather than the centre or some other part of the disc. In the case of the sun the upper limb is preferable, since the brilliance of the sun's disc may make observation difficult when the lower limb is crossing the horizon.[27] Nevertheless it is conceivable that orientations for points other than the upper limb could have been set up. In judging the significance of a solar orientation, it is also relevant to note whether this freedom has been exploited to improve the agreement between the orientation and the astronomical theory.

Solar orientations are by no means restricted to indications of the sun at the solstices. Indeed a number of people have suggested that some orientations were set up so as to mark the places where the sun rose or set at certain other times of the year. It is usually assumed that the purpose of such lines would be calendrical; thus the fact that the sun rose at a certain point on the horizon (indicated by an orientation) would indicate that a certain date in the supposed megalithic calendar had been reached.

After the solstices, the dates most usually discussed include the equinoxes, though the question of how to define these in the present context is an interesting one. One possibility – the two days in the year when the sun rises as nearly as possible on the opposite point of the horizon from the place where it sets on the same day[28] – suffers from the disadvantage that it will vary somewhat from place to place. Of course this is only an objection if the supposed calendar had to be in widespread use and therefore uniform. A second possible definition is the day which evenly divides the interval between one solstice and the next.[29] In practice this definition is almost indistinguishable from a third, in which the equinoxes are defined as the two dates which divide the year equally and on which the declination of the sun is the same.[30] Notice incidentally that any calendar based on either of the last two definitions presupposes a method of counting, since each is based on the division into equal halves of either the year or a part of the year.

Even with either the second or third definition we shall expect an equinoctial orientation to show some variation. The sun, it is supposed, was observed at any site generally only once a day, at sunrise or sunset, and the change in its declination betwen the equinox and the nearest sunset may be as much as about 12′, which can be quite noticeable. This effect occurs to a significant extent at other times of the year also, but its magnitude is negligible at the solstices.

The slow daily change in the declination of the sun at the time of the solstices, which is the reason for this last fact, leads to interesting considerations on the practicability of a calendar based on megalithic orientations to the solstices. Since the point at which the sun rises or sets scarcely changes for several days on either side of the solstice it must be comparatively easy to erect an orientation for the solstice. For the same reason, however, it would have been comparatively difficult to use such an orientation to determine the date of the solstice, unless it was of extremely high accuracy. Unless an orientation is accurate to better than about 0·2′, the sun will appear to rise or set behind the orientation for several days, and it will be impossible to determine the exact day of the solstice.[31] An orientation for the equinoxes would be much more suitable, or at least one for any other date in the calendar, as long as it is not one of the solstices. It seems reasonable to infer that, if we find a large number of megalithic orientations of inadequate accuracy directed at the solstice, then it is unlikely that their purpose was calendrical.

This conclusion requires one note of caution, for Hoyle proposed a method whereby even a comparatively imprecise orientation could yield an accurate determination of the solstice.[32] One could observe using an orientation directed to the rising or setting position of the sun a few days before the solstice. By the symmetry of the solar motion the sun will also rise or set at this position at the date which falls an equal number of days *after* the solstice. Thus the solstice can be determined by finding the day midway between the two dates near the solstice when the sun rises or sets at the place indicated by the orientation.

The very simplest proposed megalithic calendars are based on solstices and equinoxes alone.[33] The more elaborate suggestions are usually based on subdivisions of the four intervals between the equinoxes and the solstices. (In fact when we refer below to a 'calendrical' line we shall usually mean an orientation on the sun at a date which is neither an equinox nor a solstice.) Somerville's calendar, for example, had 8 'months', corresponding to a single equal subdivision of each of these four intervals.[34]

Perhaps the most complicated calendar is Thom's.[35] It runs to 16 months, so chosen that, as well as can be arranged, the declination of the sun a certain number of months before a solstice is the same as its declination the same number of months after, and that the months are of equal length. Although this definition sounds artificial, Thom makes it clear in several places that the hypothesis was evolved in an attempt to explain a number of actual megalithic orientations indicating these declinations. Thom also considered the possibility of a further subdivision into 32 months, again after the study of otherwise unexplained orientations.[36] Since Thom's calendar gives months of approximately equal length on either side of the solstice, Hoyle's method of determining the date of the solstice implicitly finds a natural place also in Thom's calendar.[37]

It is not necessary to suppose that Thom's basic calendar could only work if we find orientations at each site for the positions of the sun at all 16 months. If we suppose that the users of these sites could have reckoned forward for a whole year then only one orientation in each district would have sufficed.[38] How the reckoning might have been done in practice is a question common to most proposed megalithic calendars, and various suggestions have been made in connection with specific megalithic sites. The usual idea is that a stake was moved regularly round a stone circle to mark the passage of months or longer units of time. Thus a stake moved once a day from beside one stone to the next, round a circle containing thirty stones, could be used to count off the days in one month of thirty days.

The moon

Just as the sun takes one year to complete one circuit of our Mercator map of the sky, so the moon completes one circuit in a month. Its path lies not far from that of the sun and, as with the sun, the points on the horizon at which it rises (or sets) move periodically north and south of the east (or west) point, but in the course of a month. Again, the monthly

34

most northerly and southerly rising and setting points of the moon are determined by its extreme declinations north and south of the equator. If the moon's orbit were fixed, as the sun's very nearly is, the monthly extreme rising and setting points would not change from month to month. However, the orbit of the moon is actually changing comparatively rapidly, and this is largely due to the forces exerted on the earth and the moon by the sun.

The greatest change in the moon's orbit is a drift relative to the sun's orbit. It is most easily described in terms of the 'nodes' of the moon's orbit, which are the two points where this crosses the path of the sun. The nodes move along the path of the sun but in the direction opposite to that of the sun's motion and a good deal more slowly, taking about 18·61 years for a complete circuit. Now the maximum separation of the two orbits stays almost constant as the nodes drift, and it is evident that one result of this is a change, with the same period of nearly 19 years, in the monthly extreme declinations along the moon's path.[39]

In order to describe this important effect in a little more detail, let us fix our attention on the so-called 'ascending' node, at which the moon crosses the sun's path from below. When this node is situated at the spring equinox of the sun's path, the deviation of the moon's orbit from the sun's is adding to the extreme declination of the moon to the maximum possible extent. It is at such a time, called by Thom a 'major standstill',[40] that the moon reaches its greatest distances north and south of the equator during the whole of the 19-year period. From its position at the major standstill, the ascending node moves along the sun's path, and four or five years later it reaches the winter solstice. Here the maximum deviation of the moon's path from that of the sun occurs near the equator, and the monthly extreme declinations of the moon with its orbit in this position are quite close to the annual extreme declinations of the sun, i.e. those which the sun reaches at the solstices. By the time the ascending node has reached the autumn equinox, the maximum deviation of the moon's path from that of the sun again occurs close to the point on its orbit where the moon is at its monthly maximum distance north or south of the equator. Now, however, the deviation is acting in the opposite sense, constraining the moon so that it cannot even move as far from the equator as the sun can. This is the orbital configuration called by Thom a 'minor standstill'. When the node moves to the position of the summer solstice, the situation is similar to that when it lies at the winter solstice. Four or five years later still, after the lapse altogether of nearly 19 years, the ascending node returns to the spring equinox.

Now the maximum deviation of the moon's path from that of the sun is about 5°, or about ten times the apparent diameter of the full moon, and so the effects of the aforementioned changes in the moon's path are very noticeable. In fact at a major standstill the maximum declination of the moon is so great that the moon can then almost remain above the horizon throughout the complete course of a day at extreme northern latitudes of Britain. Conversely, when the moon

35

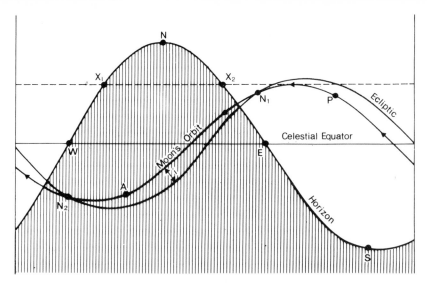

34 The path of the moon. The sky is depicted as in ill. 32. The moon traverses the whole orbit once a month in the direction indicated by the arrowheads. It rises furthest to the north at X_2, when its declination is greatest for that month. At the same time it would set at X_1. The points N_1 and N_2 are called 'nodes', N_1 the ascending node and N_2 the descending node. The maximum perpendicular distance between the orbits of the sun and moon (which occurs midway between the nodes) is the inclination, i, of the lunar orbit.

The points P and A are the positions at which the moon is respectively nearest to and furthest from the earth. These positions move forward in the same direction as the motion of the moon, but much more slowly. They take almost nine years for a complete revolution round the lunar orbit.

35 The motion of the nodes. The orbit of the moon is

shown in four configurations, when the ascending node is at the points marked (1), (2), (3) and (4). These are numbered in the order in which they occur, a cycle being completed in about 18.61 years. III. 34 shows the situation at a time between configurations 3 and 4. Those marked 1 and 3 are called by Thom the major and minor standstills, respectively. At the major standstill the monthly maximum declination of the moon takes its largest value ($\varepsilon+i$) for the whole of the 18.61-year nodal cycle. At the minor standstill it takes its smallest value ($\varepsilon-i$). At the extreme north of the British Isles the highest part of the horizon mask in ill. 32 lies only slightly above the line marked '$\varepsilon+i$'.

The perturbation on the inclination is at a maximum when the sun crosses one of the nodes. For example, the perturbation is at a maximum at the summer solstice in configurations 2 and 4 and at a minimum then when the moon's orbit is in configurations 1 and 3.

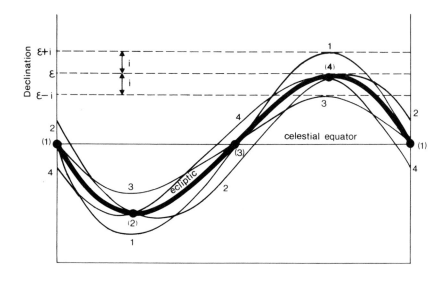

reaches the lowest part of its orbit at a major standstill, it barely shows itself above the horizon, and then only for an hour or two. J. W. Barber has noticed the awareness of what may be this phenomenon among the farming community in a district in Ireland,[41] and, as Thom has said, the 18·6-year cycle may well have obtruded itself in prehistoric times.[42]

The extreme declinations of the moon at the major and minor standstills are regarded as the primary lunar declinations to which one might consider megalithic orientations to be directed.[43] If an orientation is considered accurate to a degree or so, the lunar part of the astronomical hypothesis is as simple as that, except for one minor complication: the phenomenon of parallax. For simplicity we have drawn and discussed the paths of the sun and the moon as viewed by an imaginary observer at the centre of the earth. For a real observer situated on the earth's surface, the apparent position of a comparatively nearby object like the moon is shifted against the background of stars towards the horizon. 36 The effect is substantial, about 1°, and it obviously affects the apparent declination of the moon. (A parallax correction can also be calculated for the sun, but the effect is minute since the sun is so much more distant.)

When we move on to orientations precise to $\frac{1}{2}°$ or better, then in addition to the declination of the centre of the moon's disc we must consider the declination of either limb also, as with the sun. Thus wherever initially we had one declination we now have three against which the declination actually indicated by the orientation can be compared.

At slightly improved levels of accuracy new effects enter the discussion and considerably increase the number of possible declinations which must be considered. The first of these is what Thom calls 'the wobble'. Previously we said that the maximum deviation of the moon's path from that of the sun (i.e. its 'inclination') is approximately constant. In fact, however, it varies on either side of its average value by a small amount. The maximum variation is denoted by Δ and measures about 9′, or roughly one third of the moon's apparent diameter.[44] This has the effect of further complicating the declinations associated with each standstill, for we may consider the extreme declination of the moon

36 Lunar parallax. Relative to the stars, the moon (M) appears in slightly different positions when viewed by observers at the centre of the earth (O₁) and its surface (O₂).

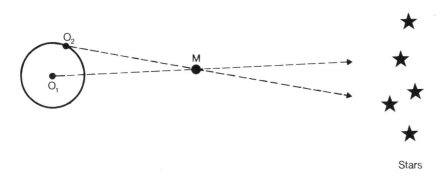

Stars

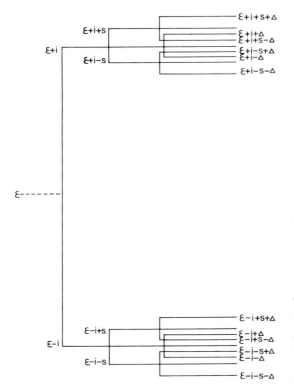

ε+i+s+Δ
ε+i+s
ε+i
ε+i+Δ
ε+i+s−Δ
ε+i−s+Δ
ε+i−Δ
ε+i−s
ε+i−s−Δ

ε- - - - - - -

ε−i+s+Δ
ε−i+s
ε−i+Δ
ε−i+s−Δ
ε−i
ε−i−s+Δ
ε−i−Δ
ε−i−s
ε−i−s−Δ

37 Extreme lunar declinations. The annual maximum declination of the centre of the sun is ε. When the moon is at a major standstill, the monthly maximum declination of the centre of its disc is given by ε+i, if the perturbation to its inclination happens to be zero. Then the declinations of its limbs are ε+i±s, where s is approximately its apparent radius. If the perturbation is a maximum or a minimum the extreme declination of the centre of the lunar disc is ε+i±Δ, respectively, and there are fresh declinations for the limbs. A similar group of extreme declinations corresponds to a minor standstill, around ε−i.

when the effect of the 'wobble' is maximum, minimum or nil. Each of the three previous declinations now splits into three.

The period of the wobble – the time between two successive dates when its effect is at its maximum – is quite short, almost six months in fact. It is really a 'perturbation', as astronomers say, caused by the disturbing action of the sun, and so it is not surprising that its magnitude is related to the position of the sun in its orbit. In fact the perturbation reaches its maximum effect when the sun is at either node; hence the period of about six months. For instance, it is impossible for the perturbation to be at a minimum when the full moon occurs at the position of the equinox at a major standstill. (It will be an exacting test of the reader's understanding of these rather complicated relationships if he can convince himself that this statement is correct!)[45]

The perturbation manifests itself in the following way. Without it, the monthly maximum declination of the moon would vary smoothly over a period of about 19 years, as previously described. The perturbation superimposes a small 6-month oscillation on the long-term variation.[46]

Evidently parallax and the apparent size of the moon's disc both depend on the distance of the moon, which varies during each month by about 5 per cent on either side of its mean value. Thus the extreme declination of the moon will not be quite the same from one major standstill to the next, even if we consider the same limb of the moon and take care that the perturbation is at its maximum on both occasions. If we were attempting to set up a precise lunar orientation corresponding to *average* parallactic conditions (and Thom has claimed that such orientations exist),[47] we would clearly have to observe the moon at several standstills. In fact it can be shown that observations spanning almost a century would be needed, and perhaps longer if we account for observations missed on account of bad weather.[48] There is a difficulty here, however, for during such a period of time, slow changes in the apparent path of the moon caused by changes in the obliquity would have led to slight but just noticeable alterations in its extreme declination. The combined effect of these circumstances is to impose a rather fundamental limit on the conceivable accuracy of a lunar orientation: this cannot be much better than about one or two minutes of arc.[49]

With observations of the sun there is no question of interference by daylight, but this must be given consideration for the moon. By day the moon can be quite difficult to see, especially when near the horizon, where the sky is brighter and atmospheric obscuration heavier. If we neglect for the moment the difference between the sun's path and that of the moon, ill. 38 allows us to understand the effects of sunlight. It shows the situation just as the moon is rising, and it is clear that sunlight will interfere if the sun is at any part of its orbit between WS and SS via SE.[50] Actually, the situation is a little more complicated, because the moon will rise in the bright dawn sky even when the sun is slightly to the left of SS; on the other hand when it is just to the left of WS the moon is full and it rises just as the sun sets; hence it will not be difficult to see

38 Visibility of moonrise. The moon is shown rising when its declination takes its maximum value for the month, and we ignore the difference between the apparent paths of the moon and the sun. The moon will rise in daylight if the sun is at any part of its orbit between WS and SS via SE, i.e. for the six months following the winter solstice.

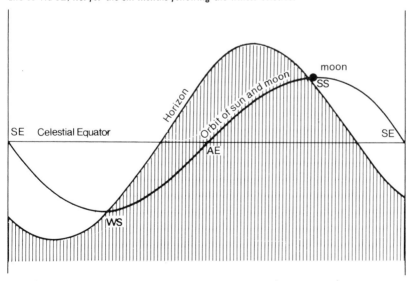

if the sky is clear. At any rate, observation of moonrise at its maximum declination will be hampered for about six months, and one may well ask whether the six-month perturbation in the moon's maximum declination already referred to could ever have been discovered. This is not in fact a strong objection, for the missing half of the year could have been filled in by using an alignment for moonset rather than moonrise, as only a little thought is needed to show.

Even when the moon rises at its maximum declination for the month in a sky sufficiently dark, it is clear that its phase will vary from month to month. When the sun is near SS, for instance, the moon is nearly new, and when the sun is at AE the moon is at last quarter. There seems no good reason for supposing that phases other than full would have been unsuitable for observation. Nevertheless several writers put much emphasis on the full moon, and one often reads such phrases as 'the midwinter full moon' in some discussions of megalithic astronomy. 'Midwinter' implies that the sun is at its most southerly declination for the year, and 'full moon' implies that the moon is at the place on its orbit as far from the sun as possible, i.e. 'at its maximum declination for the month'. We prefer this phrase because it removes undue emphasis on consideration of the full moon only. On the other hand, if it is supposed that observations did take place when the moon was not full, one must ask whether the limb of the moon to which the alignment corresponds was illuminated by the sun. If the limb was on the dark side of the moon, accurate observations may have been difficult. It turns out that the limb would have been suitably illuminated on only six months of each year, and for three of these the alignment could not have been used because of daylight.[51]

A final possible obstacle to the establishment of quite accurate lunar orientations is related to a topic introduced in connection with equinoctial solar alignments. Except near a solstice, the sun moves noticeably between one sunrise and the next. The same is true of the moon between successive moonrises, but the motion is much larger, even near its extreme declination. The difficulty is that the moon never rises exactly at the time of maximum declination on its orbit: this generally occurs between one moonrise and the next. Now it is generally argued that it is the extreme declination only which is of any significance, and so, if one supposes that accurate orientations for the extreme are indeed to be found, one must propose a way in which these could have been set up even when observations precisely at the extreme could never have been made.[52]

This is the problem of 'extrapolation' to which Thom has often drawn attention.[53] Indeed he has proposed two or three related ways in which it could have been done with quite primitive equipment.[54] It is not appropriate or necessary to describe the theory of these methods, but the practical operations they involve are worth mentioning. Suppose the observations are made by lining up variable stakes (A, B, C, etc.) with a fixed stake (Z). (The components of the orientation need not be stakes and need not even be artificial; we simply use stakes for clarity of exposition.) Suppose also that the stakes are set up to show the rising position of the

39

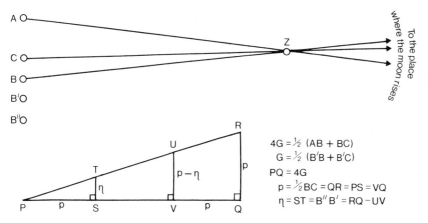

$$4G = \tfrac{1}{2}(AB + BC)$$
$$G = \tfrac{1}{2}(B'B + B'C)$$
$$PQ = 4G$$
$$p = \tfrac{1}{2}BC = QR = PS = VQ$$
$$\eta = ST = B''B' = RQ - UV$$

39 Extrapolation of stake positions. AZ, BZ and CZ point to the places on the horizon where the moon rises on three consecutive nights. The sequence of operations is described in the text. Also shown is a variant of step (iii): it would be possible to measure QV equal to p, erect a perpendicular UV, and take η as the difference between RQ and UV. Also, if G is assumed known, observations on two successive nights would suffice. We have considered Z to be a stake, but it can be any kind of foresight.

moon on three successive nights which straddle the instant when it reaches the declination maximum.[55] Then the problem is to find where the stake should be put to mark the position where the moon would have risen had it done so precisely when its declination reached its extreme value (B″). According to Thom, one possible procedure is the following:

(i) Take one eighth of the sum of the distances AB, BC. (Note that this can be found by passing a rope from A to C via B and folding it three times.) Following Thom we call the result G.[56]

(ii) Find the point halfway between B and C. Measure half the distance between B and C (called p), and measure a distance G from the midpoint to give the point B′.

(iii) Set out a line PQ of length $4G$ on the ground and measure a length p at right angles to this line at Q, giving a point R. Measure a distance p along the line PQ from P to give a point S, and let T be a point on the line PR such that ST is perpendicular to PQ. Denote the length of ST by η. (Once more notice that these operations can be carried out using ropes. Accurate right angles are probably not critical, but two people might be needed to ensure that S and T lie on the required lines.)

(iv) Measure a distance η from B′ to give B″.

The above set of operations has a number of variations. First, it may not have been necessary to measure G more than once for any particular site, for it is nearly constant. Hence it might be expedient to have this length marked out permanently on the ground, and then two nights' observations are sufficient. In fact, however, G is surprisingly sensitive to the varying distance of the moon,[57] and so if it is thought that accurate observations were undertaken then its measurement would have been necessary each time extrapolation was carried out.

A second variant is that the 'triangle' method for stage (iii) can be replaced by a 'sector' method using curved geometry rather than the straight geometry of the method we have described. According to Thom one difference between the sector method and the triangle method is that it would have been worthwhile to lay out a grid of stones on the ground to facilitate the application of the sector method but not for the triangle method.[58] The reason for this is that the operations of the triangle method take place close to the narrow end of the triangle PQR, and it would be difficult to set out accurately a grid of lines converging on P; in the sector method, however, it is the broad end of the sector that is used, and this problem does not arise. However, it is easy to devise a variant of the triangle method which resembles the sector method in this respect (see ill. 39) and so a grid with straight lines would be equally workable.

The uses of lunar lines

Having discussed something of the practical and theoretical problems in the erection of lunar orientations, we must survey some of the suggestions that have been made about their possible purpose. Some of these – such as the prediction of the tides, or the use of the moon for calendrical purposes or as a source of light – do not amount to much, because the minor variations in the declination of the moon are really not relevant for these purposes, and it is declination which any orientation measures. Furthermore the tidal theory seems somewhat at odds with the existence of supposed lunar sites far from the sea.[59] There is a way in which megalithic rings *could* have been used in connection with the tides or a lunar calendar, though it has nothing to do with orientations: a marker moved regularly round a ring with an appropriate number of stones could have served to count off the months or years of a lunar calendar, just as in the case of a solar calendar, or the succession of spring and neap tides.[60]

40, 41

Much attention has been paid to another possible reason for studying the moon – eclipses and their prediction. Just as these 'often played a dramatic part in the thinking of ancient peoples',[61] so they have played an important role in recent studies of megalithic astronomy. This is especially true of the interpretation of Stonehenge, thanks to Hawkins and Hoyle.

Referring to ill. 34, we should note first that the discs of the sun and moon are so small compared with the maximum distance between their paths that it is possible for the moon to obscure the sun (as in a solar eclipse) only when both are close to one node or the other.[62] Thus there is a possibility of an eclipse when the sun is very near N_1 and again, just under six months later, when it is at N_2. Now when N_1 is at position 1 (which corresponds to a major standstill) in ill. 35, eclipses are possible only near the equinoxes, and as N_1 moves along the sun's path the times of year at which eclipses occur become earlier. When N_1 reaches position 2 eclipses are occurring at the solstices, and by the time it has arrived at position 3 they are in danger of occurring at the equinoxes again. This is the time of a minor standstill. Now the times of a major or minor standstill can be found by reference solely to observations of the declination of the moon. Therefore, lunar orientations could have permitted the determination of the times of the year ('eclipse seasons') when eclipses were possible, at least at the time of a standstill.

We have described the situation with regard to solar eclipses, but it can be argued that we should be more concerned with lunar eclipses than with solar eclipses, since total solar eclipses are so rare and partial ones are not usually conspicuous.[63] However, the concept of eclipse seasons applies equally to lunar eclipses, and these even occur at the same times of the year as those for solar eclipses.

The problem of finding the date when the major standstill occurs has features akin to the determination of the solstice: the monthly maximum declination of the moon changes quite slowly at the time of the standstill. In fact the 18·6-year revolution of the nodes leads to a change of only about $\frac{1}{4}°$ in the first year after a major standstill. Thus the existence of *inaccurate* orientations for extreme declinations of the moon might be held to indicate that this method of eclipse prediction was not used. It might be thought that, as with the determination of the solstice, Hoyle's offset method could have been employed.[64] However, it has been argued recently by an astronomer, G. Moir, that the method is more difficult to apply to the moon, because of its more rapid daily motion, its relative dimness, and its changing phase.[65] Actually, there are ways in which eclipse prediction could be performed without the need to determine the times of the standstills. Solstitial orientations could be used,[66] or else one could observe directly whether the full moon at the solstices rises (or sets) directly opposite in the sky to where the sun sets (or rises),[67] as it must do if an eclipse is to be possible. Then, however, eclipse prediction ceases to be an explanation of orientations for the standstill declinations of the moon.

Thom has proposed a method whereby eclipse seasons could be determined by observations of the six-month perturbation.[68] We have already stated that the maximum of the perturbation occurs when the sun is at either node, whence it follows that observation of the wobble at maximum implies that an eclipse season is occurring. This would be done most easily at a standstill. There are also methods whereby eclipse seasons could be predicted from observations of minimum or zero perturbation, but the latter requires the presence of more accurate permanent orientations than do the other methods, and the limitations on the accuracy of lunar orientations which were mentioned above may render this variant impracticable. Thom has not shown that his method would have been more accurate than the standstill method and, with the implied need for extrapolation, it is more elaborate.

Both methods of eclipse prediction imply that eclipse seasons in the years between standstills were predicted by calculation. In the context of Stonehenge two ways of expediting such calculations have been developed in considerable detail. Both use the ring of 56 Aubrey Holes.

71

In Hawkins' scheme[69] six evenly-spaced movable markers, alternately black and white, are moved by one hole once each year, and three fixed

40

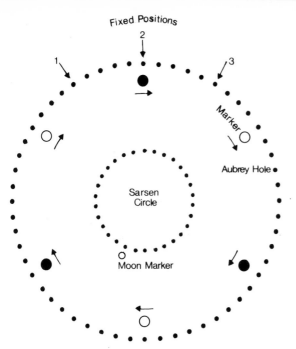

Fixed Positions

1 2 3

Marker

Aubrey Hole

Sarsen
Circle

Moon Marker

40 *Hawkins' method of eclipse prediction at Stonehenge. The seven movable markers are moved by one hole each year, except for the moon marker, which is moved each day. The scheme may be started with a white marker stone at the third fixed position at the time of a major standstill. Eclipses are occurring at the equinoxes. Nine or ten years later there is a black marker at the third fixed position, it is a minor standstill, and eclipses again occur at the equinoxes. Thus a movable stone at the third fixed position indicates the danger of eclipses at the equinoxes. The other positions, and the distinction between black and white markers, permit the prediction of other phenomena. For example, in the configuration shown, eclipses occur at the solstices. The moon marker completes one revolution about the sarsen circle in about a month, thus keeping track of the phase of the moon. (Eclipses can occur only if the moon is new or full.) In a variant, Hawkins considers that the phase of the moon was predicted using a different ring at Stonehenge, but the principle is the same.*

markers, with a separation half that between the movable ones, are situated beside the ring. First note that the average interval between the passage of (say) successive white stones past (say) the third fixed marker, is just 56/3 years, or about 18·67 years. This is very close to the period of revolution of the nodes of the moon's orbit. Suppose, then, that we begin in the year of a major standstill with a white stone at the third marker. Then eclipses will be occurring near the equinoxes, and there will be a black stone at the first marker. This will reach the second marker one quarter of a nodal period later, eclipses now taking place at the solstices. With the black marker at position 3, the next white marker will be at position 1; it is a minor standstill and eclipses are taking place once again at the equinoxes. Thus we can predict the occurrence of standstills, and can foretell the years when eclipses may occur at the equinoxes or the solstices. In fact, by inserting extra markers between those already shown, we could determine when the eclipse seasons are occurring even when they do so neither at the equinoxes nor the solstices.

41   Hoyle's scheme[70] is more economical. He takes three movable markers to represent, respectively, the sun, the moon, and one node of the moon's orbit. These markers are moved so that each completes a circuit of the Aubrey Circle in approximately the same time that it takes the real sun, moon and node, respectively, to make a complete circuit of the ecliptic. Then eclipse seasons occur only when the markers for the sun and the node lie either close together or nearly opposite each other. Eclipses may occur within these seasons only when the moon marker lies near the position of the sun marker or nearly opposite it.

Note that Hoyle's method includes the prediction of the actual day of an eclipse, since the moon marker moves so quickly. The same feature can be added to Hawkins' scheme by introducing a further marker moving

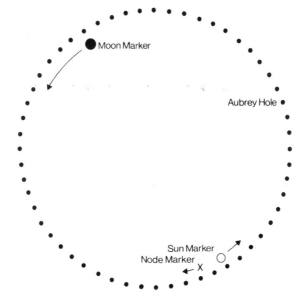

41 Hoyle's method of eclipse prediction at Stonehenge. He uses the Aubrey circle as a geocentric model of the sun and moon, including the ascending node. Three markers revolve at approximately their real rates. Eclipses only occur if all three markers lie on approximately the same diameter of the Aubrey Circle.

regularly round the sarsen circle at Stonehenge.[71] This circle consisted of 30 stones, which is approximately the number of days between successive new or full moons, the times when eclipses occur. Actually, with either scheme in its simplest form, it will often happen that a predicted eclipse will not be visible from Stonehenge.[72] Nevertheless, quite simple additional observations could have been used to furnish information on the visibility of individual eclipses.[73] Then again it is possible for an entire eclipse season to pass without a lunar eclipse occurring.[74] Further problems are caused by the variable rates at which the sun and moon move around the sky. Indeed, a recent thorough discussion by Hoyle shows just how much is involved in making such detailed predictions.[75]

40, 71

On Thom's method of eclipse prediction, eclipse seasons in years between successive standstills could have been calculated provided that the approximately 6-month interval between successive eclipse seasons was known.[76] On the other hand, the methods of Hoyle and Hawkins seem to imply knowledge of much longer periodicities, since they depend on the fact that the lunar node executes three cycles in almost exactly 56 years. Though the discovery of this fact need not have taken 56 years,[77] it seems difficult to deny that it would not have taken much less than the average working life of an observer in these primitive times,[78] even if we ignore difficulties caused by the weather. Then it becomes reasonable to ask whether such periodicities (and indeed the basic relationships between moonrises and eclipses on which the prediction methods were based) could have been determined without extensive record-keeping. The problem is that there is no archaeological evidence for such records. Against the reply that such records might have perished, Atkinson argues that it is based on an improper attitude to archaeological evidence, which must be treated as it is rather than as we would like it to be. To non-archaeologists at least, this perhaps seems too severe. After all, we may believe that most of the stones of Stonehenge were dragged from some distance. Need we deny this simply because we cannot find the ropes and rollers that may have been needed? Another archaeologist (MacKie) considers that no written record was necessary for much of the practice of megalithic astronomy as suggested by Thom and that large bodies of knowledge can be memorized and transmitted verbally.[79] However, a severe problem is surely posed by the very accurate lunar orientations whose design must have taken two centuries or more, because of the effects of parallax.

Finally one wonders, with the astronomer D. H. Sadler, why such elaborate methods of eclipse prediction need have been in use when simpler methods were available.[80] For example, suppose, as Thom does, that successive eclipse seasons can be calculated if the dates of just one eclipse season are known. In Thom's method, the time of the first eclipse season is determined by observation of the lunar perturbation. However, it could also be determined simply by observing an eclipse, since that implies that an eclipse season is in progress.

In short, eclipse prediction does not seem an impressive reason for carrying out observations of the rising and setting positions of the moon, at any level of accuracy. However, this argument does not show that lunar orientations could not have been set up, or even that they were in any sense unlikely. The motivation for them might have been some other scientific purpose, or a ritual one, in the widest senses of these words.

The stars

When considering the astronomical objects to which some megalithic sites may be orientated, we must reject the various celestial phenomena which do not recur regularly, however spectacular they are. Thus aurorae, meteors, comets, novae, and supernovae do not concern us. Of the objects visible to the naked eye which we have not yet described only the planets and stars remain.

The planets have been mentioned from time to time in work on megalithic astronomy, but are rarely given any prominence, and it is not always easy to see why. In his work on Stonehenge, Hawkins dismissed the possibility of planetary orientations,[81] but gave the wrong value for the extreme declination of Saturn. Elsewhere it has been claimed that the motions of the planets are so complicated that megalithic man could have made little progress in understanding them.[82] However, the behaviour of the extreme declination of the bright outer planet, Jupiter, for example, is not at all complicated provided that great accuracy is not demanded. Furthermore, these extremes recur about every 12 years, which is not long by the standards of the 19-year lunar period. Conditions are more difficult for the bright inner planet Venus, which reaches its extreme declination only at times when it is difficult to observe.[83] Despite this, it may be that the possibility of orientations to some of the planets is ripe for reconsideration.

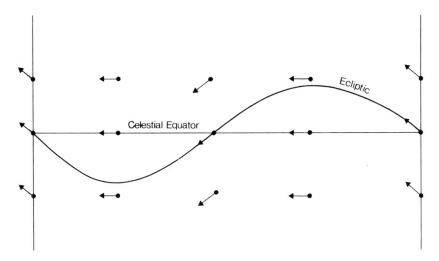

42 Precessional motion of the stars. Because of a very slow motion of the earth, the celestial equator moves against the background stars. Thus the places where the equator crosses the ecliptic are moving along the ecliptic, to the right. Since we refer the positions of the stars to the ecliptic and the celestial equator, however, the stars appear to drift in the opposite direction. The direction of the precessional drift is indicated schematically by arrows.

We turn lastly to the stars. They move extremely slowly in comparison with the sun and moon, as the old expression 'fixed stars' implies. They rise night after night at almost exactly the same position on the horizon, and if there is any difficulty in erecting an orientation to indicate this position it is not caused by their motion.

Looked at over a sufficiently long period of time, a slight motion of the stars does become apparent. The principal reason for this is not the movement of the stars themselves, but a motion of the earth called 'precession'. Ill. 42 shows the sense of this motion. Its value in declination is clearly at a maximum for stars near the extreme right- and left-hand boundaries and the middle, and there its magnitude is such that the rising position of a star is moving along the horizon by a distance equal to the apparent size of the full moon in about 50 years. Since many megalithic orientations can be defined with this sort of accuracy, it is clearly generally possible to identify an orientation with some star only if a reasonably precise date is stated also.

The declinations of the stars may also change as a result of their real motions in space relative to each other. This is normally a smaller effect than precession, but it is still important. Fortunately, the combined effect of these two motions can be calculated even for dates several millennia ago.[84]

The comparative dimness of the rising or setting sun is familiar enough, but the same dimming (caused by the great depth of intervening atmosphere) greatly affects the apparent brightness of the stars. Indeed, below a certain distance above the horizon the dimming is so great that the star cannot be seen even in the clearest air. The height at which a rising star first becomes visible is known as the 'extinction angle', and depends on the transparency of the air and on the brightness of the star. The dimmer the star the larger the extinction angle. The importance of this is that, if we suspect that an orientation served some stellar function and the altitude of the horizon is less than the appropriate extinction angle, we should not regard the orientation as pointing to the horizon. Instead, we should regard it as indicating a point above the horizon whose altitude can be determined from the extinction angle. Naturally, this modification is not made when the horizon altitude exceeds the extinction angle.

Hawkins appears to have thought that stellar orientations should be regarded with more suspicion than those to the sun and moon,[85] since even a bright star is so inconspicuous when rising or setting. However, it seems unwise to argue away the possibility of stellar lines before the evidence is examined, for one could argue that the faintness of a rising star makes an orientation all the more purposeful!

In later chapters we shall have much to say about the possibility that megalithic orientations to the place on the horizon where some astronomical object rises or sets can occur quite by chance. However, it is worth stating here that this problem is particularly acute with regard to the stars, for two reasons. The first is that, although the stars move much more slowly than the sun or moon, their declinations generally change much more rapidly than the *extreme* declinations of the sun and moon. Therefore, if the date of an orientation is uncertain, there is a much larger chance that it will accidentally indicate a certain star than that it will indicate a certain extreme lunar or solar declination. The second reason is the large number of stars: some thousands are visible on any clear night. Of course, all but the brightest are difficult or impossible to see when anywhere near the horizon, and so most attempts to identify megalithic orientations with stars have concentrated on the brightest stars. Naturally this greatly reduces the number of stars to be considered.

In order to assess the significance of stellar orientations in any investigation, it is clearly necessary to know what range of dates was considered, and how many stars were included. For example, if one considers only first magnitude stars (of which there are a dozen or so) over a period of only 500 years, there is a probability of about one third that a random line can be interpreted as stellar.[86] Thus we have to be very careful in accepting Somerville's evidence on stellar orientations, since there are at least twenty relevant stars brighter than the faintest one he considered, and he was prepared to contemplate any date between about 4000 and 0 BC.[87] On the other hand, Thom considered the twenty or so brightest stars in his first book, but dates between 2100 and 1500 BC only.[88]

There are one or two exceptions to the general rule that only the bright stars have been considered, and the Pleiades or Seven Sisters is one, perhaps because of the reference to them in the famous passage by Diodorus (see p. 212). Even fainter than the Pleiades is the Milky Way,

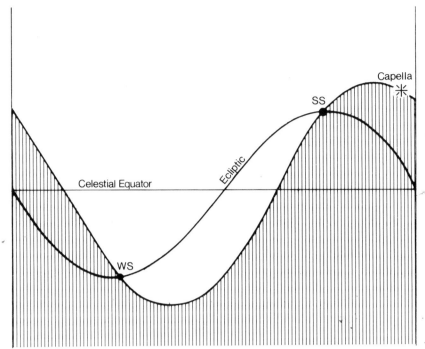

43 Stars as clocks and calendars. Capella is shown on the horizon as it is rising in prehistoric times at the latitude of the British Isles. At midsummer the sun is at SS and so Capella rises at about sunset, but at the winter solstice both the sun (which is at WS) and Capella rise at approximately the same time. Thus the time of day indicated by the rise of Capella depends on the time of the year. Finally note that the heliacal rising of Capella takes place a few days after the winter solstice.

which has not escaped at least one suggestion of an associated megalithic orientation.[89]

Several authors have restricted the choice of stars to be considered by assuming something about the purpose for which the supposed stellar orientations were constructed, and this somewhat reduces the possibility of obtaining lines by chance.[90] The purpose of stellar lines is a topic which we may also discuss for its own sake, since some critics believe that the presence or absence of a plausible purpose is itself significant evidence in the assessment of an astronomical theory. Broadly speaking, the suggestions fall into two categories: that the stars were used either as a clock or as a calendar. Why a calendar might have been useful we have already mentioned, and it is not hard to speculate in a similar vein about clocks.[91]

The use of stars as clocks is not completely straightforward, since the time at which a star rises or sets depends on the calendar date.[92] As an example, let us consider Capella, which Lockyer regarded as a possible clock star.[93] Ill. 43 shows the situation when Capella is rising. Clearly, at midsummer, when the sun is at the 'top' of the ecliptic, Capella rises at about sunset. By the late autumn it rises in the middle of the day, and by midwinter it is rising at about the same time as the sun. Thus the time of day indicated by the rising of a star varies from one day to another, and it is not entirely clear what use can be made of a clock which gains four minutes a day and cannot be reset.

When we consider the rising and setting of stars, it is not clear that orientations are necessary at all. Thom excuses the curious absence of orientations to the very brightest star, Sirius, by arguing that it is sufficiently well indicated by neighbouring stars.[94] It is not obvious that this argument does not greatly weaken the need for almost all stellar orientations on the clock theory!

As we shall see, this criticism cannot be levelled so easily against the other possible use of the stars, as a calendar. Looking again at ill. 43 we note that Capella rises at sunrise if the sun is at the point WS in its orbit. At this time of the year (near midwinter) Capella rises in a sky too bright for it to be seen, but as the days pass the sun moves to the left, and on each succeeding day Capella rises earlier, in a darker sky than on the previous day. After perhaps two or three weeks there is a certain date when it is just visible for a minute or two as it rises, before the sky gets too bright.. This is the 'heliacal' rising of Capella, and it will occur each year at almost exactly the same date. It is clear that a megalithic orientation would be of great value here, since the observation of an isolated star in a bright dawn sky is particularly difficult if one does not know exactly where to look.

The heliacal rising of Capella occurs at a certain date, and the heliacal risings of a number of stars could be used to construct a calendar.[95] Lockyer attached particular importance to stars whose heliacal rising occurred close to dates in his solar calendar; these he called 'warning stars'. Thom has claimed that a calendar based on heliacal risings has nothing like the accuracy of one based on solar orientations, because of the comparatively long twilight period at the relatively high latitudes where megalithic sites are found.[96] How great a problem this is is unclear. Anyway, we should not regard the possible use of heliacal risings as a particularly advanced activity in the context of ancient astronomy, and its occurrence in any settled society, literate or not, would not be very surprising.[97]

6 Megalithic orientations

As will have become clear from remarks in the previous chapter, the central theme of megalithic astronomy is the idea of megalithic orientations towards the places where conspicuous celestial objects rise and set at certain positions in their apparent orbits. So far our discussion has hardly at all been concerned with the evidence for or against this idea, and there remains yet the present chapter before the ground can be said to have been adequately prepared for an examination of the evidence. In the previous chapter we were concerned mostly with the astronomical aspects of megalithic orientations. Now we shall look in fairly general terms at the structure of the orientations.

First we shall attempt an informal classification of the orientations, giving examples of the various types and, for the sake of interest, the astronomical object with which each may be associated. Then there are a number of practical considerations on the use of orientations which merit discussion. Finally we need to say a little about the phenomenon of refraction, and the limitations which this and other effects impose upon the accuracy of orientations.

Types of orientation

One of the objections which archaeologists are apt to raise against any talk of megalithic astronomy is the extreme archaeological diversity of the sites which are brought into the picture.[1] To some extent, though not entirely, this apparent disregard for the archaeological framework of megalithic studies is caused by the conflation of the efforts of several investigators. Individually they have tended to restrict themselves to a less rich diversity of sites than they have collectively. Later on we shall return from time to time to the question of consistency with the archaeological record, but the point is worth mentioning here, since we are about to survey something of the variety of megalithic orientations for which an astronomical purpose has been claimed. These examples have been culled from several authors, a fact which should be remembered if the diversity of sites seems excessive.

One of the earliest investigations in which large numbers of orientations were discussed was Lockyer's. Generally, he considered the following types:[2] (i) from the centre of a stone circle to one of the stones in the circle, or to the space between two of these; (ii) alignments of menhirs;

(iii) from the centre of a stone circle to an outlying stone; and (iv) passage graves; though he extended this list from time to time.

28

A little later, Somerville was considering lines of Lockyer's type (iii), and added two more types:[3] (v) the axis of symmetry of a megalithic ring; and (vi) from a megalithic site to a distant natural object.

Thom has discussed lines from most of these six groups,[4] with one or two modifications. For example, he occasionally considers lines of type (iii) in the reverse sense. He discusses also lines of yet another type – (vii) from one megalithic site to another – though, in fact, examples of this type are not hard to find in Lockyer's work. Indeed, examples of some of these types of lines can be found in work earlier than his. Thus Lewis had previously considered lines of types (iii), (vi) and (vii).[5]

The above classification is fairly comprehensive, though a few misfits will appear from time to time as we give examples of the variety of megalithic orientations. Also, the order in which the different types occur is not logical, and we shall now consider them individually in a different order, which is given in capital roman numerals below.

One useful piece of terminology may be inserted here: that of 'foresight'[6] and 'backsight'. The backsight is the part of the orientation at which the observer is supposed to have stood, and the foresight is the part towards which he would have looked. Thus in lines of class (iii) above, the outlier is the foresight and the centre of the circle is the backsight.

I Alignments

Single slabs by themselves are not usually considered as orientations, except as indicators of natural features on the horizon, but alignments consisting solely of two or more menhirs are common enough. A fairly

44-7, 61-3, 67, 73,
81-6

straightforward example is the group of lines of small stones on Learable Hill, Sutherland.[7] Here there is a clear-cut horizon to the east, and the indications are thought to be calendrical. Some alignments are usable

58

in both directions; for instance an alignment at Duncracaig (Ballymeanach), Argyll, is thought to give a solar indication in one direction and a lunar one in the other.[8]

In some cases the menhirs are so far apart that it stretches meanings to call the site an alignment. However, it is not inconvenient to classify some of the orientations involving Le Grand Menhir Brisé, Brittany,[9] under this heading. These we shall discuss in more detail later. Likewise

12

it is convenient to include here stone fans such as Mid Clyth (Caithness) or stone rows such as Kermario (Brittany) which could act as astronomical orientations.[10]

Some alignments have special features, such as holed stones as at Men-an-Tol, Cornwall, which may be calendrical.[11] Lockyer discussed some of the numerous rows on Dartmoor, Devon, from the astronomical point of view, and he considered that the 'blocking stones' which obstruct the ends of some of these rows were sighting stones in some sense.[12] Many of the rows are not quite straight, and this can be readily inter-

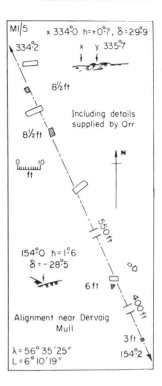

44 Dervaig B, Mull, from the north. This part of the alignment, of which a plan is given in ill. 45, consists of two upright menhirs and three lying on the ground. Other stones lie in the same line further south. Thom gives no identification for the declination indicated in the south (Thom 1967, table 8.1), but in the reverse direction the alignment indicated the place where the star Castor set in 1700 BC.

45 Plan of Dervaig B, Mull, by Thom (1966, 23). Upright stones are shaded and their heights are given. Details of the azimuth, elevation and declination for two possible foresights are also stated.

Plan of Dere Street I, Rox-rgh, by Thom (1966, 34). The ew in ill. 47 was taken from hind the stone at upper right, d the horizon profile can be mpared with Thom's sketch.

Dere Street I, Roxburgh. This an alignment with no appa-nt astronomical identification, ough Thom (1966, 11) suggested at the line should perhaps have en used in the opposite direc-n. The line was omitted in the st published by Thom in 1967 able 8.1). Some of the stones e associated with a ruined irn (G. Moir, pers. comm.).

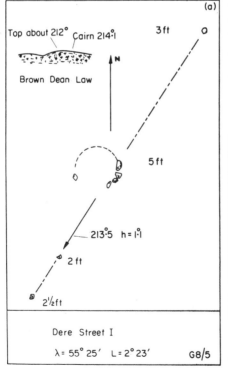

preted on the astronomical theory.[13] If a row is a stellar orientation, the explanation could be that different parts of the row were built at different times, between which the position of the star would generally have changed. Alternatively, the varying height of the horizon means that the direction of the row must vary from place to place so as to be able to indicate a constant declination. However, this interpretation is disputed by Burl, who maintains that some rows are just too sinuous to be astronomical.[14] This objection was also raised to Lockyer's astronomical interpretation of the West Kennet avenue at Avebury.[15] Nevertheless, the Dartmoor rows are deliberately orientated, however roughly.[16] Another peculiarity of some alignments, which probably deserves more attention, concerns the relation between the direction of the alignment *58, 67, 80, 96, 100* and that of the flat stones of which some alignments consist.[17] These directions are not always the same.

II Megalithic rings

Orientations of Lockyer's first type – those from the centre of a stone ring to one of the stones of the ring – are in fact rarely considered. Likewise, numerous orientations could be obtained by joining each stone in a ring to each other stone, but these are either given low weight[18] or (as is more usual) completely ignored. One reason for this is that it would just take up too much time to measure all such lines! Thom refers to Cauldside *48, 49* (Kirkcudbright) and Castle Rigg (Cumberland) as two of the few sites where such orientations may be meaningful.[19] There is an interesting

48, 49 An astronomical sightline at Castle Rigg, Cumberland. According to Thom (1967, 145 f.) this line indicated midsummer sunset when used to the north-west (shown opposite) and indicated sunrise on the day midway between the equinoxes and midwinter in the opposite direction (above). To the north-west the foresight is the small stone on the far side of the circle just to the left of the tall stone in the foreground, which is the backsight. Both stones are easily recognizable also above, but in neither case does the foresight protrude above the horizon beyond. This line also has a geometrical significance, since it is a diameter passing through both the main centre and a subsidiary centre of the geometrical construction suggested by Thom for the site. The subsidiary centre lies close to one of the stones visible in the pictures within the ring. Thom (1967, 99) assigns high weight to this line in both directions. However, the other symmetrically placed diameter is not listed at all, even though its ends also are marked by stones.

example at Clava, Inverness, where two slabs in the same circle are slewed round so as to point at each other. This may be solstitial, but Thom expressed some doubt as to its significance.[20] Another very curious example occurs at the Lios, Co. Limerick. Here two stones touch to form a V-notch which would be suitable for sighting from the 'entrance' to the ring, which lies opposite.[21] The entrances of a different type of prehistoric monument – the circular enclosures known as 'henges' – also seem to have meaningful orientations.[22]

If a ring is not circular, but is nevertheless symmetric in some way, its axis of symmetry is often considered for possible astronomical interpretation. Normally, as with flat single menhirs, this is not regarded as an orientation on its own, but in relation to a distant natural feature, as in the case of the elliptical ring at Cultoon, Islay.[23] However, the exceptions include perhaps the most famous astronomical orientation

71 of all: the solstitial orientation of the axis of Stonehenge. This example shows that the axis can sometimes be very impressively reinforced by the architecture of the site. In some cases the axis is emphasized by the fact that the stones are graded in height in the direction of the axis. Grading by itself cannot normally be used to define an orientation of any precision, but the orientation of the grading is sometimes a useful clue for the archaeologist in classifying a site,[24] and it obviously has some connection with megalithic astronomy.

Although it stretches the notion of a 'ring', it is convenient to classify
50 here certain lines at the stone rectangle at Crucuno, Brittany. Thom and his co-workers have suggested that lines from its corners to certain stones on its perimeter may be lunar.[25] Finally, if we admit the Crucuno rectangle here, perhaps we may also include the well-known orientations defined by the Station-Stone rectangle at Stonehenge.

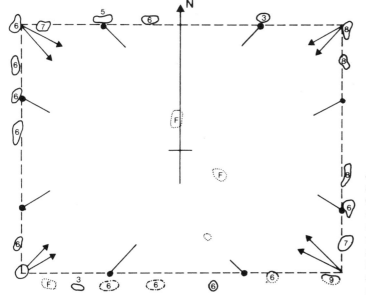

50 The Crucuno stone rectangle, near Carnac, after Thom et al. 1973, fig. 1. The arrows and dots show some possible astronomical indications. Note that the orientation of the short sides of the rectangle is approximately north-south. Fallen stones are marked F, and heights are given in feet.

0   50 feet

0   15 metres

51 Maen Mawr and circle, Brecon, from the south. Maen Mawr is the large stone on the right. The axial outlier referred to in the text cannot be seen in this view.

III Outliers
A more-or-less isolated stone lying outside but not too far from a megalithic ring or cairn is often referred to as an 'outlier'. Though the archaeologist Aubrey Burl has expressed the opinion that most such stones served no astronomical purpose,[26] there are many examples of claimed astronomical orientations consisting of an outlier viewed from the centre *52* of the associated circle. Note that a certain amount of megalithic geometry is involved here, since the choice of the 'centre' of a non-circular ring is not necessarily a trivial matter. At Woodhenge (Wiltshire), for example, Thom's geometry defines two centres,[27] and each of these is claimed to define a stellar line to a corresponding outlier.

Numerous lines of this type will be found in Lockyer's work. There is a singular example at the Merry Maidens, Cornwall, in which the outlier has a hole bored in it.[28] In this case Lockyer thought it preferable to regard the orientation as being from the outlier to the centre of the circle, in which case it yielded a line for midsummer sunset. In his earlier work Thom did not consider orientations used from the outlier to the circle, or else gave them low weight.[29] One of his examples is the stellar *53* line from the very tall menhir Clach an Trushel, in Lewis, to Steinacleit, which is really a chambered cairn rather than a ring, but he clearly found this an uncomfortably poor explanation for such a large stone.[30]

In some cases the orientation to the outlier is reinforced by some other feature of the site. For example, the ring beside Maen Mawr, Brecon, *51* has a small outlier on its axis. Though Maen Mawr itself is a large outlier which may define a stellar orientation, the axial outlier is unidentified astronomically.[31]

There are a few examples where the outlier is supposed to be viewed from some point which is not the centre. At Castle Rigg it is viewed *54* from the stone in the ring opposite to the outlier, and this defines a calendar line.[32] At Ardlair, which is a recumbent-stone circle in Aberdeenshire, the line of three outliers is supposed to be viewed from the recumbent stone, since it is closer to the line of the outliers than the centre.[33] This line is apparently identifiable only on the theory of a calendar with 32 months.

Above:

52 Stone circle and outlier at Lochbuie, Mull. The outlier is the small stone on the far side of the circle. It is too close for 'discriminating' astronomical use (Burl 1976, 142). The line to the outlier is listed by Thom (1967, 100) with high weight but it is not identified astronomically. Several other outliers stand at greater distances, and these provide astronomical indications.

Far left:

53 Dere Street IV, Roxburgh. Two stones, which might be regarded as distant outliers, indicate a circle on the horizon, though the circle is invisible on this photograph. The astronomical interpretation of the line is not known (Thom 1967, 98).

Left:

54 The outlier at Castle Rigg, Cumberland. According to Thom (1967, 99, 151) this defines a calendar line. However the outlier was buried at one time, as the scratches caused by ploughing still testify, and so its position is suspect (Burl 1976, 77).

IV Megalithic tombs

In general, the orientation defined by the passage of a megalithic tomb cannot be determined with much precision. Nevertheless there are many tombs for which an astronomical orientation is claimed, as the numerous examples assembled by Müller amply illustrate,[34] and this class includes some well-known sites. Three examples must suffice however. The first is the group of 'Hünenbetten' near Wildeshausen in north-west Germany.[35] At one end of one of these is a setting of large stones which could have acted as a foresight for the moon. Müller thought it a particularly 'conclusive' example. The other examples we shall mention are two of the three famous Clava Cairns, near Inverness,[36] and Newgrange, Co. Meath,[37] all of which are orientated for the winter solstice. Megalithic 'coves', such as those at Avebury and Stanton Drew, may also be aligned astronomically, and may be linked with megalithic tombs.[38]

V Lines between sites

This is a composite class, because of the variety of sites which can be included. Perhaps the simplest type is a line joining the centres of two megalithic rings. Lockyer gave a number of examples,[39] and in general terms emphasized those in which the centres of the rings are marked by stones. Yet examples in which this is not so are not rare, and include such a well-known site as the three rings of Stanton Drew, Somerset,[40] which has stellar and solar orientations. Writing in 1966, Thom assigned low weight to orientations of this kind.[41]

There are numerous examples of orientations between a megalithic tomb and some other type of megalithic site, especially in Lockyer's book. For example, he quotes from A. Devoir a site in Brittany where the line between a 'dolmen' and a menhir appears to define a solstitial

55 Shianbank, Perthshire. This apparently chaotic site, only part of which is shown here, consists of two rings. The line joining their centres defines a solstitial alignment in one direction and a calendrical one in the other (Thom 1967, 100).

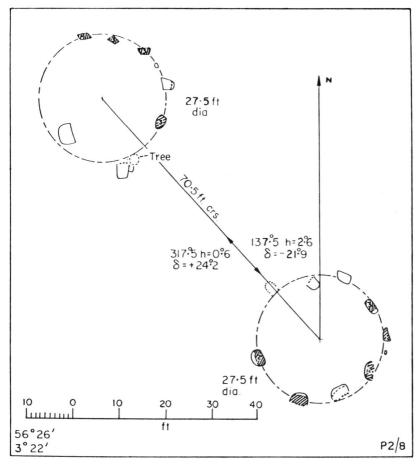

56 Plan of Shianbank, Perthshire, from Thom 1966, 39.

orientation.[42] A more elaborate instance of the same type was found by Somerville near Rhives, Lewis;[43] here the axis of a chambered cairn is continued by an outlier and a row of stones, and appears to define a calendrical orientation. There are also cases in which an astronomical orientation is defined by a line between the centre of a megalithic ring and a tomb,[44] or else between two megalithic tombs. An example of this type occurs near Carnac according to A. Devoir.[45] There is also an interesting group of such lines, which may be calendrical, on the island of Sylt, West Germany.[46]

At this stage the possibilities for composite orientations seem endless, for it is obvious that quite a number of different types can be generated by joining sites of one sort to those of any other. Since we have probably already mentioned enough examples to indicate this variety, we shall close our description of these orientations with just two more sites, which are of special interest. The first is at Odry, Poland, where there is a line for midsummer sunrise defined by no less than four rings (numbered 4,

78, 79

31

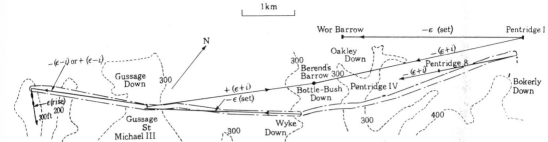

57 Astronomical indications at the Dorset Cursus, after Penny and Wood 1974, 269. Various neighbouring barrows are marked and named, and a number of proposed astronomical indications are identified. A gap in the north bank at one place is interpreted as allowing an unrestricted view to the barrow Pentridge 8 from the east end of the cursus. The dashed lines are contours, with heights given in feet.

5, 6 and 7 in ill. 31). A very curious feature is a pair of standing stones near the centre of the ring which acts as a foresight. These stones straddle the sightline, and the rising midsummer sun would be framed by them.[47] There is another line, with a similar pair of standing stones, for midwinter sunrise. Our last example is the earthwork known as the Dorset Cursus. Here lunar and solar orientations have been identified from points on the Cursus to neighbouring barrows.[48]

VI Natural foresights

The natural horizon plays a part in any megalithic orientation, since the orientation merely indicates the place on the horizon where some object rises or sets. The horizon could easily be quite featureless, but the claim has been made that conspicuous natural features were occasionally used to mark the relevant place on the horizon. Naturally, in this case the observer would have to adjust his position until he found that the object rose or set behind the selected feature, but otherwise there is no essential practical difference between this type of orientation and those types which are entirely artificial. In such cases the foresight is the natural feature, which may be a valley or 'notch', a peak, an island, or the sloping side of a hill which is approximately parallel to the apparent path of the rising or setting object.[49] When the foresight is a notch whose sides are formed by hill-slopes at different distances, it can be important to note that it will not behave like a cardboard silhouette when viewed from various positions.[50] It is even sometimes necessary to take account of erosion of a natural foresight.[51]

Although a number of orientations have been suggested in which only the observing position (i. e. the backsight) is marked by a menhir or in some other way, without any indication of the direction to the supposed foresight, it is 'indicated' foresights that play the biggest part in this subject. The indication can consist of any one of the orientations we have already discussed: a flat slab, an alignment of stones, the axis of a noncircular ring, a ring and outlier, the passage of a tomb, and so on, including the numerous possible composite types. Obviously the number of types is large, since the variety of indications is compounded by the range of types of natural foresight. Therefore a few examples only must suffice.

Some very large single slabs act as indicators, including the huge stone Clach ant Sagairt on North Uist. It is roughly orientated on the island of Boreray, which acts as a natural foresight for a calendrical line.[52] An unusual example in Brittany uses a reef out at sea as a possible solstitial foresight,[53] the backsight being a single stone.

There are numerous examples of natural foresights indicated by alignments. In the case of Ballymeanach, Argyll, which is lunar, it is indicated by a row of four slabs flattened in the direction of the row.[54] The alignment at Duntreath (Blanefield), Stirling, indicates a solstitial notch,[55] but here one of the stones has a flat face at an angle to the row itself; this face also indicates a notch, but this fits an equinoctial interpretation only roughly.[56] There is an interesting example of an indicated foresight at Strontoiller, Argyll, where the slope of the upper edge of the indicating menhir is parallel to the hill-slope containing the foresight behind them.[57] Natural lunar foresights are indicated by menhirs at the complex site associated with the Merrivale stone rows, Dartmoor, the rows themselves acting as possible backsights.[58]

68, 74, 97

59

91, 100

58

69

58 Ballymeanach, Argyll, after Thom 1971, fig. 5.3. The two alignments consist of stones which are flattened in the directions of the alignments. The row of four stones gives a solstitial indication to the south-east. To the north-west it indicates a horizon with natural foresights for the moon. The foresights are shown in the insets, where the coordinate on the left is elevation, and the coordinate on top is azimuth. The alignment of two stones gives a lunar declination to the — *south-east, though this, like the nearly parallel indication of the other alignment, is at present obscured by trees. To the north-west the smaller alignment indicates the star Capella. This star is also indicated by the hole stone, since it rises in the north-east from behind a prominent peak when viewed from this stone (Thom 1966, 20, where the site is referred to as Duncracaig). However, the stone is broken and does not seem to indicate the direction of the claimed sightline.*

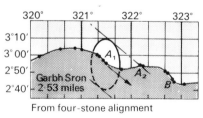

From four-stone alignment

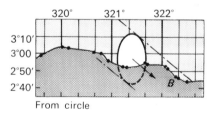

From circle

Moon setting with declination $\epsilon + i + \delta$

$140°{\cdot}7$ $h = 2°{\cdot}3$ $\delta = -23°{\cdot}7$

$332°$ $h = 3°{\cdot}1$ $\delta = 32°{\cdot}1$

Hole stone

$152°$ $h = 1°{\cdot}1$ $\delta = -28°{\cdot}6$

0 20 40 60 80 100 feet

59 Rueval Stone, Benbecula. This flat stone accurately indicates the island of Boreray (Thom 1967, 133), over 50 miles (c. 80 km) out in the Atlantic and invisible in this photograph. It indicates a calendrical declination. Boreray also marks a different calendrical declination when viewed from An Carra, South Uist (ill. 75), but it is not indicated by An Carra.

We find few if any sites in which a natural foresight is indicated simply by the axis of a megalithic ring, but there are some cases in which it is indicated by an outlier. One example may suffice: the east ring at Fowlis Wester, Perth.[59] In fact this combines both types, since the outlier lies on the axis of the ring, which is elliptical, and both features indicate a foresight to the north east. This is identified as lunar. Incidentally, excavation has shown that there are actually two concentric rings here, the inner one, which Thom has studied, being the kerb of a former cairn.[60]

Of the few cases in which a natural foresight is indicated by the axis of a megalithic tomb, one almost merits the epithet 'spectacular'. In St Kilda there is a passage grave whose axis indicates what Somerville called a 'window', which was really an oval patch of sky framed by a natural boulder wedged between two natural outcrops.[61] He could not decide whether this was lunar or stellar, however.

Orientations of the fifth type considered above, that is, lines between sites, can act also as indicators of natural foresights. For example, there is a natural calendrical foresight which is indicated by a line joining the two rings known as Long Meg's Daughters and Little Meg, in Cumberland.[62]

In the above examples, the backsight lies along the line which indicates the direction of the foresight, and this is the normal arrangement. There are cases, however, in which the observer is thought to have stood some distance away from the line of the indication. An example is the renowned site of Brogar, Orkney, where the foresights are indicated by a flat menhir (the Comet Stone) and by lines joining nearby cairns.[63] In many cases the cairns themselves are the places from which the foresights

92

are to be observed, i.e. they act as backsights. However, the Thoms also refer to a group of small stones within the ring itself which could have acted as a backsight. One might refer to this arrangement as a 'displaced' backsight, since this particular backsight does not itself indicate the foresight, though this is indicated elsewhere in the site.

A stage further takes us to 'unindicated' foresights, where a site marks a suitable backsight for a natural foresight without indicating its direction in any way. An example is An Carra, South Uist, which acts as a backsight for a calendrical foresight, without indicating it even roughly.[64] Such a foresight should be given low weight, but an unindicated foresight on (say) the western horizon might be less unacceptable if there exists at the same site an indicated foresight on the eastern horizon for the same declination.[65]

VII Miscellaneous lines

Though almost all supposed astronomical orientations can be forced into one or other of the above six types, one or two resolutely defy orderly classification. One is the unusual suggestion of an orientation related to some cup-and-ring markings on a stone at Monzie, Perth.[66] Another occurs in a group of three rings at Boitin, near Güstrow in East Germany, which lie on an approximate isosceles triangle.[67] Here Müller found some orientations by connecting the middle of the base of this triangle with the three rings. All three lines thus formed may be astronomical. The last curiosity we shall mention is a set of 'roads' radiating from Stonehenge, one of which is described as stellar, though one is unidentified.[68]

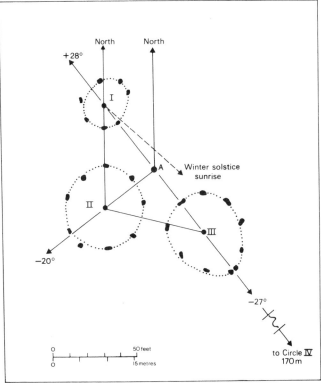

60 Three circles at Boitin, near Güstrow, East Germany, after Müller 1970, 83. The three circles are thought by Müller to be represented by egg-shapes in Thom's classification. The line joining I and II is almost exactly north-south, and the triangle I, II, III is approximately isosceles. The point A is the mid-point of the longest side of this triangle. The numbers beside three lines give approximately the corresponding indicated declinations. All three are interpreted as being lunar, but the line from II to III is unidentified.

Megalithic alignments in use

In the foregoing section we have surveyed something of the variety of megalithic orientations for which an astronomical interpretation has been proposed. It was certainly not intended as a review of evidence for or against megalithic astronomy. Now it is time to be a little more systematic in laying the foundations for a critical study of the evidence. As usual, this partly involves an examination of the practicability of the hypothesis. To some extent we have dealt with this in the previous chapter, but there we discussed mostly the sorts of limitations which are imposed on an astronomical hypothesis by the astronomy itself. Now we look at the other aspect of the theories – the megalithic orientations – to enquire whether their use for astronomical purposes was subject to any practical limitations.

The first requirement of any practical astronomical orientation is that the far end should be visible from the observer's end, and there should be nothing in between to obscure the view. However, there are cases in which the sightline is obscured by some structure in the orienta-
51 tion itself. One example is Maen Mawr, a massive outlier to a megalithic ring in Brecon. It is so bulky that it is reported to obscure the sightline which one might consider from the centre of the ring towards Maen Mawr itself.[69] Another site where this may be a difficulty is Clava, Inverness. At present the heights of the cairns at this site do not preclude sightings being taken over them,[70] but this may not have been true in the past.[71]

There are cases in which a free sightline along an orientation appears
61-3 to be obscured by the relief of the landscape. An example is Eleven Shearers, Roxburgh, an alignment which is identified as calendrical.[72] However, it stretches over a ridge, and neither end is visible from the other. Another example is at Burnmoor, a group of sites in Cumberland, where Thom has listed two sightlines from one ring to two others, among other orientations.[73] However, Burl maintains that the two rings cannot be seen from the first one.[74] Obviously the siting of a monument can be important for clear visibility along possible sightlines, and it is interesting that many sites in the Carnac area, for some of which an astronomical interpretation has been claimed, lie on good vantage points.[75]

A factor which may affect the intervisibility of the components of an orientation is vegetation, especially trees.[76] Unfortunately, even in specific cases there may be little direct evidence (without excavation) as to whether the trees were also there in megalithic times, or even if trees previously grew at a site which is now clear. Nor is it really enough to know that trees currently smothering a site were recently planted.[77]

Changes in the tree cover may have come about through two related causes: the extension of agriculture and climatic changes.[78] According to the climatologist H. H. Lamb 'there is now much evidence... that between about 5000 and 2000 BC, forest grew much nearer to the open Atlantic coast of northwest Scotland than at any time since and also in parts of the Hebrides and northern isles.' In fact the comparatively rapid decline of the woodlands is dated between 2600 and 1600 BC. To the

61 Eleven Shearers, Roxburgh. Interpreted by Thom as an equinoctial indication, the alignment continues (out of sight) on the far side of the nearer ridge. Thus not all of the alignment can be used for sighting purposes at one time.

62 Eleven Shearers. A continuation of ill. 61, the most

distant stone there being the nearest upright one here. Thus all but one of the stones shown here are invisible from the west end of the alignment.

63 Thom's plan of Eleven Shearers (Thom 1967, 149). The sightline of ills. 61 and 62 is indicated by the arrow marked 94°.5.

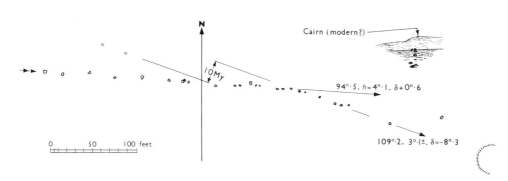

$94°·5, h=4°·1, \delta+0°·6$

$109°·2, 3°·1\pm, \delta=-8°·3$

extent that the orientations and the clearance of the forest can be dated at all, then, some doubt is cast on suggested astronomical orientations that are very early, i.e. much before the end of the Neolithic, at least in certain regions. It has also been suggested that the need for horizons clear of trees may well have influenced the geographical distribution of some types of megalithic site.[79]

Let us pass on from the intervisibility of the foresight and backsight to their structure, and consider first cases in which one or other is a megalithic ring. From the practical point of view the use of the geometrical centre of a megalithic ring is somewhat suspect, for the reason that it is not often marked by a stone.[80] It is at least odd to suppose that the position of the putative observer was unmarked, whereas the ring, which is quite peripheral to the orientation, was emphasized with impressive megaliths. This problem is all the more marked at very large rings or those with a non-circular geometry. Even allowing for their ruinous state, it would have been very difficult to determine accurately the centres
64 of the rings at Stanton Drew, Somerset, without very careful measurement. And although some rings do possess a central stone, this need not have been put up at the same time as the other stones.[81]

65, 66 There are a few cases in which a stone stands very close to, but not precisely at, the centre. Examples include some rings in the group at
31 Odry, Poland,[82] and one can argue that such an arrangement is deliberate, to make room for an observer at the exact centre. However, such cases are not common, and in general Thom had to presume that the centres must once have been marked by a perishable object, such as a wooden pole.[83] Yet this seems at odds with his discussion of backsights for lunar orientations, where he argued that large menhirs were often used since such great importance was attached to these sites.[84]

Generally the centre of a circle is regarded as a backsight, but equally interesting practical considerations arise in connection with the foresight.

64 Air view of part of the site at Stanton Drew, Somerset, by J. K. St Joseph. The small north-east circle is right of centre, and to its left, extending to the edge of the frame, are stones of the main circle. According to both Thom (1967, 100) and Lockyer (1906, 176) there are astronomically significant sightlines involving the centre of the circle, but how was the observer to know where this was?

65 The megalithic ring at Cambret Moor, Kirkcudbright, from the south-west. According to Thom (1967, 98) this is the backsight for two sightlines; and it is one of the few circles at which the centre of the circle, i. e. the observer's position, is marked by a stone. One of the lines is unidentified and the other is stellar.

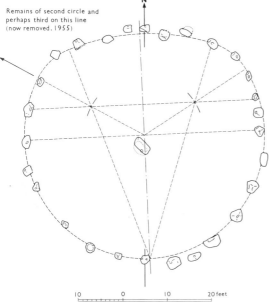

Remains of second circle and perhaps third on this line (now removed, 1955)

N

10   0   10   20 feet

66 Plan of the site at Cambret Moor, after Thom 1967, 64. Note that the central stone lies just to the side of the geometrical centre in the construction suggested by Thom, which is that of a flattened circle of Type A.

67 Na Fir Bhreige, North Uist, looking west. Thom (1966, 12, 24; 1967, 99) was unable to offer any astronomical interpretation for this alignment, and did not give it high weight. Note that the far stone lies well below the apparent horizon, and this is equally true if the line is used in the reverse direction. One of the stones is slewed to the left, and indicates both an artificial and a natural foresight; this line is thought to be equinoctial.

In particular, the foresight should appear to the observer with its tip just level with, or slightly elevated above the horizon, if the orientation is lunar or solar,[85] for if the foresight is substantially below the horizon it will be difficult to see against the glare of the sun (if the line is solar) or in the darkness (if it is lunar). An orientation will probably be most suitable if the foresight projects slightly above the horizon and is silhouetted against the disc of the sun or moon. This consideration sometimes allows us to decide that an orientation could only have been used in one direction, i.e. that it is not reversible. For example, on relatively level ground the tallest stone of an alignment is likely to have served as a foresight but not as a backsight.[86] Also, if one end of an alignment is blocked by nearby high ground, it is likely that it could only have been useful in the opposite direction.[87]

An example where this criterion applies is Stonehenge. According to Hawkins, the tips of both the foresights which are still upright (Station Stone 93 and the Heel Stone) are about level with the horizon,[88] as had been pointed out long ago by E. Duke.[89] In fact at Stonehenge conditions are a little complicated, since the surrounding bank may well have acted as the horizon, when newly made,[90] and weathering of the ground must be taken into account.[91] It has also been claimed that the great height of the car park posts at Stonehenge is accounted for by their being foresights: the car park is sited on ground somewhat lower than the main monument, and shorter posts would not have reached above the horizon.[92] A very similar explanation has been given for the great height of the fallen menhir, Le Grand Menhir Brisé, near Carnac, Brittany.[93]

When the foresight is a structure which does project above the horizon, one has to decide whether to measure the orientation to its tip or to the horizon behind it. While the latter has become general recently, Lockyer and Hoyle preferred the former option.[94]

Note that these considerations apply to lunar and solar lines, but not to stellar ones, since there is no sense in which a foresight can be seen in silhouette against a star! There are other practical differences, however. Thus, unless a stellar orientation was used at twilight, it would have been quite useless without illumination, and it would generally be difficult to arrange for a fire at a foresight if this was too distant.[95] Stellar lines should be comparatively short, therefore, though not so short that accuracy is sacrificed. In practice, an orientation for the sun or moon must not be too long either, though for a different reason. If it consists of menhirs of average size the foresight must be close enough to be distinctly visible against the disc of the sun or moon.[96]

One way of making longer alignments that still work is to make the foresight bigger, but the combination of length of alignment and size of foresight produces its own problems. These are acute if the backsight is immovable (e.g. the centre of a stone ring) and the orientation was constructed by adjusting the position of a large distant foresight. For example, the Thoms have suggested the use of distant artificial foresights at Stonehenge, and have pointed out that they would have had to be at least about $1\frac{1}{2}$ ft (c. 0·5 m) in diameter for every mile (c. 1·6 km) of

68 Clach Mhor a Che, North Uist. According to Thom (1967, 130) this indicates Craig Hasten, to the left, which marks the setting point of the star Altair in 1700 BC. 'This may or may not have been the ietention', he writes.

distance from Stonehenge.[97] For the lengths concerned the diameter may be of the order of 12 ft (c. 4 m). How could such a large foresight have been set in place to mark the setting point of the moon, say, when the moon takes only a few minutes to set? There is a second and equally troublesome problem: how could the observer at Stonehenge have communicated with the persons at the foresight and told them where to place it in such a brief period?[98] It would have been possible to adjust a nearby, smaller foresight in this time, communication being effected by voice, and then there would have been ample time during daylight to adjust the distant foresight in line with the nearby one.[99] On the other hand, this means that the distant foresight would have been no more accurate than the nearby one and would have offered, to say the least, no practical advantage over the latter.

Another way of constructing long orientations is to exploit distant natural foresights. This can only be seriously contemplated for solar or lunar lines, since a natural foresight for a star would be quite invisible[100] and artificial illumination is somewhat impractical. Despite this, Thom gives occasional examples of stellar lines using natural foresights, e.g. Duncracaig (Ballymeanach), Argyll.[101]

In connection with natural foresights for the sun, Thom introduced what has become known as the 'rim-flash' technique, first noticed at the site at Ballochroy, Argyll.[102] It only works for a foresight with a hill-slope almost parallel to the sun's path as it sets (or, possibly, as it rises). Here the idea is that the observer adjusts his position so that the edge of the sun just glances along the slope. It has been suggested that more conspicuous foresights are required for solar observations than for lunar ones, partly because of the greater relative brilliance of the sun.[103]

58, 68

100, 101

If it was desired to set up an alignment for (say) the solstice, one can imagine that the correct position of the observer would be marked temporarily for a few nights on either side of the solstice.[104] Then the position for the solstice would be obtained, possibly by some kind of extrapolation procedure. For lunar alignments the principle is the same but for an accurate line, a considerable amount of room must be available at the backsight so that observations may be made on several nights about the time of the extreme declination. Extra space would also be needed for the extrapolation process itself, and so here is another practical consideration that must be satisfied at such a lunar site. It is especially severe when the backsight is supposed to be on the top of a cairn, where the room for movement is certainly much restricted. One of the suggested backsights for Le Grand Menhir Brisé, Brittany, is suspect for this reason.[105] More space is also required for an orientation to the centre of the moon or sun, since this could only have been erected accurately by finding the observing points for each limb and then taking the point half-way between these.[106]

There is a further possible problem with any sites where there appear to be three or more natural foresights which can be used in conjunction with a single backsight. The reason is that, given three foresights, there is generally no one place from which all three would have lain in directions required by the astronomical hypothesis.[107]

There are still a few more practical considerations to be borne in mind when discussing the feasibility of any astronomical orientation, and some will be mentioned in the following sections. Here we mention just one more – the weather. Though Britain may be 'notoriously cloudy' now,[108] the same may not have been true in megalithic times. Indeed it seems that there was 'a high frequency of sunshine... as far north as 60°N' around 2000 BC, and that wetter conditions prevailed after 1200 BC.[109] Thus we may guess that, when many of the megalithic sites were being constructed, skies might have been clear at night more often than they are now. Nevertheless, when clouds appear at all in the sky, they generally give the impression of being concentrated near the horizon, where all the rising and setting phenomena which are supposed to have been observed by megalithic astronomers took place. Furthermore, any problems caused by cloudiness would have been exacerbated (in the case of lunar lines) by the need for extrapolation, which required observations on two or even three consecutive clear nights.[110] Haze too may prevent observations of risings and settings just as effectively as cloud.[111]

Finding alignments at sites

In the previous section we began to study one or two of the arguments for and against megalithic astronomy, for there are certain practical criteria which a proposed orientation should satisfy before it can be seriously considered as a candidate for an astronomical interpretation. In this section we shall consider one or two other criteria, not of a practical type, which a proposed orientation should generally satisfy.

69 *Standing stones at Duntreath, Stirling, from the east. This site is dated at about 3250 BC though the interpretation of this date is not straightforward (MacKie 1974, 187). The flat face of the central stone indicates a natural foresight to the east, which cannot be satisfactorily identified astronomically, but there is also a solstitial foresight.*

It is almost always true that studies of megalithic astronomy are concerned with remains which still lie above the ground, and these may be misleading. What seems to be a normal outlier of a ring, for instance, may well prove on excavation to be something quite different.[112] A specific example of a different kind, noted by A. Burl, is the west ring at Fowlis Wester, Perthshire. At one time interpreted by Thom from the surface remains as an ellipse with a lunar axial orientation,[113] it was actually shown on excavation to be nearly circular.[114] Thus a foremost criterion is that any proposed orientation must take account of what has been firmly established archaeologically.[115]

One consequence of this is that we must reject orientations between two features known to be unrelated.[116] For example, Lockyer generally omitted round barrows from orientations, on the grounds that these are later than the stone rings.[117]

Some critics take a stronger line, arguing that an orientation should be ignored if the features of which it is composed are not known to be related. For example, Hawkins has been criticized for including a hole at Stonehenge whose nature archaeologists were undecided about.[118] In general this point of view seems unduly severe, since it would exclude from consideration any site not thoroughly investigated by archaeologists. Likewise Hawkins' criterion that orientations should be postulated only between 'homogeneous' markers[119] can be interpreted with different degrees of severity. Certainly, however, proposed orientations must take account of any archaeologically well-established sequence of phases in the evolution of a site.

Another situation in which the archaeological evidence is of direct importance is in establishing the original numbers of stones which may have been present in a ring, for the existence of a certain number is usually the only direct evidence that some of these sites may have been used for counting up the intervals between eclipses, or other cycles. The presence of one or two more stones below the surface of the ground should quite vitiate the evidence for such theories, and Hawkins was well aware of this danger at sites which have not been excavated fully, such as Callanish (Lewis).[120]

In many cases the astronomical interpretation of an orientation will be possible only if its date lies within a certain range, and clearly this must be consistent with any date reliably determined by archaeologists.[121] Of course there will be many sites for which no such information exists, but this is a useful criterion where properly calibrated dates are available. This criterion can usually only be applied after a specific interpretation for an orientation has been proposed. However, it is worth noting here that the archaeological dates of sites for which an astronomical interpretation has been attempted appear to range from about 3300 BC to about 1600 BC.[122]

The accuracy of megalithic orientations

We have already listed a number of criteria which any proposed sightline must satisfy. As we shall see, further criteria must be applied when we attempt a statistical study of large numbers of sites. However, let us continue to consider individual sightlines, and ask now what information we need about them. First, it is necessary to measure the azimuth defined by the orientation, and the altitude or elevation of the horizon in this direction. In addition, however, it is important to know how accurately an orientation can be said to define a particular point on the horizon, for this can limit its possible uses. For instance, it is ridiculous to suggest that a short line of two or three broad stones may have been used for the sort of lunar observations required by Thom's proposed method of predicting eclipses. This method relies on observations with errors at most a small fraction of the moon's apparent diameter, and so such an alignment would furnish quite inadequate accuracy.

The accuracy that is relevant here is the accuracy with which the orientation could be set up and used, of course, and this may not be the same as the accuracy with which we can measure it now. In fact it is possible to set up an orientation surprisingly accurately with quite simple means. According to Atkinson a position on the horizon can be defined to within 5′ (about one sixth of the apparent diameter of the full moon) using a couple of poles,[123] and if these are sufficiently far apart an accuracy of about 1′ is attainable.[124]

When we turn to actual megalithic orientations we find again that accuracy is largely a matter of length. Thus orientations using distant natural foresights are generally the most accurate,[125] and are therefore capable (in principle) of being used for the most refined observations. For this reason they are given great prominence by some authors.[126] However, some other lines, such as those involving Le Grand Menhir

70 An alignment at Usk River, Brecon. It is very short, and so the indicated declination is *particularly uncertain. According to Thom (1967, 82, 101) this indicates sunrise at two dates in the sixteen-month calendar, but it is given low weight.*

Brisé, near Carnac, may be of comparable accuracy. Most of the well-known sightlines defined by the stones at Stonehenge are much less accurate, even potentially, since they are much shorter. Indeed it was presumably for this reason that Hawkins ignored the very shortest lines that could conceivably be found at Stonehenge.[127] The fact that accurate orientations must generally be long is also a convenient explanation for the fact that students of megalithic astronomy are concerned almost exclusively with rising and setting phenomena: the only practical method of arranging for a *long* orientation is to construct it along the ground,[128] and so it would be used to indicate an event on the horizon.

71, 103

In addition to the length of an orientation, the nature of its components is relevant to its accuracy. For example, a natural foresight is capable of added accuracy if it is small and well defined.[129] Likewise, as far as we are concerned an orientation is less accurate if it consists partly of mounds than if it is entirely constructed of stones,[130] since we know less precisely where the observer is supposed to have stood. Even a single slab can be surprisingly accurate if one of its faces is quite flat.[131]

72, 91

92

59

The imperfect preservation of most sites also decreases the accuracy with which we can measure the orientations. An example is the north avenue of Callanish, Lewis, for the stones there are not accurately in line.[132] In some cases the positions of stones are uncertain because they have been re-erected or otherwise interfered with. On the other hand it is not always true that, when the direction defined by an orientation does not agree well with a suggested astronomical direction, then the error can be attributed to faulty re-erection. Hawkins offered this explanation in the case of one line at Stonehenge, but Atkinson, having himself parti-

107

cipated in the reconstruction of parts of Stonehenge, did not think that this could account for the error.[133]

Another factor which sometimes limits the accuracy with which megalithic orientations are defined is the horizon altitude, which can be affected seriously by the changing patterns of tree growth.[134] To a large extent, what was said about these changes in connection with the intervisibility of sites is equally applicable here. What is normally done in this situation is to quote the horizon altitude as it would be in the absence of trees. However, as a measure of the uncertainty introduced by the possibility of trees on the horizon, it is worth noting that at Stonehenge their presence or absence affects the declination indicated by a typical orientation by roughly half of the apparent diameter of the moon or sun.[135]

91   Another example worth noting is the north-westerly notch at Temple Wood, Argyll, where much higher accuracy is claimed.[136] Patrick, however, has found that as little as a 6-ft (c. 2-m) growth of bushes would affect the indicated declination by about 3', or about one tenth of the apparent diameter of the sun or moon.[137] This is almost certainly by far the biggest source of uncertainty at Temple Wood.

It must be stressed that the uncertainty due to vegetation only affects the accuracy with which we can determine the particulars of an orientation, and need not have hampered observations in the past if vegetation was absent. This being so, it seems that some natural foresights may have yielded an accuracy of about 1'.[138]

A few other estimates of the accuracy of some orientations may also be of interest. The axes of megalithic rings are generally poorly determined. The axis of Woodhenge (Wiltshire), at about $\frac{1}{2}°$, is one of the most accu-

3   rate,[139] but the recumbent-stone rings of Cork and Kerry, Ireland, which have been studied by J. W. Barber, are smaller, and the accuracy is correspondingly poorer: between about 1° and 3°.[140] The accuracy of short alignments and of orientations defined by the axes of megalithic

108   tombs is often comparable with this.[141]

Refraction

Important as accuracy is for the discussion of megalithic orientations, the essential data which must be obtained for each orientation are the azimuth and altitude of the place on the horizon which it indicates. However, when this information is converted to declination, which is what is relevant astronomically, a number of corrections must be applied. Perhaps the most important is refraction: the fact that light does not move along straight lines in the air, but on gentle curves. It makes the apparent altitude of a rising or setting body higher than it would be in the absence of the atmosphere, by an amount which can exceed the apparent diameter of the full moon. It causes the rising or setting moon to seem flattened, and it can also affect the intervisibility of sites.[142]

The amount of refraction, even for a given orientation, varies significantly with air conditions. Thus for high accuracy the refraction correction applied should be appropriate to the atmospheric conditions thought to have prevailed when the orientation was in use.[143] In addition to uncertainties in the gross climate in megalithic times, this depends in part on whether the line is thought to have been used at night (a stellar or lunar line) or by day (a solar one). To minimize these uncertainties, it is preferable to measure the orientations under the sorts of conditions in which they might have been used.[144] However, even for fixed conditions, the values of the refraction corrections differ slightly from one authority to another.[145]

These variations limit the accuracy with which we can determine the declination indicated by a given orientation. However, atmospheric conditions vary from night to night, and the resulting variations in refraction would have limited the usefulness of very accurate orientations even in megalithic times. In other words, unless conditions then were much more stable than they are now, these variations impose a limitation on the accuracy with which a fixed megalithic orientation could have been used to record a fixed astronomical position (such as the solstitial rising position of the sun).[146]

For the Temple Wood lunar indicated foresight (the one to the north-west) Patrick calculated that refraction variations would limit the accuracy of the orientation to about 1′ (i.e. about one thirtieth of the apparent diameter of the moon), and maybe worse.[147] The actual horizon at Temple Wood in this direction is high – over 4° above the 'astronomical' horizon – and, at other sites with lower actual horizons, refraction can be much stronger and its variations still larger. Nevertheless, Thom estimates an uncertainty of only 0·5′ for the low indicated foresight (altitude $\frac{1}{5}$°) observed from Ballinaby, Islay.[148] 91

Whatever its magnitude, this limitation on the accuracy of orientations is rather fundamental.[149] For precise lunar lines it affects the accuracy of extrapolation,[150] and it is probably the chief limitation on the accuracy of solstitial lines. For instance, refraction changes would have prevented the use of the accurate natural foresight at Ballochroy, Argyll, for determining the date of the solstice, since they much exceed the daily variation of the declination of the sun at the solstice.[151] 100, 101

Refraction is particularly subject to variation just above the level of the ground, and the Thoms have pointed out that several suggested long sightlines at Stonehenge just graze over intervening ridges between the monument itself and the proposed distant foresights.[152] This tends to make refraction stronger than it would be otherwise. Perhaps it also implies that the declinations defined by these lines can now be determined only with added uncertainty, and that their possible use in megalithic times was rendered particularly troublesome. There is a possibility that the special refraction properties of such 'grazing' rays may also affect all natural foresights, for the sightline is always bound to pass over the ground in the neighbourhood of the foresight;[153] this may well quite significantly affect the details of most indicated foresights for which particulars have been published. Interestingly, Thom's earlier work had already suggested to him that refraction was a little greater than normal when indicated foresights are considered.[154]

7 The statistical evidence

The need for statistical methods

> Certainly, in the intricate and obscure study of antiquity,
> it is far easier to refute and contradict a false, than to
> set down a true and certain resolution.
>
> INIGO JONES[1]

This is an appropriate place to take stock of our discussion so far on megalithic astronomy. In chapter 5 we looked at the subject from the point of view of the astronomy: what sorts of reasons might underlie a study of astronomy in megalithic times? What are the significant astronomical directions, and how are they defined? Are there any limitations, imposed on astronomical grounds, on the accuracy with which astronomical orientations could have been established? Are there any ways in which apparent limitations of this kind could have been overcome, such as the process of extrapolation?

Then in the last chapter we looked at megalithic astronomy with special regard to the megaliths, or the other structures which may have served to define orientations. We described examples of these orientations and mentioned the astronomical objects to whose positions at rising or setting they point. We remarked on the limitations imposed by the practical usefulness of the orientations: the foresight must be visible, perhaps in silhouette against the sun or moon or by illumination; in some cases there must be sufficient room at the backsight, and in others the foresight cannot be too far away. Finally, the effects of refraction variations, and the finite widths and lengths of the orientations, impose important restrictions on the possible accuracy which can be achieved.

Now suppose we have a number of orientations which satisfy all these constraints: they could have been used in practice, there would have been no essential difficulty in setting them up, and they point with adequate (but not impossibly excessive) accuracy to astronomically significant places on the horizon. Two possible explanations for such orientations suggest themselves: either they were deliberately set up in megalithic times for some purpose with an astronomical ingredient; or else they occur by chance. Now *a priori* we do not know that the megalith-builders erected astronomical orientations, but we can be quite sure that some apparently astronomical orientations will occur by chance. Therefore it seems proper to ignore the possibility that the orientations were deliberate unless we can be reasonably sure that not all of them can have been due to chance.

It is astonishing that this simple precaution has been ignored so often, and this has indirectly done megalithic astronomy much harm. Lockyer, for instance, in his book[2] describes on page after page one orientation after another which can be interpreted in some astronomical way. It scarcely seems to have occurred to him that all or at least many of these orientations could have occurred quite by chance. *93*

Some authors appeal qualitatively to the *numbers* of astronomical orientations in an attempt to argue that they are really significant. Thus it is argued that the occurrence of an astrononomical orientation in a single site might be a coincidence, but when we find similar orientations in many sites, then we can conclude that it is deliberate. However, this is no improvement, for even if all the orientations occur by chance, one will find larger and larger numbers of them the more sites one studies. Likewise, the fact that some of the lunar and solar orientations found in the first constructional phase of Stonehenge (phase I) also occur in phase III does not of itself confirm that astronomy was practised there.[3] *103*

In his investigation of Stonehenge, Hawkins made a statement which sounds dangerously like using the mere existence of a suitable orientation as proof that it was astronomical: 'If I can see any alignment, general relationship or use for the various parts of Stonehenge then these facts were also known to the builders.'[4] Hawkins described this statement as simply a working hypothesis, which by implication does not absolve the researcher of the need for proof. However, he later accompanied it with the explanation 'Unless proved otherwise, we give them the benefit of the doubt.'[5] It is a perilous approach to the interpretation of evidence, as Atkinson pointed out.[6]

Suppose once more, then, that we have a number of megalithic orientations which satisfy all the criteria of feasibility on both astronomical and practical grounds. When, if ever, is it reasonable to abandon the view that all the orientations occur by chance, and consider instead that at least some of them might be real? We approach this question using the criterion which we discussed in the introductory chapters: is there anything about the orientations which would be surprising if we supposed that the astronomical theory were wrong? In the present case, this means that we adopt the following criterion: are there so many orientations pointing in astronomically significant directions that we cannot reasonably attribute them to chance?

Of course, even if the number of astronomical orientations we find is very significantly greater than would be expected by chance, we have not proved the astronomical theory. As Inigo Jones might have recognized, that is a far more difficult task. All we have established is that if we abandon the astronomical theory we admit the occurrence of a highly unlikely number of coincidences. Nevertheless, this criterion is the best single safeguard against the possible criticism that the orientations could be occurring by chance, and has been adopted by the few critical workers in the field. But even if we accept this criterion, it implies nothing about the nature or purpose of the astronomy; it could be ritual, practical or scientific, for example.

Before we discuss the implications of this criterion, perhaps one point should be stated. What we are essentially doing is comparing the astronomical theory of the orientations with the theory that their directions are random in azimuth. However, the hypothesis that their directions are random is not the same thing as the hypothesis that they were not deliberate. For instance, one might entertain the virtually untestable idea that they were orientated on sacred places,[7] or the idea that they acted as direction indicators for travellers.[8] However, on any such theory there would seem to be no reason to expect larger numbers of orientations in astronomically significant directions than would be expected if they were random, especially if the orientations are widely spread geographically. This last qualification may be an important one, for Jon Patrick has given an example which shows that the topography can by itself make the distribution of orientations look non-random if the sites considered are confined to one small area.[9] This may also affect the statistical analysis of a site like the Dorset Cursus.[10]

Our criterion quickly brings us into statistical considerations. What we need are large numbers of orientations. Just as it would be impossible to decide the merits of the quantum hypothesis if we had only one circle whose diameter had been measured, so it would be difficult to come to any conclusion about megalithic astronomy if we knew only one alignment, even if we also knew, say, that it happened to point within a few degrees of the place on the horizon where the sun rises at midsummer. It follows that an investigation concentrating on only one or two sites (unless they are of the complexity of Stonehenge, say) is unlikely to be of much interest to us. That is not to say that such investigations are generally of no value, for it is frequently interesting to see whether the various criteria of practicability are satisfied at a site.

Now we have stated several times that the sites we find today have been subject to many disturbances, including weathering, destruction, re-erection, and so on. Furthermore, some of our orientations may be spurious. Possibly we may be including an orientation which really should have been used only in the opposite direction, or else we are considering an orientation between two structures which were never meant to be related. At the five circles on Burnmoor in Cumberland, for instance, some of the lines joining the pairs of rings may be intentionally astronomical, but it would be too much to expect that all are.[11] How do these effects interfere with our statistical study of the orientations? The answer is quite simple. Generally speaking, none of these effects should preferentially increase the numbers of orientations close to astronomically significant positions. Hence they are not expected to bias the evidence in favour of the astronomical theory.

One implication of this is that, provided that we adopt statistical methods, the presence of a small number of undetected spurious orientations is not destructive. For example, suppose a sample of genuine astronomical orientations is contaminated with a few spurious ones. Provided that there are sufficiently few of the latter, we should still be able to detect that there are significantly more orientations pointing in the astronomically meaningful directions than would be expected by chance. On the other hand, too large a number of spurious lines could make it impossible to detect any genuine orientations even where these exist. At any rate, their presence can only make us err on the conservative side.

This discussion brings out a further fact. Even if we find statistically significant numbers of astronomical lines in a sample of orientations, we cannot conclude that every line lying close to the astronomically meaningful directions is genuine. We may conclude that some are, but in general we could not distinguish the genuine ones from the spurious or accidental ones. In consequence, the greatest care must be exercised before one can declare of a particular line whether it is or is not deliberately astronomical. Regrettably, however, almost all writers on megalithic astronomy express themselves in the most unequivocal terms on the significance of individual lines. Thom, for example, says of the line at Stillaig (Argyll) that it is 'definitely lunar'.[12] This is a rough analogue in megalithic astronomy of an attempt to deduce the value of the megalithic yard from the diameter of a single megalithic ring.

Selection of lines

In the previous two chapters we dealt at some length with certain criteria which astronomical orientations should satisfy. Some are astronomical but some are practical. Such restrictions are pretty common to most discussions of megalithic astronomy, and we should expect any investigator to pay some attention to them. On the other hand, most writers on megalithic astronomy usually apply further restrictions on the orientations they are prepared to consider. Many ignore orientations formed from lines joining two stones in the same stone ring, for example, while others ignore orientations which involve features that are not man-made, such as those in which natural foresights are used.

Often these restrictions are a matter of individual choice or convenience, and one could argue that one should perhaps go to a site without any such prior restrictions and simply measure every orientation that could conceivably (in terms of its structure) serve as a sightline. One would soon find the need to impose some restrictions, however. Consider an alignment such as the Devil's Arrows, at Boroughbridge, Yorkshire. It is a spectacular alignment of three very tall menhirs, but the three stones are not quite in line; are we, then, to consider it as one line or three (corresponding to the three pairs of stones)? If the latter, should we not also treat the Nine Maidens, a row of nine menhirs in Cornwall,[13] as a group of no less than 36 pairs, even though all point more or less in the same direction?

Clearly we need some criterion which allows us to decide when an alignment forms just one sightline and when it forms several. However, this is a comparatively trivial problem. Think of an alignment in which the stones are so far apart that we might doubt whether they form an alignment at all. Again we need a 'selection criterion' so that we can decide whether to include or exclude it. Similar problems confront us with lines from the centre of a circle to an outlier: how do we decide which stones are outliers, and how do we define what is meant by the 'centre' of a ring if this is not circular?

71   If we need another example, let us consider the axial line at Stonehenge. How is this to be defined? Do we define it from the avenue, as Lockyer did,[14] or from the remaining stones, as Lockyer's critic A. P. Trotter recommended?[15] If the latter, do we use the trilithons or the sarsens,[16] and do we regard the line to the Heel Stone as worthy of separate consideration?

Selection criteria are essential and, provided that they are decided upon in advance of an investigation and rigidly adhered to during it, they should be quite safe. However, if they allow the investigator some discretion, for example in marginal situations, there is a danger that orientations with a possible astronomical significance will be selected preferentially, either consciously or unconsciously. As Thom has emphasized, much depends on the integrity of the researcher, and it is essential that the selection of the orientations be 'honestly done and honestly reported'.[17] Since we shall later be presenting evidence which does appear to support the astronomical theory, biassed selection is one alternative explanation which must be eliminated before the astronomical theory can be accepted with any confidence.[18] For each of the studies which we shall describe we shall try to find out what care has been taken in the selection of the data, but it should be obvious that it is of particular value if we can apply some fresh test of the data after the selection has been made, so that the results may not have influenced the selection of the orientations even unconsciously. There are cases in which this is possible.

The problems of selection have been considered in a general and interesting manner by Hawkins.[19] His five criteria have had some influence on megalithic astronomy, having been adopted explicitly by J. W. Barber, for example.[20] Nevertheless, while they represent one possible approach to questions of selection, it does not seem necessary to regard all of them as obligatory, and indeed they have been firmly criticized by E. W. MacKie.[21] Hence it is not necessarily a fatal criticism of Lockyer's work that it fails to meet them,[22] or of Thom's later work.

One of the criteria, that lines should only be considered between 'homogeneous markers', has been mentioned already. Two others concern selection criteria for the astronomical hypothesis, and will be raised shortly at a more appropriate point. The other two, however, do deal with the selection of orientations. They are the second and fifth in Hawkins' enumeration.

Hawkins' second criterion is really a corollary of the one we have mentioned. It states that orientations should be restricted to man-made markers, which would imply that indicated natural foresights should be excluded. However, there seems no reason why one should impose such a restriction, provided that any natural markers are selected fairly.

Hawkins' fifth criterion is that all possible alignments at a site must be considered. We have already discussed examples which show that this criterion is insufficiently restrictive, and indeed Hawkins did go on to qualify it.

Since this subject has been raised again, it is worth describing one practical solution which has been devised and applied by Patrick.[23] It will be recalled that one of the problems in selecting orientations was to decide when a group of stones, which are roughly in line, should be taken to define one line, and when the row may be broken into smaller components. Patrick's answer was to look at the uncertainty in the directions of each individual pair of stones. This might be due to many causes, such as their finite sizes, and he argued reasonably that a row defines a single alignment when the uncertainties exceed the variation in the directions among the pairs of stones. Patrick's thesis contains several examples which show how the rigorous application of criteria such as this resolved questions which would have seemed borderline in a more poorly controlled investigation. His criteria represent an original and comparatively workable means of tightening the methodology of investigating megalithic orientations.

A different attempt to lay selection criteria on a systematic basis has been made by John Cooke, Roger Few, Guy Morgan and Clive Ruggles, a group of astronomers.[24] It depends implicitly on a number of assumptions about the accuracy and purpose of supposed megalithic sightlines, and so, while it is rigorous and systematic in one sense, it is rather arbitrarily restrictive in another. However, it at least indicates what difficulties there are in the establishment of universally acceptable criteria, and it has been applied in interesting investigations of the sites at Callanish (Lewis), Cefn Gwernffrwd (Dyfed),[25] and elsewhere.

Selection criteria also play an important role in Thom's now classic investigations of astronomical orientations. Since these will be discussed in detail later in this chapter, it is more appropriate to consider his selection criteria there.

Testing the astronomical hypothesis

To satisfy ourselves that astronomical orientations are not just occurring by chance, we have to show that there exist significantly more than would be expected by chance. That will be our strategy, and now it is time to consider how it is to be implemented.

Clearly we must compare the positions indicated by the orientations with those expected on the astronomical theory. One way of doing this might be to use the azimuths indicated by the lines. However, comparatively few investigations have been expressed in terms of azimuth. Perhaps the reason is that the azimuth corresponding to any one astronomical phenomenon varies from site to site. However, the declination does not vary (except possibly for effects due to parallax), and so, if data from different sites are being collated, it is less inconvenient to do so using the declination. On the other hand, when we are comparing the number of orientations which would be expected by chance with the number actually found, the azimuth is more useful, since the chance hypothesis is more easily expressed in terms of azimuth. However, the two choices – the use of azimuth or declination – are basically equivalent, and for different purposes either one may be more convenient.[26]

The fact that each astronomical phenomenon corresponds to a single declination at all sites, but to a range of azimuth, yields a possible test of the astronomical theory. If this theory is correct, we expect the declinations indicated by orientations to be closely grouped, or clumped, around a few values; while we would expect the azimuths not to be so clumped. Indeed Thom has stated that his results show this effect, but gives no details.[27]

There is even another method for comparing orientations with the directions expected on the astronomical theory, besides expressing results in declination or azimuth. It is usable at a site with indicated foresights. Here one can employ the astronomical theory to predict where the backsights should be, and then compare these positions with those marked by menhirs or other structures. Thom chose this method for a visual demonstration of the precision of Temple Wood (Argyll) and Brogar (Orkney).[28] However, this method is not well suited to statistical studies.

92

No matter whether one uses azimuth or declination, one must at some stage compare the values actually found at a group of sites with those expected on the astronomical hypothesis, and investigate whether the results are unlikely to have been due to chance. The simplest way of doing this is to find out how many of the actual values (of declination or azimuth) lie within a certain distance of one of the expected values.

One of the important things to decide is the size of this distance. Perhaps the most important guide is the accuracy with which the orientations can be defined, a point which we have already discussed. However, the particular aspect of the astronomical theory under test is also relevant. For example, if we were testing for the presence of solstitial lines it might be legitimate to consider lines which indicate any point on the disc of the sun at the solstice, which is a range of about 15′ on either side of the declination of the centre of the sun. On the other hand, if we were investigating whether solar orientations are directed to one or other of the solar limbs, we would only consider lines whose orientation could be determined to an accuracy of (say) 10′ or better, and count only those lying within this distance of either limb.

Many authors have taken a rather casual attitude to this question of deciding how close an orientation must be to the corresponding astronomical direction before it is counted. For example, Hawkins' treatment of Stonehenge left something to be desired in this respect, because although he discussed possible sources of error,[29] the limit of acceptability was not quantitatively related to any estimate of these. In particular

Atkinson thought it too large.[30] It is important for authors to decide in some impartial way what error they are prepared to accept. If the maximum allowable error is somehow influenced by the errors which are actually found, the result could be that the number of orientations shows a spurious excess.[31]

When we have decided on the maximum tolerable error, the next step is to calculate the probability (on the hypothesis of a random distribution of orientations) that a particular line lies within this distance of one or other of the astronomical declinations under consideration. Finally, we calculate the probability that the number of orientations in this range is equal to or greater than the number which are actually found, and for this purpose we use the binomial distribution.[32]

The smaller this last probability is, the more attention we should pay to the hypothesis that the orientations are not random. There is no precise agreement on how different values of the probability should be interpreted, especially in a subject as contentious as this. However, as a rough but useful guide, we should pay no attention if the probability exceeds 10 per cent, which means that, even supposing that the orientations are random, there is at least a one-in-ten chance that the number of orientations close to the astronomically interesting positions would be at least as large as the actual number we find. If the probability is less than 1 per cent, however, we will regard the result as significant, and reasonable grounds for rejecting the idea that the orientations are random. Obviously there is a broad borderline between these limits, and results which lie within it may be of some interest. 'Suggestive' is a suitable non-committal epithet for such results.

For most purposes, the foregoing test is quite adequate, but a considerably more refined test has recently become available, thanks to the work of P. R. Freeman and W. Elmore.[33] Their results are not expressed directly in terms of probabilities, but can be understood in much the same way. One of the refinements of their test is that they calculate their measure of the probability for various values of the maximum tolerable error, so that one can clearly observe its influence on the significance of the evidence to which the test is applied.

Tests such as these are much the most direct method of examining the significance of the astronomical orientation of megalithic sites. However, some authors have presented their results in a rather different way. What is done is to find the value of some astronomical quantity which gives the best overall agreement between the astronomical theory and the actual orientations. Then, if the value thus found lies close to the known correct value, this is taken to support the astronomical theory. An example of this procedure will be described later, and it is best to delay an analysis of the significance of such results until then.

Now we have one last major question to raise before we look at some of the evidence which has been offered in support of megalithic astronomy. What are the significant astronomical declinations with which we should compare the megalithic orientations? Of course, we have described many of the significant declinations in chapter 5 in anticipation, but it was not always possible to give a very satisfactory account of the reasons for their being regarded as significant. It is true, for example, that certain lunar lines would be useful if it were desired to predict eclipses in certain ways, and we guess that solstitial lines would be important if megalithic astronomy had been a ritual activity. However, we have no sound *a priori* reasons for making such suppositions, or for guessing that megalithic astronomy might have been done for one purpose rather than another.

The trouble is that we have turned the subject on its head by discussing the possible astronomical declinations first and studying the evidence second. In the development of the astronomical theory the order has been reversed: the various uses of astronomical orientations have been introduced piecemeal to account for the declinations which, it has been claimed, are indicated at certain sites. In fact our choice of which astronomy to discuss was largely dictated by the topics which have arisen in investigations of megalithic astronomy.

The upshot of this is that we have no *a priori* list of astronomical declinations to check against the orientations we find, or at least the list was begun and has been added to by successive investigators. In this sense the astronomical theory of megalithic sites is itself derived from data on the orientations, and often this data is the same as the data against which we wish to test the theory. Our situation is not unlike the problem of investigating the megalithic yard when its value has been derived from the data now being used to test it. In that situation we saw how much more conservative we had to be than in cases where the value of the megalithic yard was not influenced by the data. In exactly the same way, we must be much more cautious in accepting a theory on astronomical orientations if the investigator has allowed the indicated declinations to influence the details of the hypothesis he is testing.

Curiously, Hawkins writes as though this was a merit of the theory,[34] — that we are not forcing some preconceived scheme on to megalithic sites, but are discovering facts about them which are, in favourable cases, implied by the sites themselves. On the other hand, one should perhaps take the view that it is much simpler to test a preconceived scheme against the facts we find, than one which has been moulded to fit the facts.

In another sense, of course, it is quite unreasonable to attack pioneering work for adjusting the hypotheses to fit the facts, for in the exploratory early stages of a subject the hypotheses are bound to evolve to keep pace with new data as these become available. Nevertheless it is a valid criticism if it is understood as underlining the provisional nature of results arrived at in such investigations. The acceptability of the astronomical hypothesis would undoubtedly remain insecure as long as it was not met.

Thus we must try to minimize the influence of our data on the declinations which we test. For example, if we wish to test whether the orientations of Stonehenge are non-random, there is little use in testing whether the number of lines to the position of midsummer sunrise significantly exceeds what would be expected by chance. This hypothesis is clearly influenced by what is actually found at Stonehenge. To create a fairer hypothesis, we must also include sunset at midsummer, and both sunrise and sunset at midwinter, for by symmetry we would have attached comparable significance to these had one of them occurred. This is an example of one of the two remaining criteria of Hawkins which we have not yet stated, namely that 'all related celestial positions should be used in the analysis'.[35]

Hawkins' remaining criterion — that construction dates should not be determined from astronomical alignments — raises a point which we have already mentioned in passing, and which we deal with again in several places later. The declinations of the sun at the solstices and the extreme lunar declinations, as well as the declinations of the stars, all depend on the date assumed for the monument. Thus in general any astronomical theory for an orientation is of a dual nature: it is not simply that the line is directed towards a certain astronomically significant declination, but that it did so at such-and-such a range of dates.

In principle, then, it is possible to date a site from its astronomical orientation. One of Hawkins' reasons for rejecting such a step was that archaeological dating methods are more precise, for various reasons, than any conceivable astronomical method. This may be true at Stonehenge, which was Hawkins' primary interest. However, for a site whose date is virtually unknown on archaeological grounds, Hawkins' criterion would imply that we must not discuss astronomical orientations to a precision greater than a certain amount, which is the uncertainty in the relevant astronomical declinations corresponding to our uncertainty about the dates. As with some other of Hawkins' criteria, to accept this one is to act on the safe side, but it is not an obligation. Rather, if an investigator has adjusted the date of a site to optimize its agreement with the astronomical hypothesis, we try to take this into account when we come to assess the statistical significance of his results. As usual, it means that we have to be more severe.

Finally, Patrick has questioned whether solar and lunar declinations should be tested together or separately.[36] He argued that a supposed acquaintance with lunar orientations in megalithic times could well occur quite independently of a knowledge of solar orientations, and so the two should be tested separately. However, if a site contains lunar lines but no solar lines, the significance of the lunar lines will not be artificially and spuriously enhanced by being lumped with any chance solar orientations, and so no harm would be done by testing both together. On the other hand, a positive result for sun and moon taken together is obviously less informative than positive results for the two objects taken separately.

The statistics of Stonehenge

All that we have said so far about the astronomical theory has been mere lengthy preparation, and now it is time to examine the evidence itself. Much of this will be deferred until the next chapter, which contains evidence mostly of a non-statistical nature, and sometimes this can be quite striking. However, on the comparatively strict view of the evidence which we have been striving to take, almost all the best evidence on megalithic astronomy is exemplified by some of the investigations which we shall describe in the rest of the present chapter. What distinguishes them is that they afford us some prospect of deciding whether the orientations we find are just chance occurrences or something more. We begin at Stonehenge.

71, 102 Stonehenge is a composite monument, for its construction took place in several phases from about 2800 to about 1100 BC.[37] By the end of the first phase, known as Stonehenge I, it consisted of a roughly circular ditch and bank, over 300 ft (*c.* 100 m) in diameter, together with a number of stones and pits. Among these are the postholes on the causeway across the ditch; the 56 Aubrey Holes, which lie just inside the ditch; the Heel Stone; and, possibly, the four Station Stones. In the second phase a number of 'bluestones', which had originally come from the Prescelly Mountains in south-west Wales, were set up in the area within the ditch, and a long avenue, bounded by low banks some 40 ft (*c.* 12 m) apart, was constructed to the north-east. Stonehenge III is the most complicated phase, but it is enough here to say that the bluestones were taken down and re-erected, and that other stones called 'sarsens' were brought to the site and erected in two settings. One setting was a circle surmounted by a continuous ring of lintels, and the other was a horseshoe-shaped setting of five 'trilithons', each of which consists of two upright stones supporting one lintel. In addition it is worth mentioning the stoneholes known as the Y and Z holes, which lie outside the sarsen circle.

The main orientation at Stonehenge, for which an astronomical purpose is widely accepted, is the axis of the monument, which can be defined by the trilithon horseshoe, or in other ways. However, the claim has been made by Hawkins and others that many more lines of astronomical significance exist at Stonehenge, and it is mostly these claims which we intend to analyse now. But there is rather more to the astronomy of Stonehenge than its orientations, and we shall review some of the other arguments in the next chapter. Here we shall concern ourselves with the statistical results and the arguments which most closely relate to them.

While preliminary results appeared in 1963, the book by Hawkins and White is the most accessible source of material, and also gives a wealth of interesting background information.[38] However, Hawkins later regarded a succeeding paper as the definitive source.[39] Doubtless one of the reasons for this was that the paper was based on a new and accurate survey of the monument, whereas the data in his earlier writings had been based on less accurate plans, which had given rise to some of the criticisms originally levelled against him.[40] Hawkins' work has been summarized by many authors, and has become widely known and read.

Hawkins first had to ascertain from plans the positions of all the relevant stones, though there were difficulties with stones now missing: their former positions had to be estimated from those of the existing

STONEHENGE

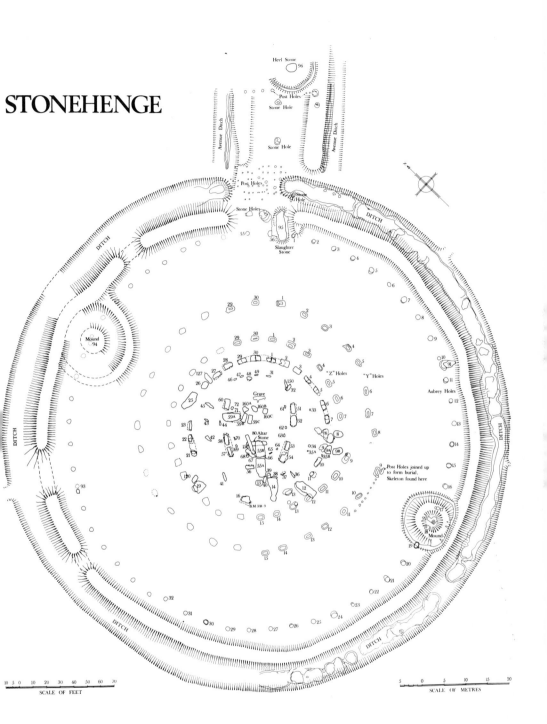

71 Plan of Stonehenge, Wiltshire. The Station Stones are positions 91—94, and the uprights of the trilithon horseshoe are numbered 51—60. The trilithons are surrounded by the sarsen circle (stones 1—30), and inside the trilithons stand the remaining stones of the bluestone horseshoe (61—72). (Crown Copyright: reproduced with permission of the Controller of Her Majesty's Stationery Office.)

stones.[41] Then the relative positions of selected pairs of stones were determined (though regrettably few details were given of the method by which the selection was made),[42] and the azimuths of the corresponding alignments were calculated. In the first paper, the conversion from azimuth to declination was based on the approximation of constant horizon altitude, refraction and parallax,[43] but by the time the book appeared, measured values of the horizon altitude had become available to Hawkins.[44] Finally, Hawkins compared the results with the significant astronomical declinations for 1500 BC – at that time the most recently available date for construction activity at Stonehenge.[45] (Since the agreement between the computed and ideal declinations turned out to be so rough – of the order of 1° – the precise date chosen was quite irrelevant for statistical purposes, at least as far as solar and lunar lines were concerned.)

Hawkins found no correlation with the stars and planets, in the sense that there were no more than would have been expected by chance, but there were substantial numbers of orientations which yielded declinations of the sun and moon.[46] The astonishing result was that the probability of their occurring by chance seemed less than one in a million.[47] The method Hawkins used for this calculation was given in the book,[48] and it is worth studying in detail.

Consider the early phase, Stonehenge I, wherein we include the Station Stones, as Hawkins did. Here he found 24 lines pointing approximately to extreme rising or setting positions of the sun or moon, including equinoctial solar positions and corresponding positions for the moon,[49] which comes to 18 positions altogether. Now we turn to the possibility that orientations are random. If an orientation is accepted whenever it lies within 2° (in azimuth) of one of the 18 astronomical positions, the probability that a random orientation would be accepted is $(18 \times 4°)/360°$, i.e. 0·2. According to Hawkins, about 50 distinct pairings of stones and other positions in Stonehenge I yield reasonable orientations, and then the probability of obtaining 24 orientations by chance was calculated by Hawkins to be 6 parts in 100,000. Together with a result of about 1 chance in 1,000 for Stonehenge III, we obtain the probability of obtaining these results as roughly 1 in 10,000,000.

Several points must be made about this, most being due to Atkinson.[50] First, there was an arithmetic mistake, and Hawkins' first result should have been even more significant: 6 chances in 1,000,000. Second, in testing the astronomical theory, one should calculate the probability of obtaining by chance *at least* the number of orientations which one actually finds, since any larger number would presumably also have been regarded as an interesting result. The new probability is obviously larger, which makes the result look less significant. However, in this case the change is small, the first probability increasing from 0.000006 only to 0.000008.

The third point mentioned by Atkinson concerned the number 50. Hawkins arrived at this number by the following argument: the solar and lunar lines which he found in Stonehenge I involved 14 stones or

103

stone-holes, and 'the number of ways these positions can reasonably be paired is no more than 50'. This may be true, but it is not the number we need for our statistical investigation. What we require is the total number of orientations in Stonehenge I which Hawkins actually studied, and although the number throughout Stonehenge was 240,[51] Hawkins does not say how many of these pertain to Stonehenge I.

Atkinson arrived at an estimate in the following way. Taking all the 14 positions in Stonehenge I and omitting all orientations shorter than the shortest accepted by Hawkins, and some other unlikely sight-lines, he found that the number of possible lines was not less than 111. Then we can repeat the probability calculation, and it turns out that the probability of obtaining at least 24 lines by chance now comes to about 0.37.[52] In other words there now seems to be nothing improbable in ascribing the alignments to chance, in contradiction with Hawkins' conclusions.

In another argument, Hawkins reasoned that the lines were unlikely to be accidental because most of the 14 positions are used in more than one line.[53] However, we have seen that 14 positions can easily lead to 24 astronomical orientations by chance; and since each orientation requires two positions, it is not surprising that each position is used on average at least three times.

Another approach is to investigate Stonehenge I and III together, because here we know that Hawkins studied 240 lines.[54] Of these, he found that 32 could be associated with solar or lunar phenomena. However, again there is nothing improbable about ascribing these to chance. Actually, by chance we would expect about 48 orientations, which is quite significantly in excess of the number which Hawkins published!

Finally we come to the errors in the orientations, that is, the extent to which their azimuths deviate from those expected astronomically. Atkinson pointed out that not all the 24 claimed astronomical orientations in Stonehenge I agreed with the ideal positions to within the limit of 2° which Hawkins used in his statistical calculation,[55] and this in itself would lead us to reconsider the statistical significance claimed by Hawkins. In fact, of the 32 lines from the whole monument only 25 have errors under 2°. The errors can be improved slightly on average by an appropriate choice of the limb of the sun or moon which the orientations are assumed to indicate, though the improvement is not great.[56]

Atkinson also considered that the limit of 2° was too large, in part because it should have been possible to position the stones with an accuracy which would have led to much smaller errors.[57] On the other hand, Hawkins did discuss semi-quantitatively several reasons why the orientations might not point exactly towards the corresponding astronomical directions. For example, the measured orientation may be uncertain if it incorporates stones which have fallen, been otherwise disturbed, or even gone missing.[58] Hawkins even claimed that the lines in Stonehenge III which are defined by stones which have never fallen 'are more accurately aligned'. However, Atkinson has disputed in specific cases that errors due to faulty re-erection were anything like large enough.[59] Another possible source of error lies in the plans used by Hawkins for measurement of the stones and other positions, and this appeared to be confirmed by the fact that the errors decreased slightly when a better plan became available.[60] Elsewhere Hawkins argued that the errors were really not important, since the supposed prehistoric observers might simply have stood to one side![61] However, before we dismiss the question of the errors completely, two more possible sources of error must be mentioned. One was again raised by Hawkins, but the other, characteristically original, was pointed out by Fred Hoyle.

Hawkins had noted that the lunar alignments exhibited larger errors than the solar ones, and he offered the following explanation.[62] We recall the fact that the daily change in the lunar declination is considerable, and this means that the moon is never quite at its maximum declination when it rises or sets. Furthermore, the error is increased if some nights are cloudy, and the extreme declination occurs only every 18·6 years. The daily change for the sun is much smaller, and, besides, its declination maximum is reached once each year. Hence it is much more difficult to get a lunar orientation right than a solar one. This qualitatively explains why lunar orientations may exhibit greater errors than solar ones, according to Hawkins, but there is more to his remarks than this.

If an observer misses the monthly maximum declination of the moon at the major standstill the resulting orientation will indicate a smaller declination than the ideal, and the same may be true of the minor standstill. Actually, the sign of the error agrees with this prediction in 10 cases out of 12. Now on the hypothesis that the errors are random, the probability that at least 10 out of 12 lines agree is about 1 in 50, which is certainly low enough to be of some interest.

Tempting as it is to give credence to this explanation (and, concomitantly, to the astronomical interpretation of the lines), it turns out that the results may have quite another explanation.[63] It is a very striking one. Hoyle thought that the errors were deliberate, and that the monument could not have worked as an observatory without them. This explanation depends logically on the supposed purpose of the alignments, which in Hoyle's view is that they were used to determine the time of the solstices and the standstills. The reason why deliberate 'errors', or offsets, would be useful in the former context has been explained in chapter 5, and a similar idea applies (in principle) to the standstills. This is obviously quite a different explanation from Hawkins', but it leads to the same predictions, except for lunar lines indicating the minor standstill. Therefore it is not surprising to find that its success is comparable. Although only 4 out of 7 lunar lines agree with Hoyle's predictions, no less than 7 out of 8 solstitial lines are in agreement.[64] If the errors were random, the probability of obtaining agreement in at least 7 cases would be about 1 in 30, which again is of some interest.

However, neither Hawkins' result nor Hoyle's is really as significant as it seems. One reason is that, if a line is included in both directions, as some of Hawkins' and Hoyle's orientations are, then the errors in the two directions will tend to be correlated. This effectively increases the probability of obtaining these results on the errors by chance.[65] Similar effects could also arise as a result of other geometrical relationships between the different lines.

What are we left with, then? The actual distribution of the orientations does not seem significantly non-random. Nevertheless it transpires that the statistical significance of Stonehenge can be salvaged to some extent if we are prepared to admit that some of the lines considered by Hawkins and Hoyle are more important than others, in a geometrical or architectural sense. One favourite candidate is the group of lines defined by the four Stations. However, the interpretation of these four positions has become so intricate that they require a rather more detailed discussion than they probably deserve. This is reserved for the next chapter.

There is one line at Stonehenge on whose significance there seems to be almost universal agreement – the solstitial orientation of its axis. Since it is so widely accepted as being deliberate, it is of some interest to find out just how significant it is in the statistical sense we have been stressing. According to the Thoms the azimuth of the axis of the trilithon horseshoe can be determined to 3′ either way, and the centre of the sun's disc would have risen within roughly this 6′ range (at midsummer) sometime between 2100 BC and 1500 BC,[66] which overlaps the archaeologically estimated range of dates for the construction of this phase of Stonehenge.[67] It would presumably have been considered equally remarkable had either limb risen within this range, or if we had been concerned with sunrise at the winter solstice, or sunset at either solstice. Hence the total range of azimuths within which the trilithon axis could have lain so as to exhibit an astronomical orientation amounts to 1·2°. The probability of this occurring by chance is one in three hundred. Of course this result depends somewhat on what one would accept as an astronomical orientation. For example, if one calculates the probability that *any* part of the disc at a solstitial rising or setting is indicated by the axis, it increases to about one in a hundred.[68]

Whatever the details, it is very interesting to have an estimate of the probability that this orientation, which is widely accepted even by archaeologists, could have occurred quite by chance. It then becomes particularly surprising, moreover, to find that similar levels of significance in other comparable investigations do not command similar widespread acceptance.

Thom's early work

The trouble with Stonehenge is that it has been overworked. There is an orientation of undoubted significance – the familiar orientation of the axis. However, when we start drawing lines through numerous pairs of positions in the whole monument – even if we ignore the implausible pairs – the very few significant lines (if indeed there are any others) are swamped by the enormous number that almost certainly have nothing to do with celestial orientations. If we wish to find out more about mega-lithic astronomy it is necessary to go beyond the study of a single monu-ment, even one as complex as Stonehenge. In fact it is preferable to restrict ourselves to only a small number of orientations from each site, and look collectively at the results from large numbers of sites. This is what Thom has done.

Modestly, Thom maintained that his work was 'complementary to a study of Stonehenge';[69] in reality it goes much further, and thanks are due to him for liberating the study of megalithic astronomy from the inconclusive evidence on which it had previously rested. Even by the time of publication of his first book, information had been gathered from about 300 British megalithic sites.[70] This vast new body of data, acquired with such care and published with such a useful attention to detail, has been invaluable in elevating megalithic astronomy to a new standard of rigour.

Many commentators have used the information in Thom's first book as a standard source for the data he had acquired up until then. However, one has to study his earlier papers to find careful statistical discussions of his results, even though the statistical analyses might be slightly modi-fied by his later discoveries.[71] Another reason for studying these earlier papers is that strict selection criteria were more closely adhered to then than in his book of 1967 and in later writings, as one example indicates: 100 Ballochroy, in Argyll.

Ballochroy has been hailed by Thom as 'the most interesting and in-structive solstitial site'.[72] Other authors agree that the flat face of one of

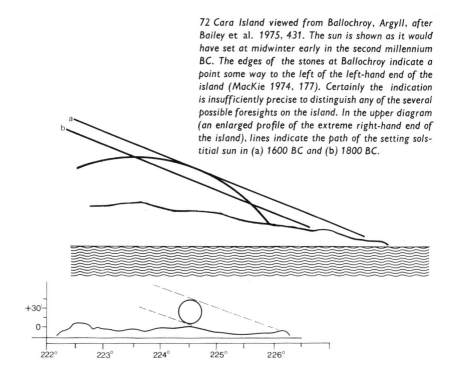

72 *Cara Island viewed from Ballochroy, Argyll, after Bailey et al. 1975, 431. The sun is shown as it would have set at midwinter early in the second millennium BC. The edges of the stones at Ballochroy indicate a point some way to the left of the left-hand end of the island (MacKie 1974, 177). Certainly the indication is insufficiently precise to distinguish any of the several possible foresights on the island. In the upper diagram (an enlarged profile of the extreme right-hand end of the island), lines indicate the path of the setting sols-titial sun in (a) 1600 BC and (b) 1800 BC.*

the stones unequivocally indicates a natural foresight to the north-west,[73] as discussed by Thom, and we shall return to this in the next chapter, but here it is the orientation to the south-west that concerns us. In his 1954 paper, this orientation was omitted from a histogram of solstitial orientations because the indication of the foresight is not unambiguous.[74] It was included in the histogram in the book published in 1967,[75] though as a second-class line 'which some people might accept and others discard'.[76] In his brief account of the site in 1971 there was little to suggest that this line had a value inferior to that of the line to the north-west.[77]

    There is some evidence, then, that Thom applied selection criteria most strictly in his earliest work. Even so, there was always a residue of borderline cases requiring individual discussion.[78] In his later work, he made this explicit by devising a weighting system to indicate the extent of subjectivity and other undesirable factors in the selection of orientations.[79] Broadly, this classification separates lines which have been chosen more or less objectively from those which have been introduced mainly because they are consistent with the astronomical theory. For example, there are lines in which the orientation is well defined by the megalithic site itself, and others in which an orientation is suspected for no other reason than that it produces one of the significant astronomical declinations. Lines of the latter type are useless for statistical purposes, because they have been selected merely for their possible astronomical significance. This Thom recognized by omitting them from the histograms which, in his first book, served as visual evidence on megalithic astronomy.

    Thom also introduced an intermediate class for borderline cases, one example being the line to the south-west at Ballochroy. One can argue that these also should be omitted from statistical calculations. Finally, there is in effect a fourth class, since in the figures in Thom's first book one occasionally finds details of a line which was not thought worth including in the main table of orientations.[80] Other untabulated lines of doubtful significance are occasionally noted in the text.

    Thom's most important papers are best taken in chronological order, beginning with that of 1954. Here Thom considers three types of site: alignments consisting of at least three stones, lines from the centre of a ring to an outlier, and natural foresights indicated by flat slabs. He stated that he had included 'every line found which complies with the above definitions'[81] which is, of course, vital. Unfortunately, details are given only of those which indicate declinations within restricted ranges close to the declinations of the sun at the solstices, the equinoxes, and the four other points in an eight-month calendar. It would have been helpful to know the total number of orientations for all declinations, but all that is said is that they numbered 'over 200'.[82]

    Detailed information is given on the lines indicating declinations within the ranges 23° to 25° and −23° to −25°, which includes the solstices, and it may be best to begin with these. The first is Ballochroy, which we have already mentioned. In order to be as strict as possible in the selection of a sample, we shall omit any line not given highest weighting in the list of 1967,[83] which means that we include only the line to the

100, 101, 97, 98 north-west at Ballochroy. The second site is Kintraw, also in Argyll. Here the indication is weak (it was given class B in 1967) and so this line is best omitted. The fourth line (Seven Brethren, Dumfriesshire) is omitted from two listings in later work,[84] and we should perhaps reject it here also. There is a suspicion[85] that the fifth line (Drumtroddan, Wigtown) has been re-erected. Of the 11th line (Colonsay, Argyll) Thom writes that the foresight is poor;[86] he omitted it in his first book and so shall we. Finally, we shall see in a discussion of Thom's next paper that the lines at Temple Wood and Sornach Coir Fhinn may *possibly* be open to doubt.

There seems little to object to in the remaining lines, which leaves the following seven:

Ballochroy, Argyll	24° 09′	± 1′
Lachlan Bay, Argyll	24 14	± 5
69 Blanefield (Duntreath), Stirling	24 03	± 5
58 Duncracaig (Ballymeanach), Argyll	−23 42	±10
Cambret Moor (East), Kirkcudbright	−23 41	±10
Long Meg, Cumberland	−24 10	±10
52 Loch Buie, Mull	−23 44	± 4

76 A histogram of these results, with the sign ignored, shows that they are clumped towards the middle of the range 23° to 25°, close to the solstitial declination of the sun in the second and third millennia BC. Now it is important to determine whether this is just a chance result, or whether it has any statistical significance.

73 (far left) *Muthill, Perthshire. In both directions this was classified by Thom (1967, 100) as class A (the highest class). To the north (shown here) it is thought to be possibly lunar, and to the south it indicates a calendrical declination.*

74 (left) *The stone near Pollachar Inn, South Uist. The righthand fall of the island (Fiary) indicates a calendrical declination. This line was given lowest weight by Thom (1966, 42; 1967, 99), perhaps because he himself had not visited it.*

75 *An Carra, South Uist, looking north-east. Its orientation 'probably' indicates a calendrical declination (Thom 1967, 133) in the direction shown, though it is not included in Thom's main list (1967, table 8.1). However it also acts as a backsight for an unindicated natural foresight to the northwest (i. e. to the left) which marks the same declination. This indication is listed, but with lowest weight. See also ill. 59.*

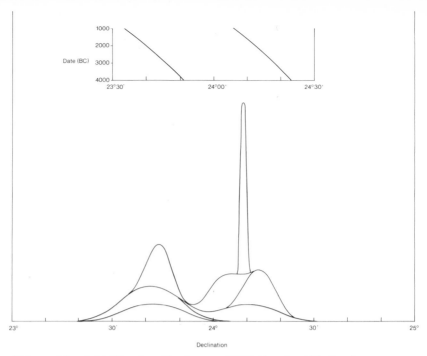

76 *Some of the solstitial lines from Thom's paper of 1954. Here the width of each curve corresponds to the uncertainty in the indicated declination, as estimated by Thom. Thus accurate lines are shown by tall narrow shapes. At the top of the diagram is an approximate graph of the declinations of the upper and lower limbs of the solstitial sun between 1000 BC and 4000 BC.*

At the solstices the centre of the sun's disc had a declination of $\pm 23° 52'$ in 1500 BC,[87] which is one of the latest dates known for a megalithic site,[88] and the disc covers a range of about 32'. On the other hand, one of the sites (Blanefield, or Duntreath) has been given a very tentative calibrated radiocarbon date of 3200 or 3300 BC,[89] when the solstitial declination of the sun must have been about $\pm 24° 03'$. Given this uncertainty in the dates, the sun's disc at the solstices occupied the range from about $\pm 23° 36'$ to $\pm 24° 19'$ during the period from 3300 to 1500 BC. All of the above lines lie within this range even if we ignore the uncertainty in the indicated declinations, and the probability of this on the hypothesis that the declinations are randomly scattered from $\pm 23°$ to $\pm 25°$ is less than one in a thousand. This is a good deal smaller than the probability that the solstitial orientation of the axis of Stonehenge occurs by chance; that is, the present result is more significant. Again, the detailed probability depends somewhat on the precise test one adopts, but we have been fairly ruthless in rejecting orientations about which there is some suspicion. The probability becomes still smaller, that is, the result becomes still more significant, if these are reinstated.

77 In Thom's discussion no statistical analysis was given, and the proof he offered was furnished by visual inspection of a histogram. He pointed out that the two main peaks in this diagram were separated by about 27', very nearly the apparent diameter of the sun, and he interpreted this as showing that it was mostly the upper and lower edges of the sun's disc that were observed. Furthermore the declinations indicated by the orien-

tations clump around the astronomically significant values when the three types of orientations are considered separately.[90]

These results strongly suggest that at least some of the orientations investigated by Thom in this paper were orientated on the rising and setting positions of the sun at the solstices. However, the paper also contains evidence of indications for other solar declinations, and it is interesting to review this. We begin with seven lines which are interpreted as equinoctial. Removing those which were later omitted or given low weight[91] leaves only four. Of these one (Na Fir Bhreige, N. Uist) was given low weight in 1966[92] and another (Clach MhicLeoid, Harris) was given low weight in the paper under discussion,[93] though it had been elevated by 1967 to high weight. Thus two lines remain, of which one (Eleven Shearers) is an alignment in which the far end is hidden from an observer at the other end by the curve of the ground on which it is built. Furthermore, Thom gave it only intermediate weight in the present paper. This leaves only one line – the famous equinoctial line at Callanish discovered by Somerville.

67

61-3

107

Thom's case for the equinoctial lines rests on the fact that, of the seven lines on his original list which indicate declinations between $-2°$ and $+2°$, all actually give declinations between $0°$ and $1°$. This is close to the range which he predicts from his definition of the equinox (which happens to yield a declination of $0·5°$ or $0·6°$), and it is important to note that no other lines were known which indicated declinations within the remainder of the range: $-2°$ to $0°$ and $1°$ to $2°$. Statistically, this is highly significant, though the low weight we assign (on the basis of Thom's listings) to most of the lines suggests that it is wisest to retain an open mind on the equinoctial lines. Similar remarks, and a similar judgement, appear warranted in respect of the lines said to indicate the positions of the rising and setting sun at dates midway between the equinoxes and the solstices. Five such lines are listed, but three are given lowest weight in this paper.

One can argue convincingly that Thom's next paper[94] is the most important single paper in megalithic science. It has already been mentioned several times in connection with the megalithic yard, where its evidence is at the very least suggestive. However, the second half of the paper was devoted to a study of 'the astronomical significance of the megalithic remains', and this is what concerns us now. Like the paper of the previous

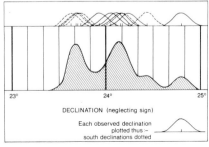

77 Histogram of solstitial lines based on a diagram in Thom's paper of 1954. Lines are shown individually at the top, and superposed below. The width is the same for all lines regardless of accuracy.

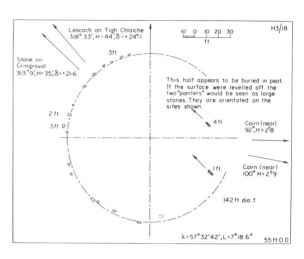

Leacach an Tigh Chlaiche
318° 33', H = 44'.8 = +24°.1

Stone on
Cringraval
313°9', H = 35'.8 = +21.6

3ft

This half appears to be buried in peat.
If the surface were levelled off the
two "pointers" would be seen as large
stones. They are orientated on the
sites shown.

2 ft
3 ft

4 ft

Cairn (near)
92°, H = 2°.8

1 ft.

Cairn (near)
100°, H = 2°.9

142 ft. dia. ±

λ = 57°32'42', L = 7° 18 6°   55 ft O.D.

78 *Part of Sornach Coir Fhinn, North Uist. The near stone, which lies within a stone circle passing through the further stone, indicates the distant hill where another site (Leacach an Tigh Chloiche, not visible here) acts as a solstitial foresight.*

79 *Plan of Sornach Coir Fhinn, by Thom (1966, 29). One of the two internal stones can be seen in ill. 78 in the foreground.*

80 *Kilmartin Stones, Argyll, surveyed by J. D. Patrick. In his 1955 paper Thom listed AB and F as outliers to the nearby Temple Wood stone circle (ill.1), but ignored the other tall pair, LM.*

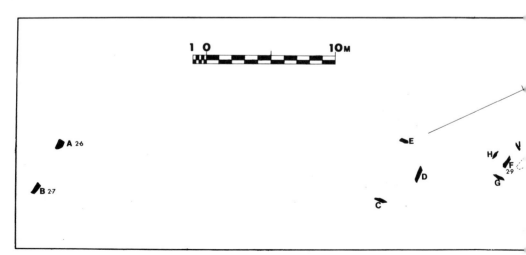

1 0   10M

A 2·6

B 2·7

E

H

V

F
2·9

D

G

C

year, it deals only with certain classes of orientations: in this case circles and outliers, pairs of slabs in line, and rows of three or more stones.[95] In fact the selection criteria are even simpler than in the earlier paper, since now there are no lines defined by indicated natural foresights on the horizon.

Of the lines defined by outliers to a stone circle, only 17 were listed later[96] with high weight, and these come from nine sites. Even when we restrict our discussion to these, a number of questionable cases appear, in addition to the two lines (one at Rollright, Oxford, and the other at Long Meg and her Daughters, Cumberland) which Thom himself cites as examples of somewhat borderline cases.[97] At Callanish only three declinations are quoted, corresponding essentially to three of the four outlying stone rows. (The one to the south is omitted because it is regarded by Thom as an indicator of the north-south line, or meridian.) At least in this case we can reinstate the missing declination, but other problematic sites are less straightforward. Two declinations are quoted for Sornach Coir Fhinn (N. Uist) and it stretches the meaning of the word to regard these as being defined by 'outliers', since the foresights are at least a mile (c. 1·6 km) off, and one is interpreted by Thom as a stone ring.[98] True, these foresights are indicated by two stones at Sornach Coir Fhinn, but it is difficult to see why they are classified as outliers. Another problematic case is Temple Wood, Argyll. Here, one of the outliers of high weight is the central tall menhir of the nearby Kilmartin Stones. One of the pairs of stones in this group is also regarded as a distinct outlier though of low weight,[99] and yet there is another pair of stones in the Kilmartin group which is not regarded as an outlier. The fact that the latter pair does not point to the stone circle makes Thom's choice perfectly understandable, but demonstrates that the selection of the lines depends partly on unwritten criteria, despite the fact that Thom paid strict attention to devising and observing his terms of reference in selection.[100] The other examples, however, appear to be reasonably satisfactory.

107

78, 79

1, 80, 109

KILMARTIN STONES

M 2·7

L 2·8

E,G,H & I   ARE FROM 0·4 TO 0·7M HIGH

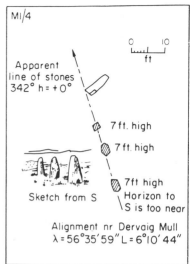

MI/4

Apparent
line of stones
342° h = +0°

0   10
ft

7 ft. high

7 ft. high

7 ft high
Horizon to
S is too near

Sketch from S

Alignment nr Dervaig Mull
λ = 56°35′59″ L = 6°10′44″

81 Dervaig A, Mull, from the north. The declination indicated in this direction was not listed by Thom in his 1955 paper, because the horizon is too close. In the opposite direction it indicates the position where Capella rose in about 1930 BC.

82 Plan of Dervaig A, by Thom (1966, fig. 8 e). All the stones in the plan can be seen in the photograph, ill. 81.

81, 82

69

61-3

83-6

     In the 1955 paper Thom also gives 34 lines defined by alignments proper, of which 21 were later listed with high weight. They come from 14 sites. As usual with alignments, there is the problem of which direction to look in. In the case of Dervaig A (Mull), Thom took the direction to the north, since the horizon in the opposite direction is too close.[101] Knockrome (Jura), Blanefield (Stirling), Drumtroddan (Wigtown) and Eleven Shearers (Roxburgh) are again alignments for which the declination is given in only one direction. Just as a precaution against the possibility, however small, of selection effects, we should put a question mark against alignments for which only one declination is given. We should perhaps do this also for two of the alignments for each of which two declinations are given, those at Loch Seil (Argyll) and Stravannan Bay (Bute). In each case the two azimuths do not differ by 180°, as they should do for one alignment used in opposite directions. What has happened is that one azimuth at each site has been adjusted a little, presumably to give the azimuth of a conspicuous natural foresight.[102]

83, 84 Alignment at Doune, Perthshire, to the north (above) and south (right). Details of the alignment in both directions were given in Thom's paper of 1955, though only the line to the north was listed in the first book (1967, 100), where it was given high weight. In this direction the alignment can be identified with Capella. The grounds on which Thom excluded the line to the south from his first book were not explicitly stated there.

85, 86 Comrie, Perthshire, to the west (left) and east (right). This is a reversible alignment. To the west it indicates the moon at the minor standstill (given weight A by Thom (1967, 100)), and to the east it gives a calendrical declination (weight B according to Thom). It is not one of the sites discussed by Thom in the paper of 1955, however.

The sites we have mentioned give some idea how difficult it is, as Thom himself pointed out, to be completely objective about the selection of sightlines. However, we may well have erred on the side of caution in some respects. As we have seen, there may be perfectly satisfactory reasons for the omission of one direction in the case of the alignments. And, while the presence of these questionable lines might cause us to be more cautious in accepting apparently significant results, there are compensating factors (cf. p. 138).

Now let us turn to the possible astronomical significance of the lines discussed by Thom in this paper. Thom himself gives a statistical discussion of equinoctial and solstitial lines together, and these have been re-analysed recently by Freeman and Elmore.[103] It turns out that the number of such lines significantly exceeds what one would expect by chance, and this remains true even if one omits lines which later Thom himself omitted or else classified as having low weight. Nevertheless it is likely that the significance of these lines is entirely ascribable to the solstitial orientations. As with the paper of 1954, the only equinoctial line that is entirely above suspicion is that at Callanish, and our previous assessment of the equinoctial lines should remain unchanged. Likewise, there is only one very good line corresponding to a declination of the sun at a date midway between the equinoxes and the solstices. This is definitely of no statistical significance.

The most interesting astronomical conclusions arrived at in the 1955 paper concern orientations to the points where bright stars rise or set. Now many writers are inclined to ignore evidence for stellar orientations

because, it is argued, there are so many stars, and by their movements they cover such a large range of declinations, that many accidental stellar orientations are bound to occur. However, such writers must surely not have digested this paper of Thom's, where he investigates just this question.

To study the possibility of stellar lines, Thom proceeded in the following fashion. In a certain 200-year period, the declinations of the stars change by calculable amounts, thus covering certain ranges. Thom counted the numbers of orientations (excluding those already ascribed to the solstices or the equinoxes) which indicated declinations within the ranges defined by the bright stars – the dozen or so brighter than magnitude 1·5.[104] This number was then compared with what would have been expected if the orientations were quite random, and this was done for each 200-year period from 2800 BC to 1200 BC, that is, eight periods.

The results are quite striking. Looking first at orientations defined by 87 outliers of stone rings, we see that the number of stellar orientations greatly exceeds what would be expected by chance for a date about 2100 BC or possibly a little later.[105] If the orientations are random, the probability that the number of stellar orientations should exceed 13 for at least one of the eight dates (on the approximation that the results for different dates are statistically independent) is extremely small. For true alignments only, the excess is not significant, though it does occur at the same date of 2100 BC, and when the results from the two classes of orientation are combined, the result is again highly significant: the probability of obtaining at least 22 stellar orientations by chance is under one in a thousand.[106]

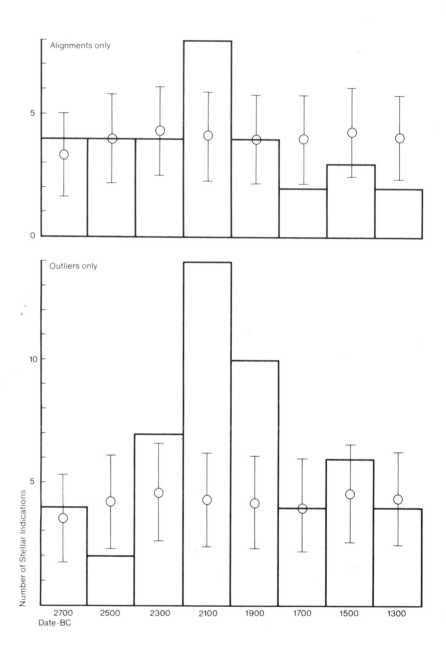

87 Indications of stellar declinations, from Thom's paper of 1955. Orientations are divided into two classes. For each class, the height of the histogram at a given date gives the number of orientations which indicate a declination within 0.2° of that of a bright star, at a date within 100 years of the date on the horizontal axis. The circle gives the number that would be expected by chance, but this is subject to statistical fluctuation. The fluctutations should lie outside the range given by the bars (which correspond to one 'standard deviation') on about one third of all occasions. However, very large excesses should occur only rarely if the orientations are random.

Such results are not sensitive to making a slightly different choice of which stars to consider, as Thom himself showed. However, their significance drops greatly when we reject the lines of low weight. There is still an excess at about 2100 BC, but there is now a large chance of expecting such an excess by accident. Also, of the 9 lines which could be identified with a bright star between 2200 and 2000 BC, 6 lie in the list of possibly questionable sites discussed previously. On the other hand, inspection of the 9 lines shows that no less than 5 are identified with the star Rigel. This is fairly remarkable, since there are altogether about a dozen other relevant stars brighter than the magnitude limit of 1·5 adopted by Thom. Nevertheless, it is not a straightforward matter to justify the possible conclusion that these lines are stellar, if only because Thom, by the time he came to write his first book, had completely reinterpreted them.

By the time this book appeared, Thom had assembled much more data. In it he lists no less than 131 lines to which high weight is attached. The types of orientations are considerably more numerous than in the paper of 1955, and it is difficult to give a satisfactory assessment of the selection criteria which Thom used. It is a help that he introduces his weighting system here, though we have seen that even lines of high weight can be questionable if we insist on being really strict. Furthermore there are some frankly puzzling features, as the discussion of Ballochroy   48, 83, 84 in the next chapter will show. In general, therefore, any conclusions drawn from the material in this book are still subject to some qualification.

Five of the lines of high weight lie within the range expected for the equinoctial declination on Thom's calendrical theory. One would have expected just over 1 by chance, and at least 5 would occur with a probability of about one in a hundred,[107] which seems quite significant. Likewise, no less than 13 lines of high quality yield declinations lying within 0·5° of the ranges corresponding to calendar dates between equinoxes and solstices.[108] By chance one would have expected only 3 or 4 and there is scarcely any doubt that the actual number is very significantly in excess of this. Taken at face value, this would imply the existence of a calendar with eight months. Again, however, such a conclusion is only as sound as the selection of the sightlines on which it is based. Furthermore, Thom's calendrical theory was adjusted to some extent to improve the fit with the indicated declinations,[109] and so our estimates of statistical significance may not be conservative enough.

When we look for evidence of orientations to the position of the sun at dates midway between those already mentioned (i.e. we contemplate a year divided into 16 parts), we find only 13 such lines of high weight. By chance one would have expected about 7, and the probability of at least 13 is about one in fifty. At face value this result seems reasonably significant, though we should be cautious about drawing firm conclusions from it, for reasons which we have already mentioned. Thom stated that 'conclusive proof' for his calendrical theory can be seen in the results for those lines which indicate declinations considered to be known to

$\pm 0 \cdot 1°$.[110] Nevertheless, not all these lines are of high weight, and furthermore we do not know the total number of lines of high precision, whence it is not possible to use them for statistical purposes. Incidentally, on the supposed 16-fold division of the year, each month lasts about 22–24 days, and Lockyer had already noted that there were orientations for the position of sunrise about 21 days before the main 8-fold divisions of the year.[111] We shall return to the evidence for Thom's 16-month calendar shortly.

We should at least mention the possibility of yet a further subdivision of the year (into 32 parts). Thom lists a number of lines which might be associated with these.[112] Six high-class lines lie within $0 \cdot 5°$ of a selection of these positions, and calculation shows that one would expect altogether about five by chance. Despite the agreement in the values of the declinations, therefore, these lines are of no statistical significance.

In Thom's first book stellar lines are again discussed, and in a manner fundamentally not unlike that adopted in the paper of 1955. However, the presentation is not statistical. Thom gives diagrams showing the dates at which those orientations which he associates with stars actually would have indicated their rising or setting positions. The dates are concentrated very significantly, and it is tempting to agree, with Thom, that it is difficult to find a reason for this, 'other than that many of the observed azimuths really were set out for first-magnitude stars'.[113] On the other hand, the date at which the concentration occurs – about 1800 or 1900 BC – is considerably later than the date arrived at in the 1955 paper.

It is of some interest to trace the origin of this change. In the paper, there was a statistically significant excess of lines which could be identified with certain bright stars between 2200 and 2000 BC. It turns out that about half the excess can be accounted for by lines to Rigel, which we have already mentioned in this connection. Now at the time in question the declination of Rigel lay very close to the declination of the sun about one sixteenth of a year before and after the winter solstice. Thus these lines could also be interpreted as calendrical,[114] and indeed that is how most are listed in the book. The removal of such lines from the list of stellar lines obviously influences the distribution of dates which we would deduce from them, and thus may well contribute to the apparent paucity of early dates in Thom's revised results. Thus in assessing the significance of the later date found in the book, it is important to know whether the reinterpretation of the Rigel lines was justified. Thom himself may have been influenced by the fact that, to the archaeologists, the date yielded by the stellar lines in the paper of 1955 seemed rather early compared with radiocarbon dates then available. On the other hand, Thom disputed this at the time.[115]

Another possible way in which to decide whether these lines should be regarded as stellar or calendrical is the following. One might suggest that it would be surprising to find markers for the position of the sun one sixteenth of a year before and after the winter solstice without other evidence of markers for corresponding dates on either side of the summer solstice, and possibly also the equinoxes. As we have said, there is some evidence in Thom's book for orientations to the sun at dates one six-teenth of a year before and after the equinoxes and the solstices. How-ever, most of this is due to the group which might equally well be attri-buted to Rigel. For the other three comparable declinations there are only 7 high-quality lines, and this is not statistically significant, since about 5 would be expected by chance. Thus the only group which shows a statistically significant excess is the group which may have been in-tended as indicators of Rigel. With this result in mind it is surprising to record Thom's conclusion that the lines at declinations of $\pm 21\frac{1}{2}°$ (which includes those which are possibly for Rigel) cannot be satisfactorily ex-plained as stellar.[116]

A quite different analysis of some of the stellar lines was also given in the book,[117] and to understand its meaning it is first necessary to sum-marize how Thom analysed lines in general. From the azimuth defined by each line and the horizon altitude along the line of sight, Thom ar-rived at a value for the declination of any object that rose or set there. If no solar (calendrical) or lunar explanation was available, he then searched for any bright star which possessed that declination at some date between, say, 2000 and 1600 BC. As we have explained in chapter 5, however, a star only becomes visible when its altitude exceeds a certain amount, called the extinction angle, and if the horizon altitude at a site was less than this, the calculation was repeated, using the extinction angle in place of the horizon altitude.

In the analysis we are now discussing, Thom reversed this modifica-tion, in the following way. He assumed that the stellar identification given by the foregoing analysis was correct, and took a trial date. Then the declination of the star was known from astronomical tables, and so Thom could calculate the extinction angle which would be necessary if the orientation was to have indicated the star at the assumed date. When this was done (for the dates 1800 and 1900 BC) for all appropriate stellar orientations, Thom found that the deduced extinction angles increased with the magnitude of the star in approximately the way that can be determined from present-day observations. There is, admittedly, some scatter, but Thom attributed this to the fact that he was trying the same date for all lines, whereas their dates may differ somewhat.

On the face of it, this appears to be striking independent evidence in favour of stellar lines, but it is something less than this. The trouble is that the only lines which are suitable for this test are those in which the extinction angle exceeds the horizon altitude. The fainter stars have larger extinction angles and so higher horizon altitudes are possible; for bright stars only low horizon altitudes are possible. It would not be surprising if this selection effect in the choice of orientations were to make itself manifest in the final results. Certainly the trend of these is what one would expect if this explanation were true.

Very recently the Thoms have pointed out that some of the lines which were assumed in 1967 to be stellar can be reinterpreted in other ways. For example, they would now regard as lunar a number of lines which were previously thought to have indicated the star Capella.[118] However, even if we take the stellar orientations in Thom's first book at face value, it is difficult to guess what their purpose might have been. There is no clear correlation between the supposed uses of certain stars (for calendrical or time-keeping purposes) and the numbers of orientations which indicate them.

To summarize the information on stellar orientations, let us begin with those discussed in the paper of 1955. When we confine our attention to the lines of high quality the most remarkable result appears to be the group of lines to Rigel about 2100 BC, though its actual statistical significance is in doubt. However, there is a possibility that these may be calendrical, in which case the residue of evidence on stellar lines in this paper is meagre. The ambiguity of stellar and calendrical lines has influenced the date derived in the book of 1967, and the discussion there of the extinction angle does little to strengthen the case. This is further weakened by the recent reinterpretation of some of the lines, and the Thoms now appear to take a rather cautious attitude to stellar lines as a whole.[119]

Summarizing now the solar lines, we recall that there is sound statistical evidence for solstitial orientations in the papers of 1954 and 1955. The 1967 book contains interesting evidence for groups of lines corresponding to the equinoxes and other dates of Thom's eight-month calendar. However, it is difficult to assess their significance, since the theoretical calendar declinations have been adjusted partly with a view to improving the agreement with the indicated declinations. Furthermore, the selection of sightlines listed in the book requires closer scrutiny than we have been able to give.

When we described the astronomical basis of megalithic astronomy, we discussed the moon at greatest length, and now it is necessary to turn to at least some of the evidence for lunar sites. There is more, but much of it is of a non-statistical nature and its description is better postponed.

In his 1955 paper, Thom merely hinted at the possibility of lunar orientations.[120] Later he explained how much he resisted the idea of lunar lines, suspecting the influence of subjective factors, until 'the final evidence came objectively'.[121] This took the form of a histogram in which Thom plotted all the indicated declinations which lay close to the four primary lunar declinations, that is, both standstills at both north and south declinations. The remarkable feature about this is that the declinations concentrate in two peaks separated (in declination) by about the apparent diameter of the full moon.[122] This must remind us of the similar double-peaked distribution of the solstitial declinations, but here there is an added bonus. To Thom the result was unexpected,[123] which suggests the very important fact that it could have had little effect on the selection of the orientations, if any.

Though this could be a crucial piece of evidence for the existence of lunar orientations, one must admit that no statistical test of the significance of the double peak has been reported, and Müller was not very

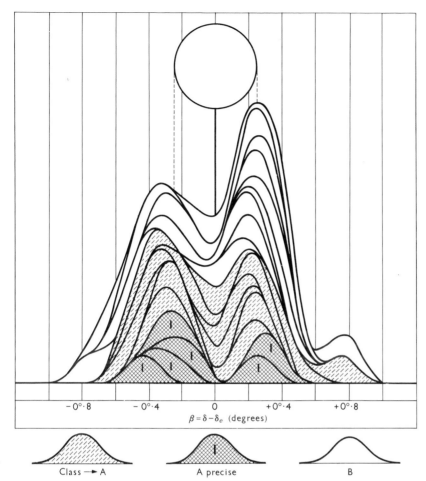

$\beta = \delta - \delta_e$ (degrees)

Class → A   A precise   B

88 Histogram of lunar orientations, from Thom's first book. Each indicated declination is plotted as a Gaussian (humped) shape at the value of $\delta - \delta_E$, which is she difference between the indicated declination and the declination of the nearest standstill. Lines of higher quality are shown shaded. The circle shows the apparent size of the lunar disc to the same scale.

impressed by it.[124] However, it cannot be denied that the declinations are concentrated in a significant way towards the lunar values: the number of high-quality lines lying within $0.4°$ of the ideal declinations (which takes account of the size of the lunar disc and the perturbation) is 14,[125] and by chance one would expect about 5 or 6; the probability of at least 14 is one in a few hundred.[126] However, this is yet another result where the difficult task of selecting sightlines objectively prevents us from arriving at a really firm conclusion.

With solstitial, equinoctial and stellar explanations only, it was possible to find an astronomical interpretation for only about one half of the orientations discussed in the paper of 1955.[127] By the time the first book was written, the astronomical theory had become much more comprehensive. In part because of the increased complexity of the astronomical theories considered, only 16 of the 131 high-quality lines lacked an astronomical interpretation of some sort. It is not necessarily an objection to the astronomical theory that it fails to account for all orientations. If a simple alignment was used in only one direction, we cannot always assume which direction was used, and so must include both, despite the fact that one or other is unlikely to yield an astronomical declination. This effect becomes still more of a problem at more complicated sites.[128]

Accurate lunar lines

We have already seen a certain amount of evidence for the existence of megalithic orientations to extreme rising and setting positions of the moon. Also, it is at least possible that some of these were aligned deliberately to one limb or other of the moon, rather than the centre or some other point of the disc. If we accept this result we might consider next the possibility of slightly more precise orientations that could distinguish the perturbation of the lunar orbit; this has an amplitude of 9′ either way, i.e. 18′ in all, which is not so very much less than the apparent diameter of the moon. There is no evidence in the histogram of lunar indications given in Thom's first book that the limits of the perturbation were known. True, in this book Thom gives the odd example of lines – in general of the type known as indicated foresights – in which extremes of the lunar perturbation appear to be orientated upon. However, though Thom implied that there were too many such sites for these indications to be occurring by chance,[129] this was not demonstrated in any way.

One of the simplest situations in which to examine statistically the possibility of accurate lunar lines is near Carnac in France – in the region around the very large, fallen stone, Le Grand Menhir Brisé.[130] There are several other tall menhirs in the vicinity, and astronomical interpretations have been offered for almost all these, though not all such interpretations are lunar.[131] However, it is only the group of sightlines involving Le Grand Menhir Brisé that has been tested statistically. The Thoms discovered that the menhir, if it was ever upright, could have been seen from several backsights which are marked by megalithic structures, and are so positioned that the menhir acted as a foresight for the moon at its extreme declinations.[132] In some cases the structures are small and unimpressive, but this is not an important objection.[133] Furthermore, the distances involved are sufficiently great that these alignments would have been accurate enough to distinguish the extremes of the lunar perturbation.

Now we shall ask whether there is any statistical significance in these results because, as usual, there is the possibility that suitable backsights have occurred by chance. Whether the backsights can be explained plausibly as coincidences depends on the number of megalithic sites in the neighbourhood. Freeman, following Atkinson, has given 250 as the number of known relevant dolmens and menhirs, though it was not known from how many of these Le Grand Menhir Brisé is visible.[134] However, Atkinson has pointed out that many of them stand on 'local eminences

89 *Menhir beside the megalithic tomb at Le Moustoir, Carnac. This stone is a backsight for Le Grand Menhir Brisé, which indicates moonrise at the minor standstill for maximum perturbation.*

of the terrain', which enhances the probability that the Grand Menhir could be seen.[135] Whatever the actual number, Freeman's important result was that, if this number exceeded about 200, the probability of obtaining the required number of backsights would not be low enough for the backsights to be regarded as significant. It is to be noted that the Thoms themselves did not claim to have proved 'mathematically' that Le Grand Menhir Brisé was a lunar foresight.[136] Still, since the statistical significance of the alignments seems so insecure, we must search elsewhere for better evidence.

One place to go is Thom's second book (1971), where he describes some 35 sites (not quite all of which, however, are lunar) in which the indications are potentially accurate enough to discriminate the perturbation in the motion of the moon. Almost every one of these is of the type known as a natural foresight, the foresight being a natural feature of the horizon which is indicated by a megalithic structure such as a single upright slab, or a line of menhirs. At most of the sites, Thom has found indicated foresights lying close to the places on the horizon where the moon rose or set at one of the standstills, for either limb or the centre of the lunar disc, when the solar perturbation on the moon was either maximum, minimum or zero.

58, 91, 107

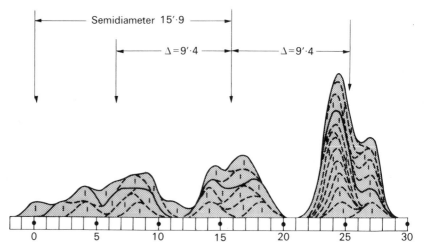

90 Accurate indications of lunar declinations, from Thom's book of 1971. Each indicated declination is plotted as a Gaussian shape at a position given by its deviation from the nearest value of ε ± i, i. e. the declinations of the centre of the lunar disc at the standstills at zero perturbation. Thus a peak at a position corresponding to half the apparent diameter of the moon ('semidiameter') would indicate a concentration of markers for one or other limb with zero perturbation. The largest peak corresponds to one or other limb at the corresponding extreme perturbation.

Thom adopted a visual display of his data to demonstrate that the foresights really did indicate the rising and setting positions of the moon for mean and extreme values of the perturbation. Certainly the histogram looks very convincing, even without any statistical test. However, before we take a closer look at it, let us decide which question we wish to ask of this data. If we accept the evidence of the earlier book, we already know that lunar orientations exist, with a concentration towards either limb of the moon. Now Thom's inference from the data of the second book is that rather precise orientations exist for the extremes of the perturbation. Is this additional inference justified?

This question could be answered in the way that we have adopted so far in this chapter: assume a random distribution of orientations, compute how many would be expected to lie by accident close to azimuths corresponding to the extreme perturbations, and see if Thom has found significantly more than this.

Such a procedure could be faulted on at least two scores. First, it takes no account of what we may already know about rough lunar alignments.[137] Second, it does not test what we want it to test: *any* set of lunar orientations, however rough, would be far more likely to contain orientations for the perturbations than a completely random set of orientations; in other words, it does not test for very accurate orientations.

To avoid these difficulties we could adopt the hypothesis that rough orientations exist, and then compute the number of orientations which would be expected, on this hypothesis, to lie by chance close to positions corresponding to mean and extreme values of the perturbation. Then, if we find significantly more such orientations than expected on this hypothesis, we have some grounds for rejecting it, and for supposing that at least some of the orientations were intended to indicate the perturbation.

This test can be put more concretely as follows. On the hypothesis of rough orientations, we might suppose that the indicated declinations should lie anywhere within about 0·6° of the ideal declinations $\pm\epsilon\pm i$ (allowing approximately for the apparent radius of the moon: about 0·25°; the perturbation: about 0·15°; and 0·2° for uncertainty in the date). Then we look at a stretch of the horizon indicated by the orientations at each site, and count how many natural foresights correspond to declinations within 0·6° of the standstill declinations $\pm\epsilon\pm i$, i.e. a range of 1·2°. Call this number N. (If there is more than one possible backsight, the numbers for each backsight must be added.) Next, suppose we accept such a natural foresight as an indicator of the perturbation if its declination lies within x minutes of arc of one of the nine declinations 37 obtained by combining the maximum, minimum and zero of the perturbation with the two limbs and the centre of the lunar disc. Therefore, on the hypothesis of rough orientations, we would expect by chance to find a certain number of such foresights, in fact about $(N\times 2x'\times 9)/1·2°$, i.e. about $\frac{1}{4}Nx$. If the actual number of foresights within x' of any of the nine declinations is significantly greater than this, we can have some confidence that the limits of the perturbation were indicated.

The above is a crude description of a statistical test which in practice might require some refinement, but it illustrates the information we need. The main point is that we need to know about all the natural foresights in the quoted 1·2°-range of declinations. Unfortunately, the list of foresights given by Thom[138] appears to be incomplete in this respect. For example, there are many sites where the indication does not pick out only one foresight unambiguously, and yet Thom lists the details of only one foresight or of a restricted selection of foresights. The line to the south-west at Temple Wood (Argyll), a site which we shall discuss shortly in 80 a little detail, is one example. In this case, as in many, the indication is at least definite in the sense that the megalithic site is orientated quite accurately and conspicuously towards the horizon close to the foresight. However, there are sites where the foresights are not indicated at all. An example of such a foresight is the Bass Rock, which is considered to be a foresight viewed from the stones at Lundin Links, Fife.[139] Several other examples of poor indications can be found in the book, and in such cases the possibility of an astronomical interpretation may well have been influential in winning them a place on Thom's list. A consequence of all this is that the histogram drawn from the data in this table cannot be used reliably to discriminate between the hypotheses of rough and accurate lunar lines. If we removed the foresights which are poorly indicated and put in the foresights which Thom omitted, it could very well be that the apparently significant peaks in ill. 90 would be largely eroded away, and the valleys between them filled in. It should be stated that the existence of foresights which do not correspond to lunar positions need have posed no problems to the supposed prehistoric observers, since they would have known the correct foresights to use.[140] However, the existence of such foresights is a problem to us when we are trying to decide whether these observations actually took place, and we have no valid choice but to include all possible foresights until the matter is settled.

If we are to estimate the number of suitable foresights at each site, we must turn away from Thom's list and look at the horizon at each site. Thom has provided very interesting sketches of the horizon as viewed from most of the sites, and so what we can do is to count N for ourselves. To do this for all sites would be a laborious process, but we can at least give an example.

Temple Wood is a good site for this purpose, since Thom says that by itself it demonstrates that the megalith builders were capable of erecting 'real lunar observatories'.[141] Also, it has been extensively studied by Patrick.[142] Taking first the orientations to the north-west, we find that there is only one notch, but there are four backsights,[143] and so we take $N = 4$. Hence we expect about x accurate orientations within x' of the relevant declinations. Actually Thom lists three within 0·6',[144] and the probability of obtaining at least three by chance is about one in a hundred.[145] In one respect we have really leaned in favour of Thom's theory by taking x to be the largest *actual* discrepancy, whereas he might have accepted a larger discrepancy had one existed. Indeed he tolerated an error of 1·5' in a different foresight at Temple Wood, which would give a result of no statistical significance. On the other hand, only at most three of the four backsights actually indicate the notch to the north-west, and if the fourth is excluded the number of indications which would be expected by chance is decreased again.

Whatever the uncertainties in the above, the situation in the south-westerly direction is definitely disappointing. Here there is effectively only one backsight, but about eight possible foresights. According to Thom, two of these indicate the moon, the largest discrepancy being 1·5'. Hence we expect about three by chance.

It cannot be claimed that these statistical tests have much precision, and refined versions should be applied at other sites. Nevertheless, they leave the strong impression that the case for accurate lunar orientations indicating the 9' perturbation at Temple Wood is by no means overwhelming. By their nature, however, these tests do not disprove the possibility that rough lunar orientations may have been incorporated into this site. Actually quite a different explanation may be available for Temple Wood, for an interesting feature of several sites in its neighbourhood is that they are very roughly aligned in the direction of the valley in which they stand.[146]

As a second example, though it does not come from Thom's book of 1971, we might consider Brogar, which stands on a commanding position on Mainland, Orkney. Suitable foresights exist in three widely separated directions, but in one of these (Kame of Corrigall) there are two suitable foresights, making four in all.[147] The Thoms list 15 declinations indicated by these foresights, and the maximum deviation from

91 An indicated foresight at Temple Wood, Argyll. The two stones (note the separate shadows) are flattened in the direction of the line joining them. This points slightly to the right of the position of the Temple Wood stone circle (ill. 1), which lies in the trees. To the left of the line to the circle there is a notch on the horizon (arrowed) which is correctly positioned for use as a lunar foresight. The stones are marked A and B in ill. 80.

suitable ideal lunar declinations is only 1·4′.[148] However, inspection shows that these require a minimum of about ten objects, mostly cairns, as backsights. With four foresights, these yield altogether approximately $N = 40$ indicated declinations. Setting $x = 1·4′$, we find that we would by chance expect about 14 of these to lie within 1·4′ of an ideal lunar declination, which is close to the number which the Thoms list.

It may be that not all 40 indicated declinations lie within the 1·2° ranges mentioned above, or that not all foresights are visible from all backsights, which would reduce the number of astronomical indications that would be expected by chance. However, we have chosen the minimum number of backsights needed to retain all the Thoms' indicated declinations, which tends to minimize the number of accidental indications while maximizing the number of those that have astronomical significance. Also our results have been biassed in favour of the astronomical interpretation because we have chosen the minimum value of x which preserves all the lines listed by the Thoms. Incidentally, they themselves noticed that the agreement between the indicated declinations and the ideal values was closer than could be readily understood, because of the variations due to parallax.[149]

In their own statistical analysis of Brogar[150] the Thoms concluded that the indicated declinations do agree, at a statistically significant level, with those expected on the astronomical theory. The fact that this differs from our conclusion may well be attributable to the way in which the sightlines were selected by the Thoms, for in several respects this is quite puzzling. For example, the two foresights at Kame are indicated by three lines of cairns, but only three of the six possible combinations of foresight and backsight are included in their lists. Again, consider the cairn L. It is listed as a backsight for the foresights at Hellia and Mid Hill (though it does not indicate Hellia), and yet the lines from L to the foresights at Kame are omitted. Until the selection of such sightlines can be made to appear less arbitrary, it seems prudent not to take the results of the Thoms' analysis at face value. It may well be that the close agreement between the indicated declinations and those expected is quite accidental.

A peculiarity of Brogar deserves to be mentioned. One of the most definite indicators of any foresight at Brogar is a menhir – the Comet Stone. It is interesting that this is the only menhir which serves this role, and Atkinson has remarked how odd it is that most of the supposed indicators consist of cairns, when in Orkney there is plentiful stone suitable for the construction of very flat menhirs.[151] On the other hand, the Thoms have argued that the extra height afforded by a cairn was sometimes necessary so that observers could be forewarned of the approaching moonrise.[152]

In a paper published in 1978 the Thoms presented a detailed statistical analysis of a number of accurate lunar lines drawn from 13 sites.[153] There they came to the conclusion that foresights really do tend to indicate extremes of the perturbation, and that this result is statistically significant at a probability level of well under one in a hundred. However, among the sites they examined was Brogar, and the lines at this site which they included are a further selection from those which they considered in their analysis of Brogar itself. Nor is Brogar the only site in the list at which some perfectly acceptable combinations of foresight and backsight are omitted. For instance, at Ballinaby (Islay) also, as an inspection of the horizon profile shows,[154] there is a possible foresight for which the corresponding declination is not listed.

Before leaving Thom's descriptions of accurate lunar foresights, we must describe briefly the analysis which he presented in the seventh chapter of his second book. In this he first assumed that each of the 40 indicated declinations he had found corresponded to one or other of the 9 usual declinations for either the major or the minor standstill. Now these ideal declinations can be calculated if four quantities are known: ε, the obliquity of the ecliptic; i, the inclination of the moon's orbit; Δ, the size of the perturbation; and s, the apparent radius of the moon. Thom then calculated the values of these four quantities which fitted best the 40 values of declination which he had obtained by measuring foresights. The values he found are here compared with the values known astronomically:

	ε	i	Δ	s
Thom (from foresights)	23°53′26″	5°08′52″	9′23″	15′55″
From astronomy	–	5°08′43″	9′	15′32″

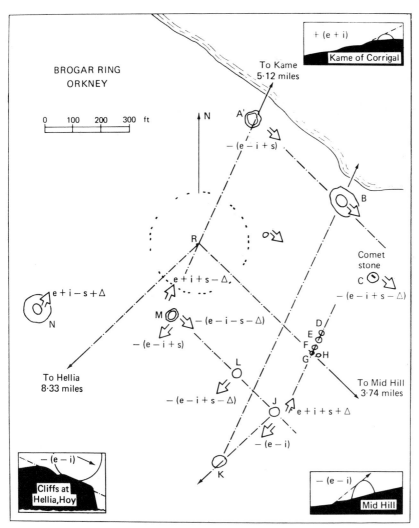

92 *Plan of Brogar, Orkney, by Thom and Thom (1973, 118). The dashed arrows indicate the directions of certain natural foresights, which are sketched in the marginal diagrams. The outline arrows indicate the backsights corresponding to certain astronomically significant declinations, which are designated as in ill. 37. The Ring of Brogar lies at the centre of the diagram, surrounded by the objects A, B, etc., which are cairns of various sizes. Other cairns are shown on a later survey (Thom and Thom 1975, 102), and the Thoms have resurveyed the horizon profiles. The Comet Stone is an upright, remarkably flat, menhir. The site is close to the edge of a loch.*

The obliquity, ε, is changing slowly, and so from astronomy we do not get a unique value. However, in about 1650 BC the value was close to that deduced by Thom. The fact that the other three values lie close to the values known from astronomy is noteworthy, and could be taken as evidence that the foresights really were chosen to indicate the nine declinations we have been discussing.

In fact however, it may not be quite true to say that Thom's values of the four quantities are generated entirely from the data on the foresights. Suppose, for example, that we have a foresight which indicates a declination of 29°11′. To decide which of the ideal declinations this corresponds to, we have to calculate the values of the ideal declinations and find which one lies closest to 29°11′. Now using the values mentioned by Thom in connection with Temple Wood,[155] we find that $\varepsilon + i - \Delta + s$ is 29°09.5′, and $\varepsilon + i + \Delta$ is 29°12.0′. Hence we would associate our hypothetical orientation with the latter ideal declination. If, however, we had started with a value of ε (or i) about 1′ larger, we would have associated it with the other ideal declination. Thus we should not be surprised that those indicated declinations which become associated with each ideal declination are scattered on either side of the expected ideal value. Therefore, when the indicated declinations are analysed, it should be no lasting surprise that the values of ε, i, Δ and s lie close to those expected, and this effect would be present even if the foresights were selected quite objectively. This analysis, then, does not strengthen the argument for supposing that these orientations were intentional.

Following Thom, we have actually simplified the discussion slightly, because the value of the lunar parallax also influences the ideal declinations. It is a little difficult to determine the value of the parallax which fits the foresights best, independently of refraction effects,[156] but Thom carried out such an analysis on those lines where refraction is smallest. He found that a value close to *mean* parallax fitted the indicated declinations best, but again this is no more surprising than the agreement of the deduced values of i and s with those expected; the foresights seem to have been discussed initially using a mean value for the parallax.

Though we have argued that we should take a very cautious position on all these results, it is worth recording a number of further comments on them. From the fact that the sites correspond to a *mean* value of parallax, Thom inferred that they must have been set up over a sufficient period of time (perhaps two centuries) to allow the effect of parallax to go through one cycle about its mean value.[157] As far as the deduced mean date is concerned, Atkinson was encouraged by the fact that it was not far from that derived from the discussion of extinction angles in Thom's first book,[158] though we have seen that this too is open to question. He also thought that the Thoms' date for Brogar may be a little late, but not seriously so.

How are we to summarize the evidence on lunar orientations? Though there is some evidence in Thom's first book for relatively inaccurate lunar lines, there is little of this which suggests that the orientations were set up so as to discriminate the fine details in the motion of the moon, in particular the 9′ perturbation. When we turn to the work described in Thom's second book and elsewhere, there seems to be little evidence that natural foresights exist preferentially for those declinations corresponding to extremes of the perturbation. Put briefly, we find a little evidence for rough lunar orientations but none of any statistical significance for very accurate ones.

Furthermore, we saw in chapter 5 that there would be some quite severe difficulties in the erection of sightlines for the fine details in the moon's motion. When we find evidence, as in Thom's second book, that lines for the lunar perturbation actually exist, we must take particular care that alternative explanations have been ruled out, and this is just where the interpretation of the data in Thom's second book and elsewhere is not straightforward. There are many sites in which one can find foresights which seem just as prominent as those which Thom lists, except that they do not fit the lunar observatory hypothesis. Fortunately, Thom's admirable descriptions of the sites contain such detail that allowance can be made for this, though little evidence of statistical significance survives.

Problems of selection are at their most acute in the case of sightlines defined by natural foresights. Fortunately, in Thom's earlier work, where we have found some positive evidence for megalithic astronomy, such sites played a relatively minor role. For example, in the paper of 1955 they scarcely enter at all, and in his first book only 30 of the 131 lines of high weight involved an indicated foresight. Finally, we have seen that Thom applied quite strict selection criteria to natural foresights when they did appear in his earliest work, as the example of the line to the south-west at Ballochroy shows. [72]

Lockyer and Lewis

In quantity, quality and originality, Thom's work on megalithic science is unique. Nevertheless, there have been other researchers who have investigated sufficient numbers of sites to make a statistical discussion worthwhile. We shall close this chapter with an account of three of these, and some mention of two or three others.

Until the work of Thom began to be published, the person who had studied more sites from the astronomical point of view than anyone else was the astronomer Sir Norman Lockyer. Though his earliest work on British megalithic astronomy had been confined to Stonehenge, he soon turned his attention to other sites, and by the time he published the first edition of his book in 1906,[159] he had come across over fifty orientations in megalithic sites.

It is of some interest to study Lockyer's results statistically, but we must be very wary of drawing any conclusions whatever from them. The problem is that Lockyer never seriously considered the possibility that astronomical orientations could occur quite by chance. Consequently he seems to have been almost unaware of the need for care and objectivity in the selection of sightlines. Worse, there is some evidence that Lockyer selected the orientations with an eye on their possible astronomical interpretation. For example, when discussing some orientations in Orkney, Lockyer first calculates the approximate azimuth for one of the calendar declinations, and then proceeds to inform us about 'the most interesting and best defined line near this azimuth'.[160] It seems probable that such a procedure will tend only to select lines which are

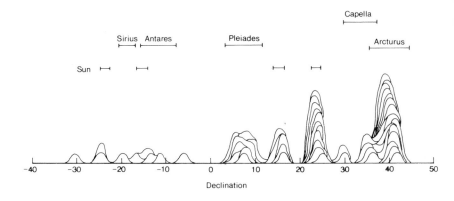

93 Indicated declinations given by Lockyer. Each declination is plotted as a Gaussian (bell-shaped) curve, different curves being added where they would overlap. Above the histogram are the ranges of declinations occupied by four stars and the Pleiades during the period 2330 BC to 850 BC, and by the sun at various times of the year: the solstices (at about ±24°) and at times midway between the solstices and the equinoxes (at about ±16°).

likely to be astronomically significant. Indeed, as far as one can tell from internal evidence such as this, Lockyer generally recorded details only of those orientations for which he could find an astronomical meaning, making at most scant mention of those which he could not identify. Therefore, if we find some result which appears to be statistically significant, it should not be taken at face value.

To be definite we shall restrict consideration to those orientations for which Lockyer quoted a numerical declination in his book. These are scattered throughout the book, and occasionally slightly different values are quoted in different places for the same line. The differences are generally slight, but it is more difficult to know how to treat the declinations given by rows such as those on Dartmoor. These vary slightly from one section of the same row to another, and we have decided to treat the different values for the same row as being independent whenever Lockyer actually quotes more than one declination for it. Thus a row with one bend on level ground would be regarded as providing two declinations if both values were quoted by Lockyer.

93 This gives 58 declinations, of which 2 are unidentified, and the remainder are assigned to the sun, a star, or the Pleiades. (Lockyer appears entirely to have ignored the possibility of lunar lines.) The solstitial lines have declinations covering the full range 22°24′ to 24°33′. The probability (assuming a level horizon at a site at latitude 51°N) of a random line giving a declination in this range for either solstice is about 0·045, and so out of 58 we might expect 2 or 3 to occur by chance. Actually Lockyer listed 13, which would definitely be regarded as highly significant if we thought that Lockyer had selected his data reasonably objectively.

Lockyer also considered the possibility of solar lines for a date halfway between the equinoxes and the solstices. The declinations to which he assigned this meaning range from 14°03′ to 16°26′, which corresponds to a variation of just over one week in the calendar date. The number expected by chance happens to be about the same as obtained for the solstices, and this time Lockyer actually listed seven, which is quite significant at face value.

Lockyer identified the remaining indicated declinations (except for two) with the stars Arcturus, Antares, Sirius and Capella, and also the Pleiades. Since the declinations of the stars vary substantially over the centuries, it is also important to note the range of dates which he considered. This is unusually wide, ranging from 2330 BC (a line at Tregaseal, Cornwall) to 850 BC (at Shovel Down, Dartmoor, where the line, as at Tregaseal, is for Arcturus). The changes in the declinations of these objects can be found from the very convenient tables published by Hawkins.[161] Converting to azimuth, we find that the rising points of these four stars and the Pleiades cover about 71° out of the 180° in the eastern half of the horizon. Thus the probability of a random line being identifiable with the rising or setting position of one of these objects is about 0·4, and we would expect about 23 out of 58 by chance. Lockyer actually found 36, an excess which is again highly significant.

If we could have been reasonably certain that Lockyer selected the sightlines objectively, such results would have provided very firm evidence that some megalithic sites had a stellar or solar orientation. However, since 58 random orientations would have been expected to give rise to some two-thirds of the number of stellar orientations which Lockyer described, we may express the results in what may be a rather more informative way as follows. Had Lockyer in effect studied only some 50 per cent more orientations than those for which he gave declinations, then the stellar lines would definitely not have seemed significant, but the excess of solstitial lines might still have seemed convincing.

To his credit, Lockyer later discussed the geographical distribution of sightlines of different types, and showed that a definite pattern emerged. In Cornwall, for instance, sightlines were predominantly for the time of year midway between the spring equinox and the summer solstice, and this gave way in North Wales to a predominance of solstitial orientations.[162] Such a result would be of substantial interest if it could be shown to survive a more objective examination of the sites in these districts.

Let us now turn, this time briefly, to some work that predates even that of Lockyer. It is also rather different in that the author, A. L. Lewis, considered the possibility that natural foresights might have been used, as well as outliers and so on. His researches are also of interest because he analysed sufficiently many sites that his results are amenable to statistical analysis, albeit imperfectly. As usual, there is the awkward question of how the lines were selected, but one has the impression that the possibilities of an astronomical interpretation had less influence on him than they had on Lockyer. He states, for example, that he included many orientations which he 'might fairly have passed over', and asserts that the effect of this has tended if anything to weight the evidence *against* the astronomical theory.[163] Nevertheless, Lewis made little attempt to lay down the criteria which guided his selection. Where he compares particularly badly with Lockyer is in terms of accuracy; the azimuths he lists are stated usually to no more than the nearest degree, and he neglected both the elevation of the horizon and refraction.

Lewis collected results from 26 sites in a paper published in 1892, and these yielded no less than 100 orientations. A great many of these were for a direction close to north-east, and Lewis interpreted these as solstitial. It is difficult to devise an entirely satisfactory statistical test of this result, partly because of the low accuracy with which Lewis contented himself, but largely because his data are given in terms of azimuth rather than declination. Nevertheless one can argue as follows. In the latitudes of the British Isles, the azimuth of the rising sun at the summer solstice lies approximately in the range 30° to 60°, and the probability that the azimuth of a random orientation should lie in this range is one in twelve. Accordingly one would expect just over 8 of Lewis's orientations to do so, whereas he actually found about 22 such orientations. This is definitely significant, but one should really consider the corresponding ranges in the other three quadrants (south-east, south-west and north-west), and analyse all four ranges together. In this case one expects about 33 orientations by chance, and Lewis actually found about 41. This does not seem significant. However, a significant result re-emerges if one allows for the other three ranges in a different way, by asking a different question: what is the probability that at least one of the four ranges contains at least as many orientations as Lewis actually found for the north-east? The answer is a probability so small as to leave the strong impression that there is a result of significance to be explained here.

Lewis also found an interesting concentration of orientations not far from due north. He assumed that these were stellar, and was here guided by a theory of Lockyer's concerning Egyptian monuments. Lockyer started to develop this theory in 1890,[164] but it seems he did not consider British sites from the same point of view until several years after Lewis, who had already made some of his results public by the early 1880s.[165]

Irish recumbent-stone circles

The last study which we shall describe in any detail is J. W. Barber's work on the group of recumbent-stone circles in Co. Cork and Co. Kerry, Ireland.[166] We have already referred to his investigations of these sites in chapter 2, in connection with megalithic geometry, and now it is time to examine their implications for megalithic astronomy.

From this point of view, the beauty of these sites is the fact that the selection of the orientations is extremely simple: we naturally choose the axis of each circle, i.e. the line joining the centre of the recumbent stone to a point midway between the portals. The main difficulty lies in choosing which direction to look in. Barber chose the direction from the portals to the recumbent, partly because of the evidence of continued

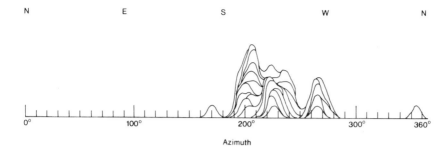

94 *Azimuthal distribution of the axes of Irish recumbent-stone circles, based on data given by Barber 1973, 32. Each azimuth indicated by a circle is plotted as a small Gaussian curve, but the widths of the curves do not correspond to the estimated uncertainties in the azimuths.*

human activity near the portals at one site, and also because of the presence of outliers beyond the recumbent at other sites.[167] These reasons are unlikely to bias the results in favour of the astronomical theory, since they have nothing to do with the azimuths of the orientations.

First – and this distinguishes Barber's study from many others – he decided rationally how close an axis would have to be to some astronomically significant azimuth to be acceptable. Guided by the size of the deviations of the rings from true circles, he settled upon 3° or 1°, depending on the size of the ring. Thus for small rings an orientation was held to be acceptable if it agreed with one of the astronomical directions to within 3°.

Considering first the main lunar declinations and the solstitial and equinoctial solar directions, Barber found that the axes of 12 out of the 30 sites pointed in these directions within the above limits.[168] He gave a statistical discussion of this result, which implied that it was very unlikely to have occurred by chance. However, Barber's data have been carefully rediscussed by Freeman and Elmore, and it now seems clear that his conclusion was incorrect.[169] In fact, considerably fewer than 12 sites are orientated to astronomically significant positions within the stated limits, and there is no statistically significant evidence that the axes of the recumbent-stone circles were preferentially orientated to the relevant rising and setting positions of the sun and moon.

It is worth noting that this conclusion does not imply that the axes are randomly distributed. Indeed a glance at the distribution of the azimuths of the axes shows that almost all of them point between west and south, a fact which had already been emphasized by Somerville.[170] 94 Therefore it is reasonable to contemplate other possible astronomical explanations for their orientation, but unfortunately no satisfactory candidate has been found. Among the solar hypotheses which Barber himself ruled out were the possibilities that the axes were aligned on the positions of sunset at random dates throughout the year, or throughout the winter half.[171] There is no evidence that the number of sites which could have served as stellar orientations exceeds what would be expected by chance, though the date tentatively assigned by Barber on their basis is consistent with what one would suppose on archaeological grounds.[172]

Barber's investigation, as corrected by Freeman and Elmore, is an unusually straightforward example of the search for astronomical orientations in megalithic sites. The selection of the orientations presents relatively few problems of subjectivity, and also the sites themselves are archaeologically homogeneous. Furthermore, as far as the lunar and solar orientations are concerned, the hypothesis which Barber was testing was not adjusted in any way to improve the agreement with his data. These are all particularly favourable circumstances for a reliable statistical investigation.

Barber avoided discussing the possible astronomical interpretation of the menhirs and stone rows which exist in this part of Ireland, but Somerville had noticed that at least one alignment appeared to be astronomically orientated.[173] Recently A. Lynch, a student at University College, Cork, has studied a sample of 37 alignments from this point of view. They define 74 sightlines, and she found that between 11 and 25 of these actually indicated one or other of the primary solar and lunar rising and setting positions, the precise number depending on how one calculates the uncertainty with which each indicated azimuth is defined.[174] Even in the least favourable case, however, the probability of obtaining so many lines by chance is calculated to be about 1 in 500, and so the alignments, unlike the circles, do seem to be significantly orientated. It would be very interesting to repeat the calculation separately for the sun and moon, just in case the significance of these findings can be explained entirely in terms of solstitial alignments. Even so, these results deserve to be better known.

It is not entirely inappropriate to conclude this section with a glance at a few other monuments in which the orientations can be determined with a precision of roughly a degree. Müller has discussed the orientations of some passage-graves in north-west Europe, the axes of which can be estimated to an accuracy of about $1\frac{1}{2}°$.[175] Some of this discussion is based on the work of Somerville, but it is not presented in sufficient detail to be amenable to statistical investigation. The identifications were mostly solar.

The cairns discussed by Somerville include those at Clava, Inverness. These and other related sites have been described systematically by Burl. As with Barber's Irish sites, the theory that they are orientated upon the position of sunset does not cover by any means all cases, and one of the possibilities which Burl entertained was that the intention of the builders may have been to orientate the sites only very approximately in the direction of midwinter sunset.[176] However, it seems that he had not yet considered lunar theories. Burl has also presented evidence, which is visually very convincing, that the tallest stone in circles of various types tends strongly to lie within a few degrees of one of the four cardinal directions.[177]

8 The evidence from individual sites

Throughout the last chapter we were concerned with one fundamental question: is there statistically significant evidence that megalithic orientations were set up to indicate extreme rising and setting positions of the sun, the moon and the stars, or is it not inconsistent to suppose that they are essentially random, and that the ones that seem to be astronomical are just chance coincidences? Being a statistical question, this involved us normally in the simultaneous discussion of data from many sites. There are some individual sites sufficiently complicated to warrant statistical study by themselves, such as Brogar, but we mentioned few such sites in detail.

In this chapter, which concludes our review of the evidence for and against megalithic astronomy, we concentrate almost entirely on individual sites, and, with the odd exception, abandon the statistical viewpoint. What we now do is to survey the large variety of non-statistical arguments which have been put forward in the controversy on megalithic astronomy. The first two cases are rare exceptions to the general remark that these arguments seldom have the persuasiveness of statistical arguments. However, they are widely used, and so we should come to some conclusion about how much (or how little) they tell us about astronomy in megalithic times.

Indicated foresights

We begin where our discussion of Thom's work ended, with those sites at which natural features on a distant horizon, usually indicated in some way, correspond to extreme rising or setting positions for the sun or moon. We take up again the discussion of Temple Wood (Argyll), or 'Kilmartin Stones', as Patrick prefers to call it.[1] Not only did it come to be regarded as an important site from the point of view of megalithic astronomy, but also it seemed to be unique in construction, at least out of those sites for which astronomical orientations had been claimed.

Patrick's attention was, however, directed to a site not far away, called Barbreck, where the arrangement of the stones corresponded to part of the very characteristic layout at Temple Wood. Patrick inferred a connection between the two sites, but that was not all. Repeatability, he argued, is the basis of scientific investigations, and he declared that one test of the astronomical theory is that, if it applies at one site, then

80

95, 96

95 Barbreck, Argyll, from the west. One of the pair of menhirs in the foreground forms a gate-post, and a third tall menhir is just visible between them in the copse. See ill. 96.

it should apply at other similar sites, especially if they are as similar as Barbreck and Temple Wood. Unless it is maintained that there is no particular resemblance between the two sites, this conclusion seems entirely reasonable.

Now there are two aspects to the astronomy at Temple Wood, the first being the orientations defined solely by the stones themselves. Thom lists several of these,[2] but when Patrick investigated the lines at Barbreck he found none of the declinations which are indicated at Temple Wood, nor even different declinations for the same body (e.g. the sun at the other solstice), though they could arguably be for different stars. The second aspect of astronomy at Temple Wood, and the one which has attracted most attention, is the occurrence of natural foresights for the moon. At Barbreck, however, it seems that there is no indicated notch that appeared to Patrick to be distinct or obvious. There are many small notches in one of the indicated horizons, but none is unambiguously indicated by the stones, and there is not yet any evidence that any of them could be lunar. The fact that the important lunar orientations of Temple Wood, a site which is architecturally so distinctive, are not repeated at the very similar site of Barbreck, is surely a very interesting argument against the suggested astronomical function of Temple Wood.

91

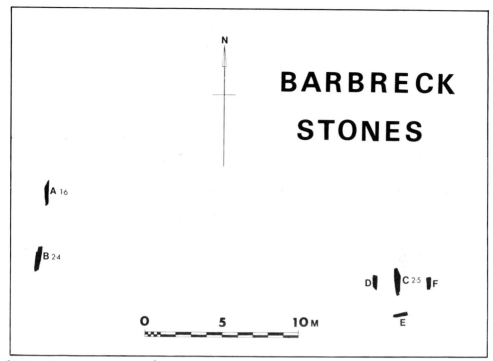

96 Plan of Barbreck by J. D. Patrick. Note the pair of tall stones and the single tall stone surrounded on three sides by small slabs. This arrangement is strikingly similar to part of the site at Kilmartin (ill. 80), which lies about 9 km to the south. The three tall stones can be seen in ill. 95.

Not all sites with natural foresights are thought to be lunar. One solstitial example is Kintraw, Argyll, and it has attracted much interest because it is the most intriguing of the few sites at which the astronomical theory has been tested by excavation. At Kintraw there is a distant, very pronounced foresight, the direction to which is vaguely indicated by a 12-ft (c. 3·6-m) menhir. Unfortunately, Thom found that the view of the notch from the menhir is obscured by an intervening ridge, and so it was difficult to understand how the menhir could have been erected to mark the exact backsight for observing the winter solstice.[3] Thom's suggestion was that the nearby cairn would probably have elevated the supposed observer sufficiently. Furthermore, in the cairn there was a posthole which may once have held an upright wooden post,[4] and this could be interpreted as a sighting device. However, there was still a problem. In order to erect an orientation for sunset at the winter solstice it was probably necessary to observe sunset for some days before and after the actual solstice, to ensure that the line did correspond to the extreme setting position. Now the difference in the observer's position between the solstice and the following night is about 19 ft (c. 6 m) at Kintraw,[5] and the cairn was probably not wide enough for this.

97

97 Kintraw, Argyll, from the south-west. The menhir, which has since fallen and been re-erected, stands beside a ruined cairn and roughly indicates a solstitial foresight formed by mountains on the island of Jura (in the opposite direction from this view). However, a clear view of the foresight is only obtained from the rising ground behind the site. On this slope is a natural ledge, on which a stone platform was found. A fence surrounds an excavated-part of the ledge, to the right of the cairn.

98 In his second book, Thom gave a more satisfactory location for the supposed observer: on a ledge or platform on the side of the hill behind the menhir and cairn, and separated from them by a gorge.[6] According to MacKie the foresight can be seen clearly from this ledge.[7] Furthermore, at the edge of the platform, on the line from the tall menhir to the foresight, is a boulder; or rather a pair of boulders, as excavation showed it to be, enclosing between them a wedge-shaped space or 'notch'.[8]

Now one can perhaps regard it as a prediction of the astronomical theory that it is on this ledge that the supposed observations took place, and so MacKie undertook a careful study of it. The ledge itself is doubtless primarily natural, but excavation did reveal a compact layer of small stones ending just beyond the pair of boulders which was supposed to mark the solstitial observing position. Such a boulder layer could be natural, but tests on the orientations of the stones seemed to show that the layer more closely resembles artificial stone pavements than natural ones.[9] However, though its limited extent lends additional support to the view that the layer is artificial,[10] no artifacts were found in it during the excavation. Perhaps it is for this reason that MacKie's discovery has not been received by his fellow-archaeologists with as much enthusiasm as he might have wished.

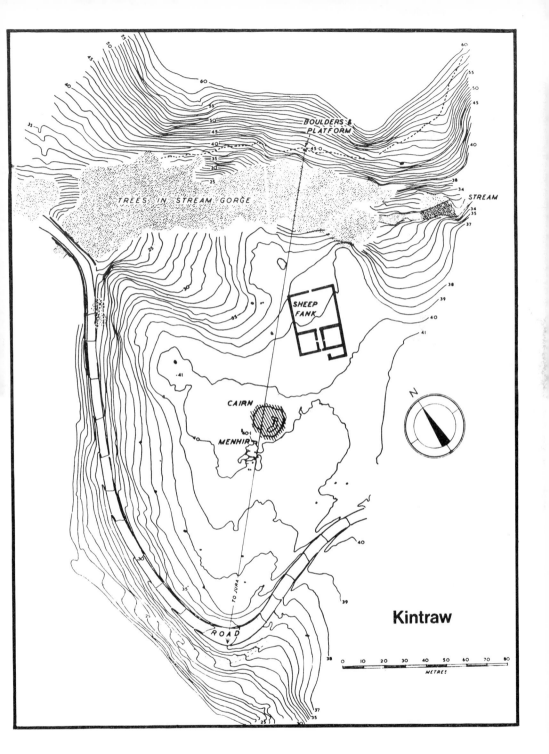

Within the map:

60

55 50 45

50 55

60

40

55 50 45

35

60

BOULDERS & PLATFORM

45

40

50

45

40

40

35

30

25

TREES IN STREAM GORGE

STREAM

38

34

34 35 37

38

39

40

41

SHEEP FANK

25

35

.41

CAIRN

MENHIR

N

40

TO JURA

ROAD

39

40

38

37 35

25

0 10 20 30 40 50 60 70 80

METRES

Kintraw

98 Contour map of Kintraw, by E.W. MacKie (1974, 179). The menhir and cairn are separated by a stream from the rising ground with the natural ledge. On the ledge, in line with the menhir and the foresight in Jura, is a pair of boulders. The stone platform was found on the ledge to the right (south-east) of the boulders, but not to the left.

There is a stone higher up the hill behind the ledge, and Thom suggested that it could have been used to mark the position of an observer who would have 'warned' those on the ledge below of the approaching passage of the sun behind the foresight.[11] However, it is possible that observation of the solstice itself could have been made from the hilltop as well as from the ledge, which is therefore not the unique spot from which observations were possible. Also it is curious that the primary backsight was located at the lower menhir when the visibility from the ledge and the higher stone was so much superior.[12]

South of Kintraw is an equally famous site at Ballochroy, which consists of three upright stones and a box-like structure of stone slabs called a 'kist'. One of its attractions is its comparative simplicity, for there are only three conceivable indications of distant foresights.[13] Two of the three stones have flat sides which indicate mountain slopes in the distant horizon to the north-west. One of these indicates the upper limb of the setting sun at the summer solstice, though the slope of the indicated hill profile is not quite parallel to the path of the setting sun, and so one obtains slightly different declinations depending on which part of the slope is regarded as 'the' foresight. (Although the menhir unambiguously indicates a single hillslope it is insufficiently exact to indicate a single feature on it.)

If there is uncertainty in the north-west foresight at Ballochroy, there is also uncertainty in the backsight, which could have been one of the three menhirs or the kist.[14] One *can* find different pairs of backsight/foresight combination which define the same declination,[15] but it is

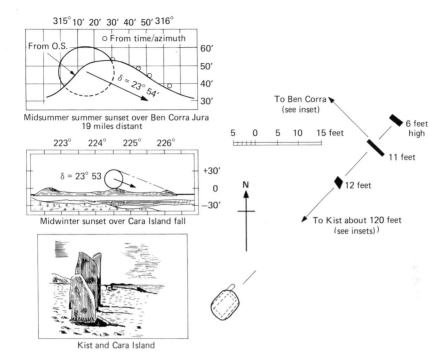

315° 10' 20' 30' 40' 50' 316°

From O.S.   o From time/azimuth

60'
50'
$\delta = 23° 54'$
40'
30'

Midsummer summer sunset over Ben Corra Jura
19 miles distant

223°   224°   225°   226°

+30'
$\delta = 23° 53$
0
−30'

Midwinter sunset over Cara Island fall

5 0 5 10 15 feet

To Ben Corra
(see inset)

6 feet
high

11 feet

12 feet

N

To Kist about 120 feet
(see insets))

Kist and Cara Island

99 (opposite) *Midsummer sunrise at Brainport Bay, Argyll. This site, the investigation of which is as yet incomplete, consists of a number of structures which can be interpreted as sighting platforms and a socket for a sighting post. It may prove to be as significant as Kintraw. The view shows the sun rising at midsummer along the principal orientation of the site, here marked by two ranging poles. (Photo E.W. MacKie.)*

100 (above) *Ballochroy, Argyll, by Thom (1967, 142). The distance between the menhirs and the kist is not to scale. The horizon profiles, which have since been resurveyed by Thom, may also be compared with ills. 72 and 101.*

101 (below) *Part of Corra Bheinn viewed from Ballochroy, after Bailey et al. 1975, fig. 2. Scales at bottom and left are, respectively, azimuth and elevation. The sun is shown setting at midsummer in 1600 BC as viewed from the kist. From the central menhir its upper limb sets along the path denoted by a broken line. Note that different parts of the hill profile correspond to slightly different declinations, even when only one backsight is used.*

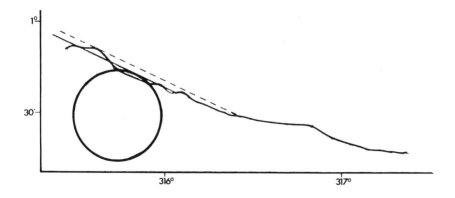

1°

30'

316°   317°

little better than an assumption that this is the unique declination indicated. When one considers the range of combinations, the indicated declination is uncertain by about 5 minutes of arc.[16]

The north menhir indicates a hillslope just as definitely as the central menhir, but no astronomical function can be found for this.[17] It is interesting to note that this indication was not listed by Thom in his first book,[18] whereas the orientation indicated by the central stone is listed with high weight. There seems nothing to distinguish the latter, except that it has an astronomical interpretation. This example shows that even the lines of high weight in Thom's book can only be used for statistical study, or as evidence for megalithic astronomy, with considerable reservation.

The three stones and the kist together define a sightline to the south-west. This passes east of the east end of Cara Island, if the line is defined by the right-hand edges of the stones. However, the *west* end of the island marks the upper limb of the setting sun at the winter solstice. Clearly the indication is inexact, and the particular foresight seems to have been chosen for no other reason than that it gives an astronomical declination.[19] Of course, even if we deny that the foresight is of any significance, we might still accept the alignment defined by the stones and the kist. However, the site at Ballochroy has a very simple geometry,[20] and the two main sightlines are roughly at right angles. Could one not equally plausibly suppose that one of the sightlines and the geometry were deliberate, and the other sightline was a coincidence? We shall see that a more striking problem of the interaction of geometry and astronomy occurs at Stonehenge.

A further difficulty with the line to the south-west is the fact that the kist, which lies between the stones and Cara Island, was 'almost certainly' once covered by a cairn, which would have obscured the sightline.[21] This is not a fatal flaw, for the observer could have stood to one side. Alternatively, one could argue, as Thom did in the context of Cauldside (Kirkcudbright),[22] that the cairn was constructed after the stones were put up. However, archaeologists appear to consider that the kist was erected before the stones.[23] We should not be too impressed by the fact that the foresights to the north-west and south-west can be fitted into the astronomical theory with the same value of the obliquity,[24] since, as we have seen, the foresight on Cara Island was chosen with this in mind, and there is some flexibility in the choice of foresight and backsight for the north-west.

Extrapolation

Without some method of allowing for the fact that the moon generally does not rise or set precisely when at its extreme declination, the 'lunar observatories' incorporating accurate indications of the extreme positions could not have been set up. Since Thom claimed to have found such indications in the form of natural foresights, he had to propose a method by which the necessary corrections could have been made.

Furthermore, not only was such a method necessary for the construction of the 'observatories', it was also needed if the observations at these sites were ever to have been used for the prediction of eclipses. Thom's answer was the process of extrapolation, using practical techniques such as those described in chapter 5. Now we have to see what evidence there is among megalithic remains that such methods were used. *39*

Following Thom, we turn to the interpretation of the stone fans of Caithness. Before he came to the idea that these were connected with the 'sector' method of extrapolation, 'no satisfactory explanation' of the stone fans had been put forward.[25] Actually, Thom himself had offered two different interpretations in his first book for one of the fans, but both are stellar, and there is only the briefest mention of the possibility of a lunar association,[26] which is of course the basis of the extrapolation theory.

The merit of the extrapolation theory is that it is not simply an interpretation of these sites; it makes predictions, and so it can be put to the test. In fact, in the form originally stated by Thom in his second book, the dimensions of the fans should take certain values (related to the extrapolation length G), provided that the lunar indication with which each site was associated can be discovered.

For the four sites discussed by Thom in his book, this prediction appeared to be borne out, and this is remarkable. At Mid Clyth, for instance, the dimensions were close to the ideal values, and similar results were returned for the other sites.[27] Yet it must be said that Mid Clyth is unusually well preserved, and at other more ruinous sites, such as Camster,[28] the dimensions must be regarded as quite uncertain. *12*

Another aspect which somewhat detracts from the value of this test of the extrapolation theory is the nature of some of the sightlines for which the supposed extrapolation was needed. At Dirlot there is no indication of the foresight from the site of the fan, and indeed no surviving practical foresight. There are stones on the horizon at the spot where a suitable foresight should have been, but these are too small to have been seen from Dirlot, and Thom had to suppose that an artificial perishable foresight had been used.[29] On the other hand, there may be some evidence that some of the sightlines associated with these fans are genuine: though no detailed justification is given for the remark, Thom has claimed that the existence of suitable foresights at Mid Clyth cannot be attributed to chance.[30] *22*

When Thom and his colleagues came to examine some of the sites in the vicinity of Carnac, new evidence became available concerning the use of stone fans or rows for extrapolation. It turned out that the fans were not all of the right size to have acted as extrapolation sectors for the sightlines to Le Grand Menhir Brisé. However, the Thoms mentioned two ways in which this could have been overcome; either by using only part of a sector, or else by inserting a 'scaling' factor during the use of the fans.[31]

The use of scaling factors does mean that there are sites which could have been used for extrapolation at Le Grand Menhir Brisé. On the other hand, it rather destroys the significance of the correlation in Caithness between the actual sizes of the fans and the ideal sizes calculated from the values of G; for it means that, even if we suppose that the scaling factors have to be integral, there is really no unique ideal size.

The fan at Petit Ménec is somewhat too large compared with the simple ideal dimensions (with no scaling factors), and the Thoms thought that this may have been done to accommodate the variations in the extrapolation length, G.[32] In fact, it was the only known sector or fan which is definitely too large, but the Thoms' suggestion leads us naturally to their proposal for the purpose of the very extensive stone rows near Carnac, which are certainly too long for the simple extrapolation method we have been considering so far in this chapter.[33] They stressed that they could not be certain that their interpretation was correct, but no harm is done by summarizing their idea if its speculative nature is borne in mind.

The value of G could actually have been determined observationally by studying the position of the rising or setting moon over three con-

39 secutive nights (see chapter 5). Furthermore it varies in step with the apparent diameter of the moon, which could have been determined simultaneously. The Thoms' idea was that a combination of these measurements was used in connection with the rows at Le Ménec to perform extrapolation in such a way as to take account of the changing distance

24 of the moon. Interestingly, the noteworthy 'quadratic relation' in the spacing of the rows at Le Ménec (see chapter 4) plays a crucial role in the working of the extrapolation method. In reality, the rows may not be quite narrow enough to be fully consistent with this interpretation of their purpose, and also it does not explain the function of the eastern half of the rows at Le Ménec.[34]

Thom has speculated that this more elaborate method of extrapolation replaced the earlier method using the small fans.[35] Indeed, it has

13, 14 been suggested that the large stones at the west end of Le Ménec may once have been arranged like a scaled-up version of one of the small fans.[36] The stones at the west end of the Kermario alignments are also especially large; and, in the form in which they are now disposed, they could have been used in a way not unlike the original sector method for extrapolation with a fixed value of G, though there are difficulties in this hesitant suggestion.[37]

In general terms, the sector method of extrapolation was quite workable, and yet there are some peculiarities. If the sectors were designed for the purpose of extrapolation, how is it that the rows of which they

14 consist are so irregular?[38] Why were such inconveniently large stones used in some cases, as at Carnac? Furthermore, how could such a subtle idea have been discovered, and how was the correct size of the fans arrived at? These are interesting questions but not fatal flaws. For example, J. E. Wood has discussed the last question in a reasonably convincing manner.[39] Nevertheless, the evidence itself hardly allows us to conclude that the fans and rows were definitely designed for the purpose of extrapolation. Nor should we feel obliged to support this explanation simply because it is the only one we have. What we can probably say is that

extrapolation was not an insuperable obstacle to the erection of accurate lunar observatories, and the stone rows and fans could have served this purpose.

So much for the sector method and its elaborations. What about the many supposed accurate lunar observatories where no fans exist? How was the necessary extrapolation there carried out? One possibility is the triangle method. If we accept Thom's original version of this, then, as we have already explained in chapter 5, there is a reason for supposing that it would be awkward to set out the method in the form of a stone grid on the ground. However, a knowledge of the extrapolation length, G, would have been just as necessary as in the sector method, and Thom supposed that this length might well have been laid out permanently.

Thom lists a few sites whose dimensions (in some sense) do seem to correspond with the value of the extrapolation length, or four times this quantity.[40] For example, at Fowlis Wester (Perthshire), where there are thought to be two lunar foresights, the extrapolation lengths appear to be marked by the distances between a stone circle and three outliers, though Thom says of certain of these that 'the agreements are probably accidental'.[41]

Thom's remark about Fowlis Wester should caution us against accepting such results as evidence that the suggested extrapolation method was actually used. As before, they merely confirm that extrapolation was possible. The important point is that enough space was available at the sites for the process to have taken place, and this is a useful practical criterion at any possible accurate lunar observatory. Most of those described by Thom appear to pass it successfully. However, an exception is the prime site Callanish I, where there is insufficient room, 107 but a special argument shows how the site could have been erected using observations at a neighbouring site.[42] On the other hand, this argument does nothing to avoid the awkward fact that the site would have been virtually useless for subsequent observation of the moon.

Stonehenge

Despite the fact that Stonehenge is the most celebrated megalithic site 71, 102 with claimed astronomical orientations, it is only comparatively late in his own research that Thom has come to express any detailed ideas about it. These were characteristically original, at least in the context of Stonehenge, but earlier Thom had confined himself to stating that his own studies of the numerous (usually smaller) sites elsewhere lent support by association to the idea that Stonehenge, too, might be astronomical. Indeed, he was even 'prepared to accept that Stonehenge was a solar and lunar observatory'.[43] Certainly, to judge by the statistical investigations summarized in the previous chapter, the astronomical theory of Stonehenge – beyond the orientation of its axis – is in need of some support. In this section we shall look at Stonehenge in a little more detail, though it must be emphasized that we are usually dealing with evidence which is of quite a different nature from that which we described previously. Here we shall normally be stating how various structures can be interpreted on the astronomical theory, and that is quite a different thing from establishing that the astronomical theory is correct. Very little of this evidence is such as would make a reasonable sceptic even consider changing his mind.[44]

We begin with the widely accepted axial line of Stonehenge. For Lockyer, who carefully measured the orientation of the avenue[45] with the specific intention of dating the monument, the solstitial orientation of the avenue and axis was the 'chief astronomical evidence in favour of the solar temple theory'.[46] We have yet to discuss the possible purpose of megalithic astronomy, but if we interpret the word 'temple' very loosely, we might guess from what we have seen of the statistical evidence that Lockyer's opinion would probably not have changed in the intervening decades.

More conspicuous nowadays than the avenue is the line from the centre of Stonehenge to the Heel Stone, though this stands a little to the right of the place where the solstitial sun rose in megalithic times.[47] Several reasons have been offered for this fact. Lockyer thought that the Heel had originally marked the solstice, but that the avenue and ditch were added later with a slightly different centre from which to observe, so that the Heel would then seem too far to the right.[48] On the other hand, Hoyle's explanation, as we have seen, is that the offsetting of the Heel was deliberate: when observed from a suitable position, the sun would rise above the Heel a certain number of days before and after the solstice, and so the solstice could be fixed. Curiously, many years ago Somerville thought that it might have acted as a 'warning' for the approach of the solstice.[49] Actually the Heel Stone is not always regarded as solstitial, for there are ways in which it could have been used as a lunar orientation.[50]

The line to the Heel Stone is just one of many orientations which Hawkins listed using stones and stone-holes which he attributed to the earliest phase in the construction of Stonehenge, Stonehenge I. Some of these lines had already been noted by E. Duke in 1846, L. Gidley in 1873,[51] and by Lockyer. Many were discovered independently by Newham, who also found others which Hawkins missed.[52] Nevertheless, these different authors do not always give the same interpretation of the same line. For instance, Lockyer thought that the line between positions 91 and 93 was calendrical (in both directions),[53] an idea that has been revived by A. R. Thatcher.[54] Hawkins, on the other hand, thought it was lunar, though without stating any clear reason for his preference.[55]

We have seen that there are no more astronomical lines in Stonehenge I than would be expected by chance, essentially because so many alignments can be found among the stones and other features of this phase of Stonehenge. Of course this statistical null result might need revision if it could be shown that those stones for which an astronomical significance is claimed were also distinguished in some non-astronomical way. Then we could repeat our statistical calculation, but modified so that we calculated the number of astronomical orientations that would be expected by chance if we now restricted ourselves to the 'distinguished'

71

102 Stonehenge, Wiltshire, from the north-east. With the aid of ill. 71, many of the features referred to in the text can be identified. (Crown Copyright: reproduced with permission of the Controller of Her Majesty's Stationery Office).

stones and stone-holes. Indeed, there is one group of positions which may be in Stonehenge I and which does seem to be distinguished geometrically – the Station Rectangle.

The Station stones and mounds were given special attention even by Lockyer, who thought they were primarily solar. For example, the view from 91 to 93 indicates the position of sunset at the beginning of May.[56] Since the Station Stones and the Heel Stone seemed to Lockyer to be unworked, and therefore early, while the later trilithons emphasized the solstitial orientation, he concluded that a calendar beginning in May had been replaced by one beginning at midsummer.[57] Hawkins too wanted the Stations to be early, but for 'astronomical' reasons.[58] Presumably this refers to the fact that the line between 91 and 93, which Hawkins and Lockyer regarded as an astronomical sightline, is blocked by the sarsens and trilithons, which were erected during the last major phase of construction, Stonehenge III. Modern archaeological opinion is that at least one of the Station Stones is late, but it may well have replaced an earlier marker.[59]

Because of their rectangular layout, symmetrically disposed with respect to the rest of the monument and its axis, it is tempting to regard the Stations as an important element of Stonehenge geometry.[60] Also, each side and one of the diagonals all define at least one astronomical line, the four Stations yielding between them eight of the astronomical lines listed by Hawkins for Stonehenge I.[61] Now the four positions yield altogether 12 sightlines, and the fact that 8 of these approximate to solar and lunar positions seems overwhelmingly significant. Actually, one of them was later removed since the error in azimuth seemed too high,[62] but the general idea that the purpose of the Stations was astronomical seems to have proved acceptable to several commentators.

A number of reservations must be made about this assessment, however. The first is that it depends on the assumed geometrical significance of the Station Rectangle; and we have seen in chapter 4 how hard it is to substantiate such assumptions even when we have large numbers of examples to study. Then again we must be careful about applying naïve statistical considerations to such a simple geometrical shape as a rectangle, for its opposite sides tend to indicate similar declinations, and if a line gives approximately a northern solar or lunar declination in one direction, it tends to give approximately the corresponding southern declination in the other.[63] (This effect is very evident in Hawkins' list.) Thus the rectangle defines only four more or less independent lines (the two diagonals and the two pairs of opposite sides), and it turns out that three of these are approximately lunar or solar. Finally, one of these follows automatically from the main axial orientation of Stonehenge, if we suppose that the Station Rectangle was deliberately made parallel to this.

This last argument was extended by the archaeologist J. Hawkes in an interesting way that parallels a remark we made about Ballochroy.[64] If we accept the fact that the Stations were set up in a rectangle parallel to the main axis, does this not adequately account for their positions, so that we can dismiss the remaining alignments as fortuitous? One possible answer to this question is that it would be a satisfactory explanation provided that the coincidence of the remaining lines was not a very unlikely one. That is what we now investigate.

On Hawkes' hypothesis one of the four essentially independent lines defined by the Stations is automatically solstitial. Is there anything surprising about the fact that two of the three remaining independent lines are also approximately astronomical? Well, their largest error in azimuth is about $1\cdot8°$,[65] and the probability that a single random line agrees with a particular astronomically significant position as closely as this is about $(2\times1\cdot8°)/360°$, or $0\cdot01$. Twelve astronomical positions must be considered in this context (corresponding to the declinations $\pm\varepsilon$, $\pm(\varepsilon-i)$ and $\pm(\varepsilon+i)$ at both rising and setting), and so the probability that a random line agrees with *any* of these positions is $0\cdot12$. The probability that at least two out of three random lines agree can then be shown to be about one in twenty-five, which is slightly significant. However, if we therefore accept that one of the two is deliberate, it may be shown that the probability of getting at least one other is about one in four. Thus, of the three astronomical alignments generated by the Stations, we may regard one as a product of their geometry, we might regard one more as of possible significance, but the third can be dismissed as a coincidence.

The sightlines defined by the sides of the Station Rectangle are thought to be astronomical, and much has been made of the fact that these two particular orientations would be at right angles only at a latitude near

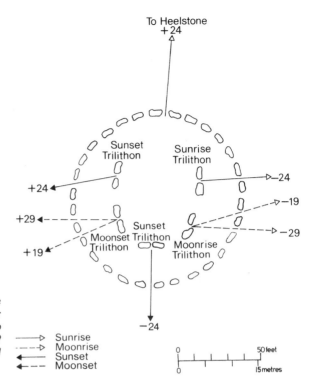

To Heelstone
+24

Sunset
Trilithon

Sunrise
Trilithon

+24 ◄   ▷—24

+29 ◄- - -   -▷ —19

+19 ◄   -▷ —29

Sunset
Moonset Trilithon
Trilithon

Moonrise
Trilithon

—24

103 Alignments at Stonehenge using the trilithons and the sarsen circle, after Hawkins and White 1966, 141. Lines to declinations ±24 are solstitial, those to ±29 are for the major standstill of the moon, and those to ±19 are for the minor standstill.

⟶▷ Sunrise
- - -▷ Moonrise
◄— Sunset
◄- - Moonset

0   50 feet
0   15 metres

that of Stonehenge. It has even been suggested that this was the reason for the choice of the latitude of Stonehenge.[66] However, it is entirely possible that one of the suggested sightlines is quite accidental, as we have seen.

Surely we can take the following view of the Stations: that the builders had no choice in the latitude; and that they laid out the Stations as a rectangle, with one pair of sides arranged parallel to the axis of Stonehenge, and the diagonal so chosen as to give a second astronomical alignment. Then the third alignment, defined by the long sides of the Rectangle, is a coincidence. It is not suggested that this view is uniquely implied by what we find at Stonehenge, but it is consistent with the facts, and leaves no surprising astronomical property of the Stations unexplained. A broadly similar view has been expressed by E. W. MacKie.[67]

Stonehenge I, which is what we dealt with mostly when assessing the statistical evidence in chapter 7, is architecturally less impressive than the structures of Stonehenge III, and astronomical orientations have been claimed for the latter also. The axis of Stonehenge III is solstitial, with an error of a few minutes of arc,[68] but several other orientations in this phase of the monument were detected by Hawkins. They are quite unlike those for Stonehenge I; here one looks between the trilithons through gaps in the surrounding Sarsen Circle.[69] Furthermore, certain hollows in the trilithons were, Hawkins maintained, deliberately carved to allow the slight 'sideways' view needed for some of the sightlines.[70]

103

There is no sightline of this type in Stonehenge III which does not indicate some significant lunar or solar declination.[71] However, the errors in some are so large, up to 8° in azimuth,[72] that they can hardly be said to indicate the solar or lunar positions at all. (It may be noted that the width of the gaps between the Sarsens, as viewed from the trilithons, is about 8°.) Another problem with these lines is that they do not define an angle to better than several degrees, and so it is difficult to see what purpose they might have served on Hawkins' theory of Stonehenge.[73] In this respect they are decidedly inferior to the lines of Stonehenge I, and in general they have had a cooler reception.

Two further possibilities should be mentioned in connection with Stonehenge III. One is that its construction must have blocked out some of the sightlines formed by Stonehenge I[74] (if we include the Stations among these). However, Hawkins has suggested that these lines were replaced by new lines in which the outlying positions of Stonehenge I were viewed from the trilithons.[75] Secondly, although the vertical structure of megalithic sites is generally ignored in discussions of megalithic astronomy, Stonehenge III is one exception. The astronomer G. de Vaucouleurs has shown that the height of the monument may be related to the shadows it casts at the solstice,[76] though there seems to be no way of determining whether this was deliberate.

Both Stonehenge I and Stonehenge III, or at least their astronomical sightlines, are laid out on a small scale, and this limits their accuracy. Without some such device as Hoyle's offset technique, they would have been hopelessly inaccurate for the observational determination of the dates of the solstices, for instance. A group of three postholes in the car park at Stonehenge, some 300 yards (c. 300 m) from the circles, may have provided sightlines of somewhat higher precision. Newham especially regarded them as having great importance.[77] Using up to five different backsights (the Stations and the Heel Stone), he showed that these posts might be related to the setting positions of the moon at the standstills, and of the sun at the solstice and one other calendrical declination. The Thoms have given a different, though related, explanation of the car-park postholes, suggesting that the posts might have been mere ancillary apparatus for setting up very distant lunar foresights on the apparent horizon beyond.[78]

The Thoms have searched for possible distant foresights for other lunar declinations, and also for solar ones, at Stonehenge. Unfortunately it would be possible to test these statistically only in the way in which the sightlines to Le Grand Menhir Brisé have been tested; and we do not possess any estimate of the number of suitable features which lie on the horizon at Stonehenge. Despite this, A. Burl has stated his opinion that the foresights found by the Thoms at Stonehenge are unlikely to be coincidental, though MacKie has expressed some well-reasoned scepticism about the suggested solstitial foresight.[79] His doubts were subsequently justified further by the discovery, through excavation, that the foresight is of modern date.[80] Actually, Lockyer appears to have been the first to claim the existence of a distant natural foresight at Stonehenge. He

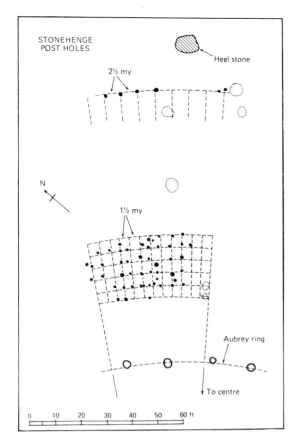

STONEHENGE
POST HOLES

Heel stone

2½ my

N

1½ my

Aubrey ring

To centre

0 10 20 30 40 50 60 ft

104 The causeway post holes at Stonehenge, after Thom, Thom and Thom 1974, fig. 11. They are situated between the Aubrey ring and the Heel Stone (ill. 71). The design superposed on the lower group is an extrapolation fan, which was an interpretation suggested by the Thoms.

thought that Sidbury Hill was a natural foresight for the rising sun at the summer solstice,[81] but in fact an intervening ridge obscures the view.[82]

According to the Thoms the distant horizon to the north-east (including, presumably, Sidbury Hill) would have come into view had Stonehenge been positioned slightly to the north-west,[83] the implication being that the position of the monument was selected to avoid this. Earlier the Thoms pointed out that a hilltop site would have been unsuitable for this sort of reason.[84] This is not the first time that the site of Stonehenge has been connected with its purpose; much earlier, H. Browne came to the opposite conclusion, arguing that Stonehenge could hardly be an observatory, since it did *not* stand on a summit![85]

If we accept the suggestions for accurate distant lunar foresights at Stonehenge, then there is the necessity for some accompanying extrapolation procedure, such as one of those devised by Thom. In fact the Thoms tentatively suggested that a certain scattering of postholes, which 104 had been discovered by excavation on the causeway across the ditch, may have been set out as an extrapolating sector, and indeed the size of the pattern is appropriate for one of the lunar lines.[86] However, a worrying aspect of this interpretation is that the date of this part of Stonehenge is much earlier than that of any other site at which extrapolation is thought to have been carried out. But this is not the only astronomical interpretation of these postholes, for Newham had a quite different one.[87] To him they represented markers for the monthly extreme rising position of the moon in successive years, with gaps for those missed because of bad weather. (There are not quite enough postholes to fit the theory in its simplest form.) Newham's explanation seems a poor one, for it would imply that the holes should be more thickly distributed on the left, near the standstill position, than on the right, whereas they are not.[88] Also, on this theory we would not expect the holes in different rows to line up with the centre of Stonehenge, and yet they give the visual impression of doing so. In both respects the Thoms' interpretation seems preferable. There is also a separate line of four postholes beside the Heel Stone, and Hoyle thought that they were offset markers for determining the date of a standstill.[89]

When we look back over the evidence from Stonehenge which seems statistically of any significance, the ground appears amazingly barren. There is the axial line, which has been known for a long time, and is widely accepted, if only as a ritual orientation. After this, however, there is only the likelihood of one further astronomical orientation in the Stations, and it is by no means a strong one. It is very hard to square this bleak record with the enthusiasm and confidence with which most accounts of the astronomical theory of Stonehenge are usually coloured.

The dating of Stonehenge

Some of the researches into the astronomy of Stonehenge have centred on dating the monument by astronomical means. Again it seems advisable to restrict such attempts to those alignments whose significance is least in doubt, for we can have no confidence whatever in a dating if we use a line which might easily be a coincidence. For those orientations whose significance is not demonstrated, all we can do is to record the range of dates on which they indicated the claimed astronomical positions, and verify that these are consistent with dates determined archaeologically. However, this should be regarded as a test of the viability of the astronomical theory, rather than as an independent dating procedure.

The one alignment whose significance is not usually disputed – the axis – has been used most frequently for attempts at dating. Even before Lockyer's well-known attempt to date the monument, two or three estimates had been made. Petrie had derived a date of AD 730, but he appears to have been quite mistaken in calculating the way in which the solstitial rising position varied with time.[90] Whitmell's estimate of AD 425 was also very late, and it differs from the date arrived at by Lockyer because Whitmell used a different value for the azimuth of the axis.[91]

71   The study by Lockyer and Penrose was the most careful. They chose as the axis the central line of the avenue, and described in some detail the procedure by which they measured it.[92] But the azimuth they used for the purpose of deriving the date was not obtained from the measurements of the avenue. Instead, Lockyer and Penrose noticed that this lay very close to the azimuth of a certain Iron Age fort on Sidbury Hill, and

they very curiously used the azimuth of the fort. Anyway, the date they obtained came to 1680 BC or, when account was taken of the slight uncertainty in the position of the axis, a date within about 200 years of this.[93] Whatever the precise date, it was a matter of satisfaction to Lockyer that it agreed well with the date arrived at independently, but very cautiously, by the archaeologists of the time.[94]

The question has often since been raised as to whether the astronomical date really is independent. Lockyer had some choice in how to define the axial line of Stonehenge[95] and in the astronomical declination which was thought to have been indicated. Although his choice of the avenue was a rational one, at least in the context of his previous researches abroad, it was not the only possibility; Trotter, for example, preferred to define the axis by the remaining stones.[96] Anyway, even if we accept the avenue, how can we justify Lockyer's choice that it was orientated upon the *upper* limb of the rising solstitial sun? (This is an important point, since the difference in date obtained by the choice of upper or lower limb amounts to about 4000 years!)[97] To decide this we could look at the other lines at Stonehenge and see which choice fits these best, but the evidence seems unclear.[98] Again, underlying Lockyer's dating was the assumption that the axis was aligned by the builders with an accuracy at least as good as the accuracy with which Lockyer determined the azimuth.[99] Finally, even if Lockyer's choice in all these matters was incontestable, archaeologists would be interested to know which phase of the construction the date should be referred to.[100] In short, there seems little justification for Lockyer's assumptions apart from the fact that they yield a reasonable value for the date. Thus it is clear that his estimate adds little new to the dating of Stonehenge.

Eclipse prediction at Stonehenge

To complete our review of Stonehenge astronomy, which is already much longer than the significance of the evidence justifies, we must review a few ideas for the underlying purpose of the many supposed lines. There is virtually no direct evidence that any of these ideas is correct. However, if one is determined to find an astronomical use for Stonehenge, it may be of interest to compare the merits of the various ideas that are already available. No doubt others will turn up.

Hawkins' ideas centred on the hypothesis that the Stonehenge astronomers were interested in observing and predicting eclipses *near the solstices*. This restriction arose from the fact that Hawkins normally considered lines to the rising and setting positions of the *full* moon. The moon is full only when it is opposite the sun in the sky, and if it is at one of the extreme declinations indicated by the orientations, then the sun must be at the opposite extreme of its orbit, i.e. at one or other solstice.

As has already been explained in chapter 5, eclipses occur at the equinoxes if the moon is close to a standstill, and at the solstices if it is halfway between successive standstills. Now the lunar orientations can be

34

used to inform us about the occurrence of standstills; hence we can find out directly when equinoctial eclipses occur, and then we could infer when they occur at the solstices. Furthermore, Hawkins found that the Heel Stone informs us directly of the occurrence of eclipse seasons at the solstice,[101] which Atkinson cautiously accepted as the best available explanation for this stone.[102]

Hawkins' most striking idea, however, was that these events could have been predicted, without the need for repeated observation. As we have seen, Hawkins introduced the idea that the 56 Aubrey Holes were used for this purpose. On this theory, the alignments were used merely to start off the prediction machinery in the correct configuration, and then to check it from time to time.

In his first paper on Stonehenge, Hawkins had looked on the Aubrey Holes as probably a sort of protractor for the measurement of azimuths,[103] but in the eclipse prediction theory they became a kind of tally, used essentially to record the passage of a period of 56 years. Hawkins proposed analogous functions for the other rings at Stonehenge, and Newham also made suggestions of this general type.[104] Their interpretations of the same ring were not always the same, however. Thus Hawkins thought of the existing horseshoe of 19 bluestones as a tally for the 18·6-year revolution of the lunar nodes;[105] Newham, on the other hand, associated them with the 19-year Metonic Cycle.

These were not the first times that such ideas had been proposed, for in the eighteenth century J. Smith suggested that the 30 stones in one of the circles was associated with the number of days which the sun spent in each sign of the zodiac.[106] Nor were such ideas confined to Stonehenge. A paper by P. Stephan is a prolific source of ideas on how circles with various numbers of stones can be turned to astronomical or calendrical use. For example, two of the circles at Odry (near Czersk, in Poland) had, respectively, 18 and 20 stones, which could have been used to record the passage of 18 'months' of 20 days each.[107] At another site, Stephan ingeniously devised a calendar with 52 months of 28 days, making 4 years, to fit a circle with concentric rings of 52 and 25 stones.[108] (He occasionally had to adjust the actual numbers of stones slightly to make the theories fit.) The lesson of all this is that it seems comparatively easy to devise some quasi-astronomical purpose for any stone circle, no matter how many stones it may contain. Furthermore, A. Burl has concluded, from a study of a great many rings, that the numbers of the stones in them do not seem specially related to calendrical purposes or those of eclipse prediction.[109]

Following Atkinson, Hoyle was puzzled by why a circle of such a large diameter as the Aubrey Holes was needed on Hawkins' scheme, when the holes were thought to act merely as a tally. The idea is that one could understand a large diameter if the markers were moved continuously, because a large diameter would make it possible to measure the angles between the markers more accurately.[110] In Hawkins' scheme, on the other hand, the markers were moved by one hole each year, and the angles between the markers were irrelevant. Therefore something like a pegboard would be much more convenient. Actually, however, Hoyle's own original theory of eclipse prediction using the Aubrey circle would be open to the same objection, for it is clear from certain of his descriptions[111] that, like Hawkins, he too thought the markers were moved from hole to hole. Indeed it now seems that the sole advantage of using a large structure like the set of Aubrey Holes is that it would be less liable to accidental disturbance than a small device such as a pegboard. One of Hoyle's recent suggestions is that the Aubrey circle was not itself used for eclipse predictions; these would be made using a pegboard, and the Aubrey markers would act simply as a record, so that the pegboard could be reset after predictions had been made.[112]

Other problems with the proposed use of the Aubrey Holes concern their nature, for Atkinson found it strange that *permanent* tally marks should be represented by pits that were filled in very soon after being dug.[113] Furthermore, though the imagined eclipse predictors are supposed to have been started off with information from sightlines that may have involved the Station Stones, one of the Aubrey Holes was actually destroyed by an enclosure around one of the Stations.[114] Newham thought that the original purpose of the Aubrey Holes was to hold sighting posts, and that the project was later abandoned and the holes, which had been made large enough for a certain amount of adjustment, were therefore filled in.[115]

In some respects Hoyle's theory for eclipse prediction at Stonehenge was simply an elegant elaboration of Hawkins' idea. He has recently re-examined his theory in great detail, and shown that it would not have worked very well in its original form.[116] For example, the original scheme would not have been able to predict the exact day of an eclipse more than a month or two in advance. In this case the remedy is simply to prescribe a better rule for moving the moon marker around the Aubrey circle. Actually, similar limitations might be revealed if Hawkins' scheme were subjected to similar detailed study.

What direct evidence is there that either Hawkins' or Hoyle's method of predicting eclipses was ever used at Stonehenge? Is there anything about Stonehenge, especially the Aubrey Holes, which would be surprising if the eclipse prediction schemes were wrong? Hawkins pointed to their number, 56, declaring that his was about the only explanation for it.[117] It is certainly a curious number, but should we be surprised that one of the rings at Stonehenge contains a number of holes which happens to be suitable for eclipse prediction? The fact that other cycles could have been used for eclipse prediction, as was shown by Colton and Martin and by Sadler,[118] certainly makes 56 less special, and Hawkins himself showed how other numbers of stones could have been used for this purpose, though perhaps less effectively.[119] If Stephan's imagination had run to eclipses, who knows what prediction schemes he would have been able to devise?

Hoyle prefaced one explanation of his ideas for eclipse prediction at Stonehenge by the statement that he was concerned largely with showing how *we* could have gone about the problem using only the sort of materials and tools available to the builders of Stonehenge.[120] However, he then argued that, since he had found his method of eclipse prediction by a study of Stonehenge, it would be strange if Stonehenge had nothing to do with astronomy.[121] (Hawkins makes a rather similar point when he remarks that he discovered the 56-year eclipse cycle while working on Stonehenge.)[122] Hoyle later even argued that, since *we* could use Stonehenge for eclipse prediction, it would be fantastic if the builders of Stonehenge did not do so.[123] These arguments are quite unacceptable, for using them what should we conclude from Hawkins' statement that Stonehenge could be used to predict the date of Easter and the Passover?[124] Furthermore, between them Hoyle and Hawkins showed that it could be used in at least two rather different ways to predict eclipses;[125] does this imply that it *was* used in both ways?

Hawkins' attitude to eclipse prediction was generally more cautious: he recognized that there was no statistical support for the eclipse-prediction theory.[126] Nevertheless, he concluded that the combined theory of alignments and eclipse prediction accounted 'for every stone, hole, mound, archway and geometric position now marked at Stonehenge I and III.'[127]

Despite its comprehensiveness, Hawkins' theory of eclipse prediction drew little unreserved support. Müller thought it hypothetical yet plausible; to Newham, who often led the field in finding alignments, it appeared invalid; Colton and Martin thought it safe to assume that the Aubrey Holes were not used for eclipse predictions on a 56-year cycle; and Renfrew considered the theory to be 'very ill-substantiated'.[128]

Sites with multiple explanations

Many authors appear to regard the astronomical purpose of a megalithic orientation as established as soon as it is shown that it indicates an astronomically significant part of the horizon. This is an example of the convenient but treacherous argument which says that, if a certain hypothesis is consistent with the facts, then it is correct. The fallacy of such an argument is immediately exposed when we have two distinct hypotheses which are both consistent with the facts. As we have seen, this occurs in connection with eclipse prediction at Stonehenge, and Hawkes stressed how damaging this is to the supposed validity of the theories.[129] In this section we shall describe some other examples of monuments which have been interpreted in different ways by different authors, or even by the same author at different times.

An example of multiple explanations from Thom's work is a site to which we have referred before: Mid Clyth in Caithness. It is approximately symmetrical about the north-south line, and Thom's first suggestion was that it could have been used as a sundial near local noon.[130] Then in his first book he suggested tentatively that it might have been used in the direction to the north for observing the star Capella, or alternatively to the south as a sort of stellar clock,[131] which is similar to the sundial theory. At this time Thom also briefly mentioned a possible

105 The stone rows of Kerlescan, Brittany, after Freer and
Quinio 1977, 53. According to
Müller (1970, 104f., cf. Devoir
1909, 74) row I is solstitial and
row XIII is equinoctial, but the
orientation of row XIII does not
seem to fit this interpretation
well.

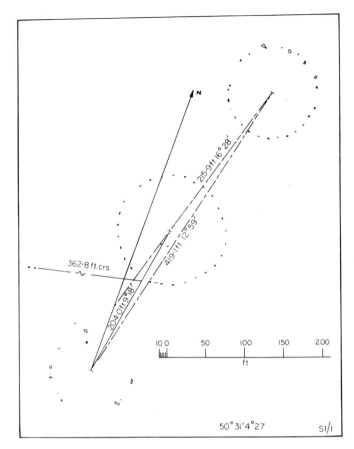

362·8 ft.crs

50°31'4°27

SI/I

106 The Hurlers, Cornwall, after Thom 1966, 40. According to Lockyer the lines from the south circle to the central one, and from this to the northern circle, are indications of the places where Arcturus rose in 2170 BC and 2090 BC, respectively. He noted that the later astronomical date for the north circle was consistent with archaeological evidence, since some of its stones appear to be more carefully worked than those in the south circle. However, according to Burl (1976, 117) the stones of the central circle were, 'uncommonly', smoothed by hammering.

connection of the site with lunar sightlines, and it was this explanation which was expanded in his second book, where the purpose of the fan was said to be for extrapolation.[132] None of these explanations has statistical support, and, though the slope of the site is not favourable to the clock theory, the existence of at least two different theories does nothing to help make *any* astronomical interpretation of Mid Clyth seem inevitable. This is particularly unfortunate, since Thom regarded Mid Clyth as a very important site for showing us how extrapolation was carried out.[133]

More than one astronomical explanation is also available for some other stone rows, especially those at Carnac in Brittany. The Thoms, as we have seen, tentatively suggested that those at Le Ménec were used for extrapolation, rather in the manner of Mid Clyth, but Lockyer thought that they were an early calendrical site.[134] Likewise Kermario, which, according to the Thoms, may also have had something to do with extrapolation, was taken by Müller to be a solstitial sightline.[135] Again the fact that we have more than one interpretation to choose from does not help to make any of them more convincing.

The Hurlers is an interesting Cornish group of three circles, almost in line, which has been investigated by several workers. The centres of the circles, taken in pairs, define three sightlines in both directions, and two of these Lockyer associated with the star Arcturus for two dates about a century apart – 2170 BC and 2090 BC.[136] Thom agreed with Lockyer in identifying these lines with Arcturus, though for a slightly different date in at least one case. Furthermore, there was a possibility, which Lockyer had missed or ignored, that one of the lines was for Vega.[137] To Stephan the numbers of stones in the circles were evidently of greater interest; he interpreted them as providing a tally system for a calendar.[138]

The disposition of the circles at Stanton Drew in Somerset bears some similarity to that of the Hurlers, and here also Lockyer ascribed an orientation to Arcturus, though for a date of 1410 BC.[139] Such a date seems very late on archaeological grounds.[140] Thom identified three sightlines at Stanton Drew, but none is for Arcturus, presumably because the date would have had to be later than Thom was prepared to contemplate.[141] All are of low weight in Thom's classification; one is solar, one unidentified, and one lunar. To Stephan, Stanton Drew again meant a calendar.[142]

Another case where we can compare the interpretations of different authors is the Nine Maidens in Cornwall, an impressive alignment which both Thom and Lockyer identified as stellar.[143] However, Thom gave it to Deneb, while Lockyer thought it was for Capella at a date of about 1480 BC. Incidentally in this and similar cases there is not very great disagreement on the essential details of the alignments, as distinct from their interpretation; the azimuths and horizon elevations differ by no more than 2° in this case, and the resulting declinations by only 1° or so. It is just that, once again, Lockyer was prepared to consider a slightly later date than Thom.

Our final example of the same monument studied by different authors is a more substantial one: the main circle at Callanish, Lewis. It was discussed by Lockyer in 1909, and in the same year it was studied by Somerville, who published his results in 1912. It has been investigated by Thom, and Hawkins found eleven lunar and solar lines there.[144] More recently a substantial investigation has been carried out by Cooke and his three co-workers, who also conveniently collated much of the earlier work.[145]

One of the most impressive lines at Callanish is the avenue leading approximately north from the main circle. It is defined by two nearly parallel rows of standing stones, and both rows yield very similar declinations, which Lockyer and Somerville both identified with that of Capella, in about 1720 BC and 1800 BC, respectively.[146] (Somerville rejected two other possible stellar explanations partly because the dates were inconsistent with the date of another supposed stellar line at the same site.) Hawkins, who disapproved of stellar lines,[147] thought that the avenue would have been used to the south, as a lunar indicator. He found that the avenue indicated a distant peak, Mt Clisham, behind which the moon set at the major standstill. This was elaborated by Thom as an indicated foresight for observation of the perturbation of the moon's motion.[148] However, Hawkins subsequently found that Mt Clisham, being obscured by ground just to the south of the monument, is invisible to an observer at the north end of the avenue.[149]

Somerville, Hawkins and Thom appear to be in agreement about the line of menhirs running to the west of the circle: all assigned it to the sun at the equinox,[150] though Hawkins used it to the east for sunrise, and the other two thought it indicated sunset in the west.

Differences appear again in relation to the line of menhirs on the east of the circle. Somerville favoured the explanation that this was an indication of the Pleiades. There were three other possibilities, but they yielded quite late dates, and the Pleiades identification was the only one which gave a date close to that for the Capella line. Rather circularly, however, Somerville used the existence of the Pleiades line, for approximately the same date, as confirmation of the date found from the Capella line.

It is of some interest to assess the statistical significance of this result. For the north line Somerville found the following possible identifications, with the corresponding dates:

Capella	1800 BC
Castor	650 BC
Arcturus	320 BC

and for the east line the following:

Pleiades	1750 BC
Spica	1270 BC
α Arietis	1130 BC
Aldebaran	800 BC

Somerville said that he gave all possible stellar identifications for any date between about 3500 BC and 0 BC,[151] and so we can calculate the probability that at least one date in the first list should lie within 50 years of at least one in the other, assuming that they are picked at random from a 3500-year interval. It turns out to be about one in three, and so the agreement of the dates is not significant evidence that the lines have been correctly identified. Furthermore, difficulties caused by atmospheric extinction will be particularly acute with stars as faint as those in the Pleiades.

To Hawkins the line to the east was one of the so-called equinoctial lunar lines, but Thom assigned it to Altair in 1800 BC.[152] He must have had some doubt about this, for he says cautiously only that it was 'perhaps intentionally' aligned to Altair.

After the alignment to the south, which may be interpreted as being meridional, only one other line need be mentioned here; it runs from an outlying menhir on the south-west to another on the north-east. Somerville said that the only star with which he could associate this was Pollux.[153] However, the date would have had to be quite late, and he favoured the lunar explanation which Hawkins was later to adopt.[154] Thom did not list it, though he mentions a nearby solstitial line which is not described by the previous two authors.[155] It is not strictly megalithic, but involves one of the construction points for the Type A flattened circle

107 The main circle and alignments at Callanish, Lewis. Note that the alignments to the north are not perfectly straight. (Plan by courtesy of Dr D.A. Tait, University of Glasgow.)

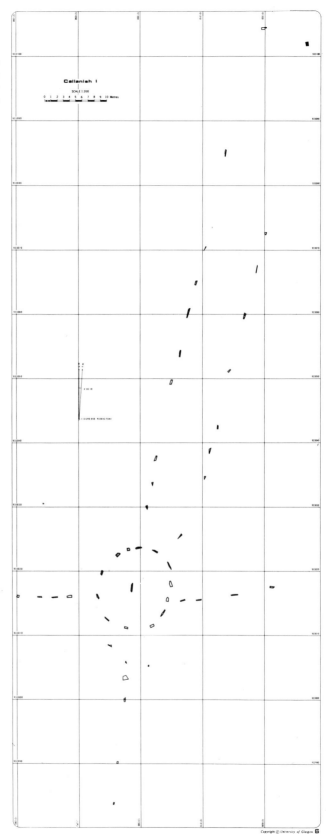

which, according to Thom, describes the geometry of the main ring at Callanish. This geometry is related in a curious way to a discovery of Somerville's. He noted that there is a point which is simultaneously in line with the row of stones to the east, the row to the west, and the centre line of the avenue to the north. Now the rows at Callanish define six lines, if we include the central line of the north avenue, and perhaps we should not be too surprised that three of these nearly intersect. However, it is remarkable that the point of intersection turns out to lie very close to the geometrical construction point mentioned by Thom.[156]

To Somerville, then, Callanish presented lines for the moon (with its approximately 19-year cycle of standstills), for the equinoctial sun, and for the Pleiades. Thus he had all the major quasi-astronomical ingredients contained in a well-known quotation from the classical writer Diodorus Siculus about a race known as the Hyperboreans. In this passage Diodorus refers to a 'spherical' temple on the island which they inhabited, to an event recurring every 19 years, and to the interval between the equinox and the rising of the Pleiades.[157] In fact Lockyer, and most later writers who have interpreted it in the context of megalithic astronomy, have linked this quotation with Stonehenge.[158] Of course we cannot be sure to which monument Diodorus was referring, or even that he was referring to the British Isles, but at least Callanish does exhibit a Pleiades alignment.

It was the Diodorus quotation which inspired Hawkins to study the possibility of a connection between eclipses and Stonehenge, and it is interesting that Callanish is the one other monument to which he has applied the same general idea. However, he had to conclude by admitting that his suggestion was conjectural.[159]

Whether the number of astronomical indications found at Callanish significantly exceeds what woul be expected by chance, has been considered by Cooke et al., and their results have also been analysed by Freeman and Elmore.[160] The upshot of these investigations is that the number of indications does not seem significant. However, it must be said that the selection criteria used by Cooke et al. were quite involved, as they necessarily will be in such a complex group of sites. They may also have been unduly restrictive, for one or two of the assumptions on which they are based seem questionable.

One last curiosity about Callanish should be mentioned, for it is certainly odd that the disposition of the alignments radiating from the circle is not symmetrical. According to Thom this implies that the design of the monument was not chosen on simple geometrical grounds. He went further by arguing that the only obvious explanation for the asymmetry was an astronomical one.[161] Such reasoning does not clinch the matter, for the positioning of the alignments might have been influenced by the topography of the site,[162] but as qualitative arguments go it is quite an appealing one.

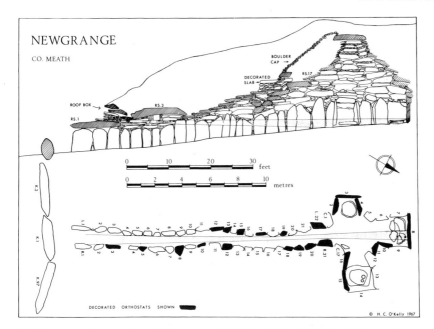

108 *Newgrange, Ireland, after J.D. Patrick and H.C. O'Kelly (Patrick 1974, 517). The roof-box is a gap above the lintel stone at the threshold. At midwinter, as the sun rises, the sun illuminates the chamber by the beam shown shaded in the section (top) and plan. Key: RS, roof slabs; K, kerb stones.*

Other astronomical structures

Much of the evidence on megalithic astronomy that we have looked at so far has been based on orientations defined by standing stones, though of course some of it, such as the eclipse prediction theories, is of quite a different nature. In this section we shall group together a number of other, rather disparate structures which are associated with megaliths, and for which an astronomical interpretation has been offered.

One of the more curious is Newgrange, one of a group of burial mounds in the Boyne Valley, Ireland. The passage is approximately aligned on the position of the rising sun at the winter solstice, as Lockyer had already noted,[163] but immediately above the entrance to the passage is a gap which J. D. Patrick calls the 'roof-box'.[164] It was discovered by the excavator of the site, Professor M. J. O'Kelly, that the sun, shining through this gap, illuminates part of the chamber of the tomb a few minutes after sunrise at midwinter. Patrick invoked the uniqueness of the roof-box and the impressive size of the tomb to support the notion that the orientation was deliberate. However, the sun would illuminate the chamber if its declination lay between $-22°58'$ and $-25°53'$, and the probability of a solstitial orientation in the corresponding range of azimuths (including the summer solstice) is about one in ten or fifteen, which is not really significant enough to excite much interest. Also, presumed movements of the stones have constricted the passage since the tomb was built, and so the range of declinations would have been

108

213

greater still at one time. Nevertheless, if the orientation of Newgrange was deliberate, it is the oldest orientated megalithic structure known (i.e. before 3000 BC).[165]

Newgrange is famous for the decoration of some of its stones, and there was a tradition that one of these carvings, situated in the burial chamber itself, was illuminated by the sun at certain times of the year. This is just one instance of the way in which megalithic art at various sites has been drawn into the debate on megalithic astronomy. Müller has given some notable examples, including what appear to be representations of the sun and moon, but cautions us not to place too much weight on such interpretations.[166] However, there is no harm in mentioning some if his warning is borne in mind. One is a stone in the passage-grave known as the 'Table des Marchands', near Carnac.[167] It is inscribed with 56 marks looking like stalks of barley, and the significance of their number will be familiar from the discussion of Stonehenge. A calendrical interpretation has been offered for an inscribed stone which was found during excavations at the famous prehistoric village of Skara Brae, Orkney.[168]

The cup-and-ring marks, which are one form in which megalithic 'art' often occurs, occasionally appear to have astronomical significance in some sense. This is true, for example, of the stone settings known as 'Four-Posters', which have their greatest concentration in Perthshire. Each of these sites consists of four standing stones, and H. A. W. Burl has shown that any cup-marks are nearly always to be found on the stone to the south-east. In the same way he has noted that the cup-marked stones in the Clava Cairns of Inverness, and other sites, often have a broad preferential orientation.[169] The largest menhir at Temple Wood in Argyll, regarded by Thom as a very important lunar site, is cup-marked.[170] Conceivably, though entirely speculatively, the marks could

109

109 Temple Wood (Kilmartin Stones), Argyll, showing the cup-marked south-west face of the central menhir (i.e. stone F in ill. 80).

represent some sort of writing in which were recorded astronomical events, or else the purpose of the stone on which they were carved.[171] In some cases, though these are rare, they can be interpreted as constellation figures, such as the Plough.[172]

Lockyer had another idea, also astronomical, for the purpose of hollows such as cup-and-ring marks; he thought they held oil, so that the menhirs marking the sightlines could be seen sufficiently easily at night.[173] Furthermore, the use of oil lamps also made it desirable that the astronomer-priests should observe from sheltered places; and Lockyer was convinced that this, rather than entombment, was the purpose of dolmens and passage-graves. He even regarded them as homes for the astronomer-priests, an idea which had already been voiced by Lewis.[174] Finally, he had little doubt that the area at the middle of Stonehenge was originally roofed over to make the solstitial sunrise more impressive.[175]

General arguments on megalithic astronomy

Most of the evidence for or against megalithic astronomy in this chapter has been of a fairly detailed nature, concerning a study in some depth of a small number of individual sites. Now it is time to draw that discussion to a close, and to consider a few more general arguments bearing on the question of whether some megalithic sites had an astronomical function.

Many people have expressed the view that the megalith builders could not possibly have been clever enough or sufficiently knowledgeable to have carried out the sorts of activities which are implied by the hypothesis of megalithic astronomy. For example, John Barber has argued that certain of Professor Thom's theories on megalithic astronomy carry implicitly the notion that the prehistoric astronomers used our scientific method, which, he asserts, is completely alien to the context of the circle-builders.[176] Jacquetta Hawkes likewise argues that the sort of intellectual abilities implied by Hawkins' theories and those of Hoyle fit uneasily with the primitive conditions in which the megalith-builders lived.[177] Yet we are concerned here not with technical skills but with reasoning power, and it must surely be difficult to arrive at a firm opinion on this. Indeed it has often been said that the primitive state of technical skills is no guide to intellectual powers.[178] Hoyle has argued that we should instead see whether suitable conditions existed for intellectual advances, if that is what we think megalithic astronomy represents, and among such conditions he listed a sufficiency of food, leisure, social stability and communications.[179] Another astronomer, D. G. King-Hele, has spoken similarly of the need for the security and leisure which an economic surplus can provide.[180] He emphasized that language was not one of the essentials, interestingly enough, and gave other very general reasons for supposing that people in megalithic times were probably capable of much of the astronomy with which they are credited.

Then again, how primitive were the technical skills of the megalith builders? There is plenty of spectacular evidence for skill in engineering which still strikes us as astonishing, such as Silbury Hill in Wiltshire, and examples of megaliths weighing a hundred tonnes or more.[181] Indeed we would surely have difficulty in crediting such accomplishments to primitive people were the evidence for them less incontrovertible. The technological background is very relevant in a general way to the economy of even a primitive society, as archaeologists themselves are well aware, and we have previously mentioned the idea that this in turn is possibly related to that society's potential for intellectual accomplishment.

Another point to be made is that, if this general objection to megalithic astronomy has any force at all, it must surely depend on precisely which aspect of the astronomical theories is contemplated. Thus the setting up of a rough marker, a pair of stones for instance, for the position of sunrise at midsummer, is a task which requires no intellectual gift beyond simple powers of observation and the recognition that the phenomenon repeats itself from year to year.[182] Even the simple lunar alignments require little more, though the longer periods involved may raise practical problems, which have been mentioned in chapter 5.

At a somewhat different level, controversy has arisen because of conflicts between the astronomical interpretations of some sites and those which archaeologists had come to accept on the basis of quite different evidence. Thus Stonehenge was for long regarded as a kind of sanctuary, which seems at first sight to be in sharp contrast with the astronomical interpretation as it is usually expressed and understood. Without doubt, certain inadequacies of the astronomical interpretation lie partly at the root of this contradiction, for there are many features of such a monument which a narrowly astronomical theory just does not explain. If we set out to predict eclipses on the method suggested, for example, by Hoyle, we might indeed build something on the lines of Stonehenge I,[183] but we would not then need the structures of Stonehenge III at all, and even if we did we would not have to make them so tall and put lintels on top.[184]

102, 103

In general terms megalithic sites are much more elaborate than the simple astronomical hypothesis demands. An alignment such as the Nine Maidens in Cornwall, for example, goes far beyond practical astronomical requirements, as Thom himself recognized.[185] Also the astronomical theories have nothing to say about the association of megalithic sites with burials. On the other hand these are not comprehensive objections to all astronomical theories of megalithic sites. Thus, while it is true that many sites have structures which seem quite superfluous to a narrow astronomical function, there are others which exhibit little more than the basic minimum needed to define a sightline. In any case, these arguments may simply tell us that the motivation behind megalithic astronomy was not purely practical. We shall return to this question in the following chapter.

92, 97, 100, 108

59, 68, 73-5, 85, 86

A related argument in favour of the astronomical interpretation of straightforward alignments was expressed by Somerville.[186] He supposed first that any alignment must have been erected purposefully, and that its purpose must have had something to do with its orientation. Next, arguing that the purpose was to direct the eye along the line of stones, and noting that this indicates nothing noteworthy on the ground in some cases, Somerville concluded that the purpose must have been the indication of something in the sky. Attractive as this argument is, it does depend on certain assumptions, and can hardly be regarded as proof of the astronomical theory. Nevertheless, true alignments are the most directional of all megalithic sites, and one might surmise that it should be in a study of these that the evidence for or against megalithic astronomy should be most clear-cut.

One of the miscellaneous arguments occasionally raised in connection with the astronomical theory concerns the *numbers* of supposed astronomical orientations. For instance, if we study the orientations at Stonehenge listed by Hawkins,[187] we find that there is often more than one orientation for a single astronomical phenomenon, and this duplication might seem puzzling if the purpose of the orientations is thought to have been practical. However, Hoyle accounted for this by noting that it safeguarded against interference by the weather.[188] Note that this explanation makes most sense, in the case of a *single* site, like Stonehenge, if we accept Hoyle's offset theory for the errors of the orientations. For example, suppose we consider solstitial orientations. On Hoyle's theory, several orientations might have been erected to indicate the position of sunrise at various dates close to the solstice, and there would be an improved chance of having at least one clear day. There would be no point in having several orientations pointing to the *exact* solstitial sunrise position, since these would all have to be used on the *same* day.

The weather has also been invoked to explain why there are so many supposedly astronomical sites, even within quite small regions, all devoted to the observation of the same phenomenon.[189] However, this would perhaps be more convincing if Lockyer had not used the bad weather in winter as an explanation of why he found so *few* sites for the winter solstice![190] This example illustrates that such arguments may be so flexible that they should be ignored.

Origins, derivatives and parallels

If we are prepared to accept that some megalithic sites were deliberately orientated in an astronomically meaningful way, it is natural to enquire into the chronological development of this custom. Are its origins, for instance, to be sought entirely within the period during which these megalithic sites were erected? Did the astronomical knowledge acquired in this long period, however meagre it might have been, survive until historical times? Aside from possible derivatives of megalithic astronomy, one may also ask whether parallels, in societies essentially unconnected with those we are interested in, are a legitimate source of supplementary evidence for the debate on megalithic astronomy. These two aspects of the subject will concern us in this section.

There are few claims for prehistoric astronomy at times before the period of the megaliths, and perhaps the best known are those of Alexander Marshack.[191] The evidence consists of sequences of incised marks on palaeolithic bone and other material, and they are considered by Marshack to be essentially calendrical. However, this is so far in advance of the late Neolithic that, despite its West European occurrence, it does not make the possibility of megalithic astronomy any more or less plausible.

Early writers, most notably Lockyer and Somerville, took a strongly diffusionist view of the origins of megalithic astronomy.[192] In this they were presumably much influenced by diffusionist ideas in mainstream archaeology itself. Now that such ideas seem untenable, at least in anything like their original form, most modern writers, if they take the claims for megalithic astronomy seriously at all, incline to the view that it originated in north-west Europe.[193] Thus the search for the origins of megalithic astronomy does not lead us to any helpful new evidence.

What can be said about derivatives of megalithic astronomy? We do in fact begin to find evidence for some kind of astronomical activity in north-west Europe in the centuries following the close of the megalith-building period, though it is comparatively rudimentary. It takes the form of rock pictures which may depict the sun, the moon, and certain constellations. For instance, there is a Swedish example, dated to between 1000 and 500 BC, which may be a representation of the familiar W-shape of the constellation Cassiopeia.[194]

Despite the fact that there may well have been contacts between north-west Europe and the literate civilizations in the East Mediterranean, early sources in these civilizations make no mention of astronomical activity in north-west Europe.[195] With the possible exception of the quotation from Diodorus, the first historical references to any form of astronomical activity in these parts refer to the Celtic priesthood known as the Druids. Lockyer and MacKie both quoted passages from classical authors indicating that the Druids of Britain and Gaul were well acquainted with various astronomical matters.[196] Indeed there is evidence that this knowledge was at its most advanced in Britain. Nevertheless, tempting as it is to use such evidence as an argument in favour of the acceptance of some form of megalithic astronomy, this is hardly justified. For instance, there is nothing which even suggests that the Druids were capable of observing with the sort of precision which one of Thom's indicated foresights could yield. And is it really legitimate to cite such evidence at all? For example, if one accepts Druidical astronomy as supplementary evidence for megalithic astronomy, one might as well also take into account the present activity in astronomy in the twentieth century. We are living only about 2000 years after Julius Caesar wrote about the Druids, and he was writing some 2000 years after the major period of megalithic construction. On the other hand, a supposed connection between megalithic and Celtic cultures in Britain would become more credible if one could accept MacKie's conclusion that the geometry employed in the design of megalithic sites was still in use in late pre-Christian times.[197]

When we turn to one of the more particular aspects of megalithic astronomy – the calendar theory – we find more specific derivatives to look for, including the division of the year by the solstices, the equinoxes, and the dates midway between these. Indeed Lockyer did find evidence for this in early Irish agricultural calendars, and Thom also thought that the placing of the Scottish Quarter Days may have been derived from a megalithic calendar.[198]

If these suggestions are to be regarded as evidence at all, it is evidence of a most indirect kind. Nevertheless a marginally more direct link between megaliths and calendars is afforded by instances of seasonal festivals or rites held in historical times in connection with certain megaliths, as at Rollright in Oxfordshire.[199] Lockyer made much of these, and indeed the fact that Stonehenge was still a centre for various activities at midsummer was to him sufficient grounds for assuming that Stonehenge was a solar temple.[200] In his book, Lockyer developed such ideas into a complex web of speculations, and it is usually quite hard to discern what relevance these could have as evidence on the possibility of the astronomical orientation of megalithic sites.

A number of writers have sought to relate the supposed astronomical use of megalithic sites to surviving place-names. For instance, it has been suggested that the name of Newgrange (Co. Meath) may be derived from an Irish name meaning 'cave of the sun'.[201] Also in Ireland, there is a circle on a hill called Beltany Hill, near Raphoe (Co. Donegal), from which a neighbouring hill indicates the position of sunrise at a date midway between the spring equinox and the summer solstice, i.e. the date known as *Beltane* in the Celtic calendar.[202] A more far-fetched example is given by Lockyer, who notes that the Hurlers (Cornwall) stand in a parish named after St Cleer.[203] At the Hurlers there is a sightline for Arcturus, which would have acted as a warning star for a date in Lockyer's calendar, about 8 August. It turns out that the day dedicated to St Claire in France is 12 August.

If the search for derivatives of megalithic astronomy seems to be taking us ever further from anything remotely resembling hard evidence, we may fare better in the search for parallels. Although the existence of orientations in other primitive societies is not direct evidence for their existence in prehistoric Britain, the search is worthwhile for two reasons. First, parallels may serve to make some of the theories of megalithic astronomy more plausible, at least if the examples are well attested. Second, if an archaeologist accepts at least some of the evidence for megalithic astronomy, parallel activity in other societies may furnish him with some ideas on the kind of society in which such activity can flourish.

There is no shortage of monuments for which an astronomical orientation is claimed. A site which is often mentioned as a parallel for structures such as Stonehenge is Sarmizegetusa, near Gradiste in Romania.[204] It is a complicated stone circle which could have been used calendrically, though it was constructed in late pre-Christian times. Then there are the taulas of Minorca,[205] the nuraghes of Sardinia,[206] a number of Egyptian temples,[207] the medicine wheels of North America,[208] certain Japanese temples,[209] and a unique coral trilithon on Tongatapu (Tonga),[210] all of which may exhibit astronomical orientations. Unfortunately the evidence that these orientations are deliberate is not irrefutable, and so to cite these analogies is hardly to argue from a position of strength. However, one historical parallel – the Maya of Central America – may well be a very important one. E. W. MacKie, for example, suggests that their society may be a useful model for the kind of society that existed in north-west Europe during the megalith-building period.[211] Certainly the Maya appear to have incorporated solar and other orientations into their cere-monial sites, as at Uaxactun in Guatemala.[212]

There seem to be specific parallels for the use of natural foresights as calendar markers. In other words, there are places where the relation of the rising or setting positions of the sun to natural features of the horizon has been used to determine the time of the year. The Hopi In-dians of the south-western United States had a practical calendar based on this scheme, which served both ritual and agricultural purposes.[213] A calendar run on similar lines was still in use at the beginning of this century in North Ossetia, in the Caucasus.[214] In the same way the passage of the sun across a mountain horizon can be employed to estimate the time of day, and several examples of such 'mountain clocks' have been found in the Alps by G. Innerebner.[215]

As a final example of a possible parallel for the astronomical orien-tation of megalithic sites, we should mention the roughly east-west orien-tation of Christian churches. It is a useful reminder of the complex links, even at the present day, between orientation, religion, ritual, and burial practices. We should bear it in mind when we come to discuss the mean-ing of megalithic astronomy, which is one of the topics we must take up in the closing chapter.

110

110 A mountain clock in the Alps, after Innerebner and Müller (Müller 1970, 143). The figure, drawn from a photograph, shows the motion of the sun around midday as viewed from a posi-tion near the village of Moos, at the north-east margin of the Dolomites. The time is indicated at the top of the figure, and the sun passes certain peaks at times corresponding to their names. There is another peak to the left called Neunerkofel.

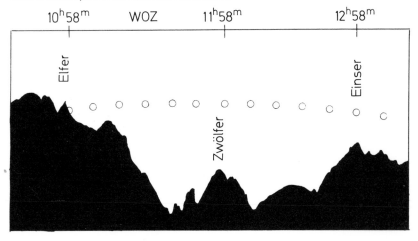

9 The implications

Our review of megalithic astronomy has finally brought us to evidence whose relevance is really quite questionable. If no direct link can be established between the megalith builders and the later Druids, it is quite possible that astronomical expertise in Celtic Britain tells us nothing about the purpose of megalithic sites. We have come rather far, then, from the type of evidence which we originally sought – evidence which would be puzzling if we denied the correctness of the theories of megalithic science. Moreover, we now intend to investigate cautiously some implications of megalithic science, and it seems incorrect to do so on the basis of anything but the most informative evidence. What we shall do first, therefore, is to review the evidence on megalithic science and pick out that which seems least equivocal. As will be seen, the result is a considerably more cautious assessment than is often found. This is the outcome, however, not of an attitude of wanton scepticism, but of a positive desire to base any conclusions on the very best evidence only.

Résumé of the evidence

After a brief preliminary look at the geometry of stone rings, we began by studying the possibility of megalithic units of length, in particular the megalithic yard discovered by Thom. We found satisfactory evidence for something like this in Thom's data on the diameters of megalithic rings, 10 in the sense that the distribution of diameters is significantly non-random in a manner consistent with Thom's quantum hypothesis.

When we examine individual sites such as Avebury, we cannot deny 27 that their design is consistent with the use of a unit of length related to the megalithic yard, but there is nothing compelling about such an explanation. Therefore, though these sites can be interpreted as giving precise information on the value of the megalithic yard, there is no inconsistency with the idea that no such unit was used there. Even the evidence for the megalithic yard in the diameters of megalithic rings cannot be used to support the notion that a very accurate unit was employed, although it might be possible to determine something like the average value of the unit with considerable precision. The statistical information on the rings does not persuasively support the view that the geographical distribution of the supposed unit was very wide; if we divide the rings geographically we find that the statistical significance of the evidence survives almost exclusively in Scottish sites.

Some of the most intriguing evidence is to be found in the stone rows of Carnac. The fact that the positions of the stones at the east end of some of the rows seem linked to their positions at the west end strongly suggests that they were set out with a high regard for accuracy. However, the direct evidence that the stones of the rows were set out at intervals related to the megalithic yard is not good in general.

The case for particular types of megalithic geometry is very weak. While it is possible to provide, as Thom has done, a sequence of designs which provide satisfactory fits for the shapes of almost all megalithic rings which he has surveyed (at least, satisfactory in a qualitative sense), and though these shapes are built up of a few comparatively simple elements, his sequence may not be unique in these respects. All that prevents us from giving more positive support to some of the alternatives, such as Angell's designs or Cowan's, is the fact that they have not been applied to nearly as many sites. If Thom's geometry is not a unique explanation for the design of the megalithic sites, it cannot be assumed that the elements of which it is composed, such as Pythagorean triangles, were used in the design of these monuments. Furthermore, there is no compelling evidence that the lengths used in these constructions were preferentially integral in units of the megalithic yard, except possibly with regard to the diameters.

When we turn to megalithic astronomy the ground becomes firmer again, and indeed, of the three major facets of megalithic science, this is the one for which the evidence speaks most positively. That is not to say that the best-known evidence is necessarily the best. At Stonehenge, for example, as much as we can say, at least as far as orientations are concerned, is that the axis of the monument has a solstitial orientation. If we concede that the Station Stones, by virtue of their geometry, form a group of individual significance, then there is a little evidence for a lunar orientation as well. There is no reason to adopt the suggestion that the latitude of Stonehenge was chosen in order to satisfy any astronomical or geometrical condition. The only direct evidence for eclipse prediction at Stonehenge – the number of holes in the Aubrey circle – loses its force because several other numbers might have functioned equally well, and for other reasons.

The most interesting evidence is to be found when we leave Stonehenge and examine some of the many other megalithic sites in Britain. The results are almost entirely due to Thom. In his first paper there was significant evidence for solstitial orientations, and, in the second paper, evidence for stellar orientations, especially for the bright star Rigel. However, by the time Thom's first book appeared, many of these orientations had been reinterpreted as indications of solar declinations in his sixteen-month calendar. Furthermore, the significance of the stellar orientations depends on whether one includes or rejects those which are doubtful for any reason.

From the data in Thom's first book there is significant evidence for an eight-fold division of the year, although at least some of the agreement may be due to adjustments by Thom in the detailed specification of the calendar. However, of the solar declinations corresponding to the further division into sixteen months, the only very significant evidence is for a group which may instead be interpreted as indicating Rigel. The discussion of stellar lines in Thom's first book adds little to what we learn from his second paper, since the apparently significant grouping of the dates could be due partly to the reinterpretation of some lines using the calendrical hypothesis. In the same book there is some evidence for lunar orientations capable of distinguishing between the 88 upper and lower limbs of the moon. The statistical significance of this result may be uncertain, but at least it is not subject to the doubts which surround the selection criteria used by Thom in choosing lines for inclusion in his first book.

Most of the lines discussed in Thom's early work would not have been capable of giving much precision, compared with sites using natural foresights or, as at Le Grand Menhir Brisé, a large distant artificial foresight. On the other hand, it has not been demonstrated satisfactorily that such lines were actually used to observe the perturbation in the motion of the moon. When we attempt a statistical examination of this theory, at such sites as Temple Wood, Brogar, or Le Grand Menhir 91, 92 Brisé, no definitely significant result emerges. But the evidence at Kint- 97, 98 raw, though neither statistical nor absolutely incontrovertible, gives some support for the notion of very accurate solstitial orientations.

Whenever we mention results of statistical significance in these different contexts, it is reasonable to accept them as providing evidence for astronomical orientations in megalithic sites provided that two other possibilities can be ruled out. One is that the details of the astronomical hypothesis have been adjusted so as to improve the agreement with the declinations indicated by the orientations. The second possibility is that the orientations have been selected in a way which somehow biases the results in favour of the astronomical interpretation.

We have minimized the first difficulty for the solstitial and stellar orientations by considering a range of dates sufficiently wide to encompass most reasonable estimates for the dates of the sites. We considered too the possibility of orientations to *any* point of the solar disc, and so we have covered the full flexibility of the solstitial theory. For stellar orientations there is also the choice of the limiting magnitude, but Thom himself showed that his results were insensitive to small changes in the choice of this. It is difficult to take account of the flexibility in the design of a calendar, however.

It is not easy to eliminate fully the possibility of selection effects. We have tried to minimize these by (a) concentrating on Thom's earliest papers, since there is internal evidence that selection criteria were most strictly applied here; (b) by ignoring lines which Thom later omitted or gave anything less than highest weight; and (c) by ignoring the surviving lines over which some doubt still remains. It is quite likely that we have been over-cautious in this last step.

The cultural meaning of megalithic science

Having sifted through a great deal of evidence on megalithic science and rejected what seems not to be significant, we find that there remains a small but interesting core of results. These are the results which are difficult to reconcile satisfactorily with the view that megalithic sites were *not* laid out using certain designs and that their orientation was *not* determined astronomically. If we accept these results as facts, it is tempting to try to interpret them, either in the sense of trying to find out why megalithic sites were constructed in this way, or else as a clue to the nature of the society in which such monuments were designed.

Just as it is difficult to sort out the evidence into facts and speculations, so in the absence of written evidence it is a hazardous venture to try to interpret even those facts of which we feel reasonably sure. Somerville, for example, though convinced that megalithic sites had been deliberately orientated, did not venture to conclude why it had been done.[1] Unbridled imagination is not helpful for this purpose, but neither is it wise to limit the possibilities too much, lest our conclusions have a look of inevitability which the evidence does not warrant. These difficulties are not unique to megalithic science, and are shared in most areas of prehistory. Nevertheless this could be one reason why the interpretation of megalithic science has generally received much briefer treatment than the raw evidence itself. Another reason is, perhaps, that the collection and analysis of the data, rather than its broader interpretation, lie closest to the interests and skills of those who have developed the subject. On the other hand, it is the interpretation of some of the claimed results of megalithic science, in terms of prehistoric mathematicians, astronomers or (more emotively) 'geniuses', which has probably been responsible for much of its popular appeal.

The interpretation of the megalithic yard is far from clear. As we have seen, there is no incontrovertible evidence for a highly standardized unit with a widespread distribution in space and time, and all that that would imply in terms of the society in which the monuments were built. There are, it is true, many individual sites, including the stone rows of Carnac, where great care was taken with the necessary measurements, but there is no unequivocal evidence that any *accurate* unit used at one site was also used at another. For the generality of sites as much as we have is some evidence for a comparatively imprecise unit, and we are not dealing with the sort of accuracy which led Thom to suppose that there must have been a sort of 'standards bureau' for regulating the size of the unit.[2] The recognized unit might well have been a pace, or something of the kind.

There can be little doubt that some megalithic sites, especially rings of standing stones, were set out to careful geometrical designs. However, there is no satisfactory evidence which allows us to assert with reasonable certainty just which designs were used. For this reason we cannot yet determine how much geometry was known by the people who designed the monuments. They *may* have been aware of comparatively advanced pieces of geometry, such as the properties of some Pythagorean triangles, and yet there is no evidence which is inconsistent with the view that they were not. Likewise we cannot tell whether ellipses were in use; nor can we infer anything about the level of megalithic mathematics from the theory that the perimeters of stone rings were frequently integral, for there is no significant statistical evidence for this, except in the case of Wood- [10] henge.

As there is more evidence for megalithic astronomy, its implications are altogether more interesting, at least potentially. Some of the best evidence is for solstitial markers, and these are quite informative, since it has been mentioned more than once that a solstitial marker is a poor way of determining the time of year. E. W. MacKie considers that very accurate sites, such as Kintraw, could have been used to determine the precise day of the solstice,[3] but the problems caused by variations in refraction may well have been insurmountable. Thus it is unsatisfactory to suppose that a solstitial marker was part of a calendar, or constructed in order to determine the date when some seasonal festival or rite had to be celebrated. A better explanation would be that the orientation played a part – perhaps, as at Stonehenge, a central one – in some rite or festival associated with the solstitial sun, the time of the solstice having been determined in some other way, if it was needed at all.

There seems to be some evidence for at least an eight-fold division of the year, but we cannot be as sure about this as we can about solstitial markers. Even if we accept the calendrical explanation of these lines, the purpose of such a calendar may remain a mystery. The existence of the solstitial lines, which can be construed as being associated with the calendar (though not assisting in its observational regulation), might be taken to suggest that the other calendar lines also served a ritual purpose, as well as being used for the determination of the date when some ceremony was to be enacted. On the other hand, the calendar lines could have had a quite different purpose, which we would regard as more practical, for they could have been used to assist agricultural operations. If this were so, perhaps it is a little more difficult to see why the eight-fold division of the year would be so important, when one might have thought that the times of important agricultural events would have been given greater prominence.

Of the stellar lines, those for Rigel are much the most significant, if we consider lines of highest weight and reject the alternative calendrical interpretation. However, Rigel seems to have no special practical role either as a clock star or as a warning star for sunrise on any calendar date.

By analogy with solstitial orientations, the evidence for orientations to *extreme* declinations of the moon argues against the possibility that these were used for determining the time of the standstills (which in turn is one way of predicting those times of the year at which eclipse danger-periods occur). Whether one regards the prediction of eclipses as a scientific or religious activity, then, there is no satisfactory evidence for it from the orientations themselves. By elimination, these and what stellar lines we have sound statistical evidence for, can perhaps only have served some ritual, superstitious or religious purpose, unless there is some other practical or scientific purpose which we have not considered.

It is not only the targets to which the sites are orientated which suggest that megalithic astronomy was not an activity motivated by what we would call practical needs. The orientation of megalithic tombs and the association of many other astronomically orientated megalithic sites with burials and cremations (of which there is no statistical doubt whatever) strongly underlines the plausibility of a religious purpose. Then there is the curious inappropriateness of the sites for practical needs. The impressive architecture at some sites, for example, does nothing to enhance their usefulness as sightlines; and at many stone circles, where the astronomically important central position goes unmarked, the peripheral 'decoration' – the circle itself – is constructed so solidly that much of it has survived for thousands of years. Again, *if* we are to accept the remarkable geometrical designs in accordance with which some of the sites are supposed to have been built, it becomes clearer still that we are not dealing with astronomy of a simple practical nature alone. According to Thom, Castle Rigg in Cumberland exemplifies this type of site, where the sightlines must be inferred to be of a 'symbolic, mystical' nature.[4] They are clearly sites dedicated to some ritual in which astronomy was an ingredient. The existence of orientations which could have been of no further use after having been set up, such as some involving concealed cup marks, further underlines this view.[5] Finally, if we take seriously the analogy that has been drawn between the society of the megalith-builders and that of the Maya,[6] we come face to face with a civilization which developed a considerable body of astronomical knowledge for what were, ultimately, ritual purposes.[7]

It is dangerous, despite the persuasiveness of the idea of an astronomy linked intimately with religion, to accept this as a comprehensive framework within which all the significant evidence on megalithic astronomy can be understood. Thus it might be that sites such as Castle Rigg represent only one class of megalithic monument with astronomical orientations. Thom has picked Temple Wood in Argyll as representative of another 'functional, scientific' class,[8] and it is entirely possible that the quite different architecture of these sites may imply a quite different purpose, just as in more conventional archaeology.[9] However, the significance of the astronomy at Temple Wood cannot be accepted without question, and this is true generally of all the very accurate orientations to which Thom has drawn attention. Furthermore at several of the supposed very accurate lunar sites, such as Brogar in Orkney, the association with burials is strong, and this suggests again that these were not simply observatories in a narrow sense.[10] Nevertheless Thom maintains that the purpose of the lunar observations was not ritualistic but scientific.[11] Perhaps, of course, this whole argument is misguided. It may be that the distinction between 'scientific' and 'mystic' is one which would have seemed perplexing to the megalith-builders, as it might have done to Kepler.

Whatever we think of the purpose behind megalithic astronomy, the intellectual level it represents does not seem very remarkable. It is true that much more is implied if we accept all or even some of the advanced theories of megalithic astronomy. However, when we look only at the astronomy for which the evidence is comparatively satisfactory, what we see is empirical science rather than theoretical science. The megalithic astronomers knew something of the motions of the sun and (possibly) the moon, but they were primarily observers and, so far as we can tell, had no general theory of the natural phenomena they observed.

The archaeological implications

It will perhaps dismay many readers to find that we have come so close to the end of this book without analysing what seems to be one of the most important arguments in megalithic astronomy: its apparent inconsistency with the orthodox archaeological picture. It has been claimed, for example, that this picture must be changed substantially on account of the recent 'discoveries' in megalithic astronomy. The strength of such claims is something we shall discuss shortly, but this is not the only sort of implication which the study of megalithic astronomy can have for archaeology. For example, the archaeologist Aubrey Burl has used an analysis of orientations to help strengthen a possible link between two types of site: Clava-type cairns and recumbent-stone circles.[12] However, for the practising archaeologist perhaps the foremost potential contribution of megalithic astronomy is in the field of dating, for some of these sites are difficult to date adequately using any of the more conventional methods.[13]

Dating is in theory potentially much more precise with stellar lines than with those to the sun or moon, since the critical lunar and solar declinations vary much more slowly than the declination of a typical star. Thus for a lunar or solar line whose accuracy is poorer than about $\frac{1}{2}°$ nothing can be learned using the method of astronomical dating. Furthermore, in the case of a *single* solar orientation we cannot be sure of the point on the sun's disc to which it is directed, and it was partly for this reason that Hawkins totally rejected the use of astronomy for dating purposes.[14] As we shall see, it is not necessary to be as pessimistic as this on the prospect of dating by solar lines, but first we shall consider stellar lines, since even quite crude stellar orientations can in principle yield a date.

Hawkins gives the impression that stellar orientations cannot be used to date sites because it is so difficult to establish that a stellar line is not just a coincidence. However, we have already seen in our discussion of Thom's second paper that it is possible, at least in principle, to demonstrate statistically the significance of a group of stellar lines. The only factors which make Thom's results doubtful are the fact that the significance of the lines becomes rather poor if we impose very strict criteria on the admissible sightlines, and also the possibility that some of the lines could be interpreted as calendrical or lunar. But if we accept the

87

significance of these lines, we have clear evidence that, as a group, they may be dated at about 2100 BC. It certainly could not be argued that *all* the lines were erected close to this date, for some could still be coincidences. The statistical result was, however, that the majority of them were unlikely to be coincidences, and the above date must thus represent something like a mean date for the majority. Since the evidence in Thom's second paper is probably the most secure evidence for stellar orientations that we have reviewed, this rather guarded result is the best estimate we have for a dating based on such orientations.

Let us come now to the lunar and solar lines, especially those for the solstices, since they are statistically the most significant. Some of them are accurate enough to provide information for dating if it can be shown to which point of the solar disc they were directed. Now if we simply had a concentration of indicated declinations close to the solstitial declination of the sun, it might well be impossible to decide whether this represented a group of lines all directed to the sun's centre but at very different dates, or a group erected at the same date but not specifically to the sun's centre. Thus it is unlikely that even a group date would be of value. However, the real data is actually more informative. For the solstitial lines there is evidence, from the double-peaked distribution of the indicated declinations, that it was one limb or the other which was observed. This removes one of the most important sources of ambiguity which normally makes dating by solar lines so uncertain. The statistical significance of the two peaks has not been investigated, but if we accept their significance it becomes possible to arrive at a group date for the solstitial lines. In fact, from data given by Thom,[15] the date turns out to be about 1700 BC. Although this seems later than the date suggested for the stellar orientations, both dates are subject to considerable uncertainty, some of which is statistical, and it is unlikely that the difference is all that significant.

Even if we are satisfied with the significance of the evidence on which these dates are based, it must be stressed again that they are dates for each group as a whole, rather than for individual sites within each group. It is rather like the situation with the megalithic yard, where statistically significant evidence for its presence in a group of sites does not imply that any one site had a diameter intended to be an integral number of megalithic yards. Likewise, it would require very special circumstances to justify the application of a group date to an individual site within the group. Even if the orientations in a group seemed statistically significant, in most cases a few lines would be expected by chance, and it would normally not be possible to decide which were accidental and which were deliberate. Perhaps at a very unusual site such as Kintraw we see the sort of local peculiarities which *might* justify the astronomical dating of an individual site, but in general it seems not to be possible to arrive at reliable dates for individual sites by astronomical means. Furthermore, a seemingly well-defined group date may be quite consistent with a substantial spread in the ages of individual sites. Again it is like the question of the accuracy of the megalithic yard: although we may

76, 77

97, 98

be able to determine an average value quite precisely, it does not mean that the individual values of the megalithic yard agree to within this precision.

Despite such considerations, there are many individual sites to which dates have been assigned on astronomical grounds. Unfortunately, at almost all of these the significance of the suggested astronomical orientations at the site has not been established. In such circumstances the best we can do is to note that, *if* the astronomical interpretation is correct, then the date of the site would have to fall within the given range. Clearly, such information is a most unreliable source of dates for an archaeologist wishing to arrange a group of sites into chronological sequence. On the strict statistical attitude which we have tried to adopt, the two group dates mentioned above are virtually the only astronomically determined dates in which any confidence can be placed. They imply that the use of astronomical orientations flourished for a period around the beginning of the second millennium BC.

Now it is time to turn to the broader archaeological implications of megalithic science. It is only quite recently that a serious attempt has been made to assess these.[16] Nevertheless it has become almost a cliché to say that the discoveries made in recent years about megalithic science demand a substantial or even radical revision of the archaeologist's standard picture of life and society in the late Stone Age and early Bronze Age.

The first thing to be asked here is whether 'revision' is the correct word, for perhaps it is only necessary to *add* something to the standard picture. After all, as Atkinson said in his critique of Hawkins' book, the development of certain types of science is an aspect of prehistory which has been undervalued frequently by prehistorians.[17] It is not that there is an absence of very obvious evidence on this: the careful design of many megalithic sites is as intriguing and obvious a problem as the question of how such large stones were manoeuvred into place, and yet it has taken the investigations of a non-archaeologist to make this plain. Thus the approach to the past which prehistorians customarily adopt cannot be claimed to be really comprehensive. If, therefore, a theory of megalithic science is developed, it can hardly be regarded as being in conflict with the standard picture when the latter has been drawn with such little regard for the questions which the theory tries to deal with.[18]

Despite this general observation, there does seem to be a widespread feeling among archaeologists that the claims of megalithic science seem incompatible with the standard archaeological picture of megalithic monuments, their purpose, and the societies by which they were built. One of their most serious worries, which has been spelt out clearly by Atkinson, is that the old orthodox picture of the prehistory of north-west Europe, whereby ideas and technology spread by diffusion from the higher cultures of the Middle East, seems very much at odds with the new picture of scientific activity in north-west Europe which was at least as well developed as in the contemporary societies in the East.[19] Another aspect of the problem is a conflict between, on the one hand, scientific activities supposedly carried out uniformly over most of the British Isles and even beyond, and, on the other, the traditional view of a society broken into local tribal units – even though it is realized that the construction of giant works of engineering such as Avebury required something more.[20]

If these are serious dilemmas, there seem to be several possible ways out. One is to note that the 'standard' archaeological picture, which is already quite old, can scarcely be said to exist any more, for it has been considerably shaken by evidence which has nothing directly to do with the subject of this book. Interestingly, one of the casualties has been the old diffusionist theory which lies at one of the principal points of conflict between the conventional picture and the general hypotheses of megalithic science.[21] Thus the standard archaeological model has already changed radically, and it may be as well to postpone the resolution of these conflicts until what Atkinson calls 'this nascent model of prehistory' has matured.[22]

A second possibility is that archaeologists may simply reject the evidence for the scientific theories, or at least its interpretation. The fact that the techniques for investigating megalithic science are quite unfamiliar to most archaeologists, making it difficult for them to acquire a feel for the strengths and weaknesses of different parts of the theories, may tend to encourage this attitude. But it can only be adopted if one ignores a significant body of evidence, and here we exclude the evidence that is simply *compatible* with the theories of megalithic science. We are thinking rather of the evidence that seems incompatible with a sceptical position – the evidence which we have tried to stress in this book.

A third possibility is justified if the theories of megalithic science are regarded as being sufficiently well established to be able to exert some weight in the revision of the archaeological model. Atkinson himself has taken this view,[23] and recently MacKie has shown how a great deal of orthodox archaeological evidence can be reinterpreted in a way that offers no apparent conflict with the claims of megalithic science. Not only is this reinterpretation possible; some aspects of it, according to MacKie, seem 'inescapable'.[24]

The essence of this revision has two features. First, MacKie supposes that the practice and knowledge of megalithic science were restricted to an élite class in society, of whom Lockyer's term 'astronomer-priests' is a quite accurate description. They lived in dwellings set apart from the ordinary people and enjoyed a higher standard of living, and it is they who organized the great projects such as the building of Stonehenge.[25] According to MacKie, there may even be evidence for them in legend.[26] Now Lockyer's term shows that some aspects of this idea are not completely new, but a second assumption in MacKie's theory does represent a considerable departure from usual thinking. It is the idea that this society might have been widespread throughout Britain and beyond (perhaps with a centre of power at Stonehenge),[27] instead of being split into various tribes in scattered localities.

To what extent MacKie's theory reconciles the claims of archaeology and megalithic science is open to question. The idea of a skilled professional élite naturally makes it easier to accept the more elaborate ideas of megalithic science, if that is what is needed. However, there are some problems of dating. The site of Brogar in Orkney, for example, is dated by the Thoms, on the basis of its claimed lunar lines, at no earlier than about 1700 BC.[28] Brogar is regarded by MacKie as the 'temple' for the astronomer-priests whom he considers to have lived at Skara Brae, the famous prehistoric village about 5 miles (c. 8 km) away. Yet Skara Brae is in fact thought to have been largely abandoned before the end of the third millennium BC.[29] One can avoid this difficulty, perhaps, by arguing that Brogar was used in different ways over a long period of time. Nevertheless, all the archaeological sites which MacKie has reinterpreted in detail are dated at earlier than about 2000 BC, while the most reliable lunar sites have been given a group date of about 1600 BC by the Thoms.[30] Of course we have argued that the evidence for accurate lunar lines at sites such as Brogar is not convincing, but if we abandon this interpretation of the sites then the need for an élite of astronomer-priests diminishes.

If the majority of archaeologists are going to be carried by new theories such as MacKie's, it is important to base such theories on evidence that is likely to be significant. Thus Atkinson testifies to the importance which he attaches to probabilistic arguments,[31] and it would surely be irresponsible of archaeologists to be content with less, in cases where such arguments can be constructed and tested. They could scarcely justify changing their view of prehistory on the basis, say, of a group of orientations which might just as easily be distributed at random as deliberately orientated towards declinations corresponding to subtle features of the moon's orbit. If megalithic science is to be used as evidence for changing the model of prehistory, it is first very necessary to distinguish those aspects of the theories which seem to be statistically significant from those which might be as easily wrong as right. This is one reason for the comparatively strict statistical approach adopted in this book.

In general the conclusions in this book are considerably more cautious than those in the sources, such as Thom's books, to which MacKie refers. If the evidence is actually restricted to the conclusions which seem to be significant from a statistical point of view, it is no longer so clear that the radical revision suggested by MacKie is necessary to bring the views of archaeologists into harmony with the conclusions on megalithic science. Perhaps a little grafting on to the orthodox archaeological view of a tribal society is all that is needed. On the other hand, the claims of megalithic science were not the only reasons for MacKie's attempt to construct a new model of the society of the megalith-builders. Whether the other reasons are sufficiently weighty by themselves may be seen from the reactions of other archaeologists to his bold and interesting theories. Some of their responses have been very cool.[32]

Prospects for the future

Interest in megalithic astronomy grew explosively on the publication in 1966 of the book by Hawkins and White on Stonehenge, and the quantity and quality of the evidence on megalithic science was revolutionized by the appearance of Thom's first book just a year later. Since then the developments have been a little more gradual and less vigorous. However, there is no reason yet to regard the subject as exhausted. Not only are there valuable lessons still to be learned by reviewing the evidence that is already available, but there is every prospect that new evidence can be sought and gathered that will go some way towards clarifying conclusions that still seem uncertain. At the end of a book where we have been limited to picking over the data which have already been published, can we see any particular directions in which progress should be made? Does our review of past research have any lessons for the conduct of research in the future?

The theories of megalithic science make many specific predictions at individual sites, and the experience of the excavation at Kintraw indicates that intriguing results can be obtained if these are tested by excavation. In some other situations the astronomical theories imply complicated interrelations between different sites. For example, in cases where sightlines are formed by pairs of sites scattered over the countryside, as on the south-west side of North Uist, the astronomical theory would imply that the positions of the sites were determined from each other. In the case cited, Thom has remarked how the position of the site known as Leacach an Tigh Chloiche must have been determined, and how it in turn dictated the positions of several neighbouring sites.[33] It may be that such predictions are susceptible to testing by more conventional archaeological techniques.

In quite a few investigations the astronomical theory has suggested the possible former existence of features which are now presumed missing, but evidence of these might be established by excavation. For example, if an alignment was set up for the extreme rising or setting position of the sun or moon, one can expect to find evidence of temporary markers that would presumably have been used while the position of the permanent marker was being decided upon.

There are fewer explicit tests of the other aspects of megalithic science – mensuration and geometry. One of the most interesting is a suggestion by A. E. Roy and his colleagues that their proposed elliptical geometry for one of the rings on Machrie Moor, Arran, could be tested by excavation of the foci.[34] Similar tests could be devised for Thom's geometrical theories.

Not all suggestions are as definite as Roy's. If a suggestion is peripheral to a theory, little would be learned by either confirming or refuting it. It is obviously more instructive to test a suggestion if a theory depends crucially on its correctness. The Thoms have stated fairly explicitly, for example, their view that the lunar observatory at Brogar, Orkney, could not work if the obliquity of the ecliptic were significantly different from the value they obtained,[35] and this is something which can be tested in principle by an independent method of dating. A confirmation of the Thoms' dates would undoubtedly be a significant piece of evidence in favour of their theory. Likewise a discrepant date would be most damaging, even if it turned out retrospectively to be possible to reinterpret the monument astronomically using the new date, for it would imply that the original interpretation did not have the inevitability that might have been claimed for it. The whole question of dating is an area where quite critical tests of parts of the astronomical theories could be conducted. The theories, especially in Thom's hands, have yielded fairly definite estimates of dates for many supposed stellar lines and accurate lunar and solar lines. Every new independent date would considerably clarify the question of the significance of such lines.

One interesting question which should be taken up is the archaeological distribution of sites with supposed astronomical orientations. This question has been raised by MacKie, who enquired whether the various types of orientation can be correlated with the way in which the sites can be classified on archaeological grounds.[36] One reason why megalithic science fails to win the respect of many archaeologists is its rather cavalier grouping together of a great diversity of sites under the misleadingly convenient heading 'megalithic'. If it could be shown that traits in the astronomical interpretations are related to the classification that can often be constructed on the grounds of architecture or associated artifacts, a significant step forward would have been taken.

As far as future survey work is concerned, it is useful to consider whether this should concentrate on re-surveying sites which have already been studied, or whether attention should be paid to fresh sites not so far investigated. There is no evidence that careful re-surveying of azimuths and elevations already measured by Thom and others has ever led to anything but quite trivial changes, and re-surveying is unlikely to alter the picture significantly. But it would be useful to have fuller information on the nature of the indications at the sites which they have studied, so that a clearer impression might be had of the selection criteria applied.

In the matter of surveying, then, most is to be gained by the examination of sites which have not yet been studied from the point of view of megalithic science. After all, not even the statistically most reliable results in megalithic astronomy are really secure, for one reason or another, and one of the prime tasks for future research is to continue testing the statistical foundations of megalithic astronomy. To be as foolproof as possible, these tests should be applied to completely new material. The extensive monuments on Dartmoor could be studied with profit, for example, despite the fact that Lockyer has picked them over already; and even in parts of Britain which have been intensively studied by Thom, the coverage is not complete.[37] With the continuing rapid destruction of many sites, the preservation of what remains cannot be relied upon, and so the need for good surveys of surviving sites is urgent. This is a large project, and the measurements must be taken with care, but even those who are amateurs at surveying can make useful contributions – as they have done already.

There is a more subtle sense in which the remaining material must be conserved. It has occasionally been stressed that future research should be more disciplined than it has often been hitherto.[38] This means in particular that every effort should be made to avoid repeating the mistakes of the past, which have rendered many of the results of megalithic science so inconclusive.

There have been three basic flaws in most of the previous research on megalithic astronomy. One of these is the nature of the selection criteria; difficult though it is to make these objective, the effort must be made. It is especially important that they should be decided in advance of the analysis of the surveys, and preferably in advance of the surveys themselves. Enough information is available from existing surveys to indicate the variety of sites which any criteria must be able to cope with.

The second problem has arisen in cases where some adjustment of the theory has been suggested by the data on the megalithic sites themselves, and then the theory has been tested statistically on the same data. This is one factor whieh has made most analyses of the megalithic yard so difficult, and it affects also the statistical study of certain types of astronomical orientation. One answer is that future investigators should decide in advance precisely which theories they will test, and even the manner in which they will be tested. Again, the theories of megalithic science as they already exist are quite rich enough to suggest a wide range of possibilities.

The third mistake of the past, especially in the field of megalithic astronomy, has been the frequent disregard for the possibility that sites can fit a theory quite by chance. In a sense it has been the purpose of this book to review the existing evidence while keeping this danger very much in mind. But this is a difficult task to undertake retrospectively. When all is said and done, some uncertainty still remains in all the conclusions which we have drawn, and no improvement is in prospect until more rigoroùs standards are applied in the selection and analysis of new data.

Unless a more disciplined approach is adopted, it is unlikely that the status of megalithic science as a respectable field of enquiry will improve. We might simply be faced with new theories, probably of greater complexity than those that already exist, but the evidence will be no more secure. On the other hand, if a strict method of enquiry is pursued, we have the much more attractive prospect of removing the vestigial doubt that still attaches to even the best of the theories which already exist.

Encouraging as this prospect is, it brings a rather pessimistic reflection in its wake. If future research is conducted along the lines advocated here, it can be seen that much energy will be expended in collecting new data for the purpose of testing those theories which already exist. If this effort is successful, this new information may also suggest a number of new theories on megalithic science. However, the only reliable way of testing such ideas would be through the acquisition and analysis of yet more new data on sites which had not so far been studied. But there is a limit to the number of surviving sites, and so this process of devising new theories and then testing them on fresh sites cannot continue indefinitely.

If this conclusion is correct, it is likely that we already have before us the broad outlines of as much about megalithic science as we are ever likely to discover, unless somehow a completely new method of analysing megalithic sites can be devised. As Thom has written, 'We do not know the extent of Megalithic man's knowledge of geometry and astronomy. Perhaps we never shall.'[39] What we do know about megalithic science may be less than is often claimed, but yet it is intriguing enough, and it is largely Thom's remarkable contribution which has shown us how to turn some of the speculation and guesswork into fact.

Notes on the text

Chapter 1: The Stonehenge controversy
1 John Aubrey, quoted by Dick (1972, 55).
2 Quoted by Hawkins & White (1966, 39).
3 Hawkins & White 1966, 15.
4 Newham 1966, 458.
5 Hawkins & White 1966, 185.
6 Atkinson 1966b.
7 Atkinson 1966.
8 Piggott 1974, 275.
9 Thom 1955, 275.
10 Thom 1966b, 128; 1967b, 96.
11 Atkinson 1975, 51.
12 Barber 1972, II 126.
13 Piggott 1974, 276.
14 Maxia & Proverbio 1972, 2.

Chapter 2: The study of megalithic science
1 Cf. Smith 1974, 125; Burl 1976, 11. Radiocarbon dates quoted in this book are calibrated dates. For a readable, profusely illustrated general account of the archaeological background, see Hadingham 1975.
2 Thom 1971, 123.
3 Thom 1971, 123; Wood 1978, 63.
4 For a list of those published in or before 1967, see Thom 1967, Table 12.1.
5 For example, Avebury (Thom 1967, 89).
6 See, for example, Atkinson 1966, 213. It would be useful if plans could be supplemented by tables giving the coordinates of plotted stones, as Thom *et al.* have done for their survey of Avebury (Thom, Thom & Foord 1976, 184).
7 For some useful notes on the special aspects of survey technique which arise in the study of megalithic sites, see Thom 1971, 119f.
8 For example Thom 1964, 533.
9 Thom & Thom 1978b, 2f.
10 MacKie 1977, 48.
11 Lockyer 1906, 148.
12 For example Thom 1971, 45.
13 Thom 1977, 4f.
14 Renfrew 1973, 275.
15 Thom 1967, 35.
16 Angell & Barber (1977, 15f.) have published a Fortran computer program for carrying out this task.
17 Thom & Thom 1973, 120f.
18 Personal communication.
19 Lewis 1895, 6f.
20 Windle 1912, 304.
21 Thom 1955, 275. See also note 10, above.
22 For another example, see Roy *et al.* 1963, 61.
23 Barber 1972, II 72f.
24 The ellipse is an oval shape which can be constructed in the following way: insert two pins in a drawing board and cast a loop of thread around them; insert a pencil in the loop and, while keeping the loop taut, move the pencil around the pins; it describes an ellipse. Other ellipses can be drawn by varying the length of the loop or the distance between the pins. The points marked by the pins are called 'foci', and the largest and smallest diameters of the ellipse are referred to as the 'major axis' and 'minor axis' respectively. The ratio of the separation of the foci to the major axis is called the 'eccentricity'. See also Thom 1967, 30f.; Thom & Thom 1978b, 60f.

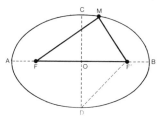

111 The ellipse. AB is the major axis, CD is the minor axis, and F, F' are the foci. The loop MFF' is kept taut by the marker M. If OD, OF' and OB are integral in some unit, then the triangle ODF' is Pythagorean.

25 For some variants, see Thom & Thom 1978b, 18.
26 Thom 1955, 275; 1966, 2.
27 Thom 1967, chapter 7.
28 Actually Thom limits the choice by using dimensions integral in terms of certain units of length. See chapter 4.
29 Thom 1955, 280.
30 For example Müller 1970, 84.
31 Müller 1970, 45f.
32 For another, due to B. R. Hallam, see Hadingham 1975, 130.
33 Cowan 1970.
34 Angell 1976.
35 Angell 1977.

Chapter 3: Mensuration
1 See, for example, Burl 1976, 72 (and 1979, 150 for the application of the same idea to Avebury). Newham has investigated a number of such suggestions (see Hawkins & White 1966, 192), and proposed one of his own (Newham 1972, 20, 26f.).
2 Lewis 1895, 9.
3 Stephan 1916, 216f.
4 Thom 1967, 43.
5 Thom 1955, 280; Hammerton 1971.
6 Thom & Thom 1972, 25. Practical considerations like these are discussed by Burl (1976, 324) and by Thom & Thom (1978b, 42).
7 Kendall 1974, 233. For an updated version of this paper, see Kendall 1977.
8 Atkinson 1967, 93. The spacing of stones around some other circles has been discussed by Thom & Thom (1978b, 22f., 146).
9 Thom 1967, 55.
10 Kendall 1974, 241.
11 Thom 1955, 280, 290f.
12 Barber 1972, II 51.
13 Thom 1955, 275.
14 Patrick 1975, 12.
15 For example Kendall 1974, 231f.
16 For example Thom 1955, Tables 2 and 3.
17 Broadbent 1955.
18 See also Hammersley & Morton 1954, 26.
19 See, for example, Thom 1967, 9.

20 For example, Thom 1967, 42. Broadbent himself (1955b, 292) underlined the importance of knowing which multiple to associate with each measurement.
21 Broadbent 1955, 56.
22 Thom 1955, 282.
23 Broadbent 1956, 33; Kendall 1974, 239f.
24 Broadbent 1956.
25 Kendall 1974.
26 One essential difference between the studies of Broadbent and Kendall is in the choice of the numerical measure. For a technical discussion of their relationship, see Kendall 1974, 263.
27 Freeman 1976.
28 Freeman 1976, 25.
29 Porteous 1973, 23.
30 Kendall 1976, 39; Kent 1976.
31 Thom 1967, 44. In our analysis (below) we omit the measures for Stonehenge, for reasons stated by Thom.
32 Thom 1955, 289f.
33 Stephan 1916, 217.
34 Müller 1970, 37. Müller concludes (p. 38f.) that a significant result emerges (for a unit very close to Thom's megalithic yard) if the diameters are supplemented by the distances between the circles.
35 Müller 1970, 48.
36 Barber 1972.
37 Yet another sample is a group of rings in Cornwall, discussed by Lewis (1895, 9). However, the agreement with the unit of 25.1 in. (about 0.638 m), which bears no obvious relation to the megalithic yard, is so good as to invite suspicion.
38 Based on Burl 1979, 125.
39 Kendall 1974, 233.
40 Hypotheses of this general type were considered briefly by Thom (1955, 283).
41 Kendall 1974, 250f.
42 Hogg 1974.
43 Thom 1966b, 121.
44 Broadbent 1955, 47.
45 Thom 1967, 42.
46 Freeman's paper (1976, 24) contains a useful summary of the results of Broadbent's and Kendall's tests applied to various subgroups. Parallel investigations have also been carried out by J. D. Patrick (unpublished).
47 Kendall 1974, 254.
48 Thom 1955, 282; Kendall 1974, 255; Freeman 1976, 24.
49 Thom 1961, 83. Recently Thom has concluded that the use of the megalithic yard extended as far north as Shetland (Thom & Merritt 1978, 60), but the supporting evidence is not of proven statistical significance.
50 Burl & Freeman 1977.
51 Thom 1967, Table 5.1. Likewise Thom's own measure of the deviations does not vary much from sample to sample (e.g. Thom 1967, 41).
52 Kendall 1974, 253.
53 Also Kendall's formula for σ (Kendall 1974, 253), which is a measure of the deviations, depends weakly (in fact, logarithmically) on the parameters of the sample, when the unit is fixed.
54 Burl 1976, 121, 318; 1979, 67.
55 Thom 1967, 36.

56 MacKie 1977, 39.
57 Thom 1955, 289; 1967, 54. Thom's basic contention is that the megalithic yard was the unit used for radii, and so the principal unit for the diameters was 2 my.
58 Thom 1967, 32. See also Thom & Thom 1978b, 27f.
59 Thom 1967, 45f.
60 A similar comment applies to an alternative investigation of the perimeter hypothesis by Behrend (1976, 44), though in other respects his method is appealing.
61 Atkinson 1979, 131; Thom & Thom 1978b, 144.
62 Atkinson 1979c, S99.
63 Thom & Thom 1978b, 22.
64 Thom 1967, 75f.
65 Thom 1968; Thom & Thom 1978b, chapter 5.
66 Thom 1962, 249f.; 1978.
67 Thom & Thom 1972.
68 Atkinson 1975, 46f.; 1979c, S99f.
69 This can be demonstrated explicitly for a version of Kendall's test in which the quantum is specified in advance.
70 Thom & Thom 1972, 13; 1974, 36. Even this much choice makes Broadbent's first test invalid; but cf. Thom & Thom 1978b, 86.
71 Patrick & Butler 1974, 34. The Thoms attribute the failure of the test used by Patrick & Butler to disturbances in the rows (Thom & Thom 1978b, 69).
72 Thom & Thom 1974.
73 Wood 1978, 131f.
74 Wood 1978, Table 7.2.
75 Freeman 1976, 31.
76 Thom 1967, 33.
77 MacKie 1977, 53f.
78 Crawford 1976, 42.
79 Burl 1979, 169.
80 See MacKie 1977, 60.
81 Thom 1967, 43.
82 According to Freeman (1976, 32) about 7 per cent of circles may be associated with the wrong multiple.
83 This distinction, already noted by Childe (1955, 293), is clearly expressed by Kendall (1974, 260) and is demonstrated in a simple artificial quantum situation by Porteous (1973, 24).
84 Kendall 1974, 258.
85 Thom & Thom 1973, 121.
86 Thom 1967, 90; Thom, Thom & Thom 1974, 83; Thom, Thom & Foord 1976, 190.
87 Hammerton 1971. See also Burl 1979, 97.
88 Porteous 1973, 22.
89 Lewis (1895, 15) suggested that the length of a spear could have been used, and this is controlled to some extent by the size of the human frame.
90 Kendall 1974, 258.
91 Thom 1974, 149.
92 See, for example, Renfrew 1973, 250f.

Chapter 4: Megalithic geometry
1 Thom 1962, 249.
2 Thom 1967, 38, 39.
3 Thom 1966, 2; 1967, 72, 77. The sides of the relevant triangle are *half* the major and minor

axes and the focal separation; hence the unit of one *quarter* of the megalithic yard.

4 Thom 1967, 72. Among the 'less-definite' ellipses in this list is one at Leacach an Tigh Chloiche (Unival), N. Uist, but recent research has shown how unsatisfactory the geometrical interpretation is in this case (Moir, Ruggles & Norris 1980).

5 Thom 1966, 4.

6 Thom, Thom & Thom 1974, 83. For other remarks on the geometry of Stonehenge, see MacKie 1977, 114f.

7 Thom 1967, 89f.; Thom, Thom & Foord 1976, which contains a very useful list of the positions of the stones.

8 Thom & Thom 1973b, 172. For another example, in Shetland, see Thom & Merritt 1978, 55.

9 MacKie 1977b, 68f. For a different construction see Cowan 1970, 323.

10 Thom 1969, 77; Thom & Thom 1978b, chapter 5.

11 Hadingham 1975, 151.

12 Thom 1971, 96.

13 Thom & Thom 1972, 15.

14 Thom & Thom 1977, 490.

15 Thom & Thom 1972b, 157f.

16 Thom & Thom 1974b, 40, 43; 1978b, 75.

17 MacKie 1977, 65f.

18 Wood 1978, 42f.

19 Thom 1967, 88.

20 Thom 1971, 101.

21 Burl 1979, 180f.

22 Stephan 1916, 216f.

23 Atkinson 1975, 48.

24 Hoyle 1977, 35.

25 Thom 1967, 157.

26 Thom 1967, 164f.

27 Thom 1967, 3.

28 Thom 1967, 91; Thom & Thom 1978b, 17.

29 Thom 1967, 164.

30 Thom 1967, 75f.

31 Thom 1967, 68, 69, 75.

32 Wood 1978, 51.

33 Thom 1961b, 293.

34 Thom 1967, 164.

35 Thom 1967, 158.

36 Thom 1971, 91f.

37 Thom & Thom 1972b, 159f.; 1974, 45f.

38 Hoyle 1966, 272f.

39 See Lysaght 1974, 232.

40 Thompson 1976, 35.

41 Angell 1978, 256f.

42 Hawkins & White 1966, 192f.

43 Burl 1976, 45; 1979, 171f.

44 Burl 1976, 227f.

45 Burl 1976, 74; for another possibility at one site see Burl 1976, 271.

46 Hogg 1974, 267.

47 Barber 1972, II 47.

48 Thom 1967, 86; 1966b, 125f.

49 Thom, Thom & Foord 1976, 188.

50 Thom & Thom 1971, 155.

51 Patrick & Butler 1974, 31. This does not imply that the Thoms' theory for the use of the site as an extrapolating device is incorrect (see Thom & Thom 1978b, 97).

52 Angell 1976.

53 Hammersley 1955, 292.

54 Patrick & Wallace 1979; Patrick 1979b.

55 Barber 1972, II 57.

56 MacKie 1977, 44f.

57 Thom 1961, 87.

58 Thom 1955, 280.

59 Roy *et al.* 1963, 61.

60 For example Thom 1967, 87.

61 Thom 1967, 82.

62 This result was obtained in the following manner. Let N random numbers be chosen, and find for each number its signed deviation from the nearest multiple of the unit 2δ. Let X be the arithmetically smallest of the N deviations. Then it is easy to show that the variance of X is $2\delta^2/(N+1)(N+2)$. Now Thom found (1967, 82) that the mean square deviation was approximately $0.100 \, \delta^2$, which corresponds to $N = 3$ approximately. A similar result is obtained for a more recent sample listed in Thom & Thom 1978b, 25f.

63 Thom 1967, 72. We suppose that the smallest axis is meant to be integral in the largest unit in which the focal distance and longest axis are integral.

64 Hogg (1968, 208) has made a somewhat similar point.

65 Thom & Thom 1978b, 26.

66 Thom 1967, 70.

67 Roy *et al.* 1963, 66.

68 Thom & Thom 1978b, 25.

69 Thom 1967, 89f.; Thom, Thom & Foord 1976, 185f.

70 Angell & Barber 1977, 14; Freeman 1977, 134f.

71 Cf. Thom & Thom 1978b, 42, 62.

72 Dibble 1976, 141.

73 Thom 1955, 280.

74 Thom 1967, 89.

75 Müller 1970, 111.

76 Burl 1976, 45f. The Thoms prefer to think of the smaller circles as being older (Thom & Thom 1978b, 177f.).

77 Thom 1969, 81.

Chapter 5: The astronomical hypothesis

1 Hawkins & White (1966, 37f., 134f.) give an interesting history of early ideas on Stonehenge. Many interesting comments on the history of megalithic astronomy in general will be found in the book by Lancaster Brown (1976), and Michell's history of the subject (1977) is interesting and entertaining, if over-enthusiastic.

2 A relevant page from Wood's book is reproduced by Michell (1977, 8).

3 See Hawkins & White 1966, 41.

4 Lysaght 1974, 223, 232. Actually Stukeley had referred to the two inner circles at Avebury as lunar and solar temples as early as 1721 (Burl 1979, 48).

5 See Lockyer 1906, 35.

6 Lewis 1895, 3.

7 See Lockyer 1906, 97.

8 Lockyer first published many of his results in articles in *Nature*, but these were later collected (often with few textual changes), together with fresh material, in a book (1906). Information on many more sites was added for the 1909 edition.

9 Lockyer 1906, 294.
10 Lockyer 1906, 43.
11 Much of the continental work is reviewed by Müller (1936, 1970), and I am grateful to Professor H. A. Brück for drawing the earlier reference to my attention. See also Baity 1973, 391, 396, 423f.
12 See Michell 1977, 40.
13 Somerville 1912, 29.
14 See Hadingham 1975, 104.
15 Nevertheless, useful statistical discussions of continental sites are to be found in Müller 1936.
16 Atkinson 1974, 126. But see Burl 1976, 127, and Wood 1978, 98.
17 These definitions are not universally used. See, for example, MacKie 1977, 96.
18 Astronomers sometimes adopt a different convention for measuring azimuth.
19 Somerville 1912, 30, 36.
20 Thom 1966b, 127.
21 For example, Thom 1967; 1971; Müller 1970, 9f.; Krupp 1979, 8f. For a simple working model of some of the phenomena, see Gingerich 1977, 67. Hoyle (1977, 54f.) is especially good on eclipses.
22 Hoyle 1966, 264.
23 This relation is tabulated by Thom (1967, 18) and, for certain declinations, by Penny & Wood (1973, 66f.). A graphical representation under idealized conditions is given by Lockyer (1906), 113).
24 The variations in the past can be determined using modern observations and some theory. De Sitter's formula (see Thom 1971, 15) should be sufficiently reliable for the dates considered for megalithic sites. According to Dr A. T. Sinclair (private communication) the error is unlikely to exceed 0.4' in 2000 **BC**.
25 The apparent diameters of the sun and the full moon are both about 30 minutes of arc (30'). The unaided eye cannot normally distinguish two objects if they are separated by less than about 1'. The obliquity is currently decreasing at a rate of approximately 47" per century, where 60" = 1'.
26 Thom 1954, 401.
27 Hoyle 1972, 38; Atkinson 1979c, S101.
28 Hoyle 1966, 271f.
29 Somerville 1927, 33.
30 Thom 1954, 396. It may be shown that both definitions lead to almost exactly the same values for the declination of the sun at the equinoxes. In practice Thom's may be superior, as it is not necessary to determine the date of the solstice on his definition, and this can be difficult.
31 MacKie 1977, 76, where a particularly clear discussion of solstitial orientations will be found.
32 Hoyle 1966, 270f. Curiously, Lockyer (1909, 428f.) noted that solstitial orientations tend to deviate from the ideal direction in a manner consistent with this idea. His interpretation, however, was that such orientations gave a 'warning' of the approaching solstice.
33 An example is Spence's, published in 1894 (see Hawkins 1974, 160).
34 Somerville 1923, 198.
35 Thom 1966, 30f.

36 Thom 1967, 116.
37 Thom 1967, 117.
38 Thom 1971, 114.
39 This cycle, with a period of about 18.61 years, has nothing to do with the Metonic Cycle, although the two have been confused by some writers. The point is clearly explained by Hawkins (1968, 61) and by Wood (1978, 74).
40 Thom 1971, 18.
41 Barber 1973, 37.
42 Thom 1971, 23. It was apparently known in Norway by the 4th century **BC** (see Müller 1936, 70).
43 Another possibility is the declination of the moon when it crosses the right- or left-hand margin of ill. 35 at a time when its orbit is in either configuration 2 or 4. An orientation indicating one of these declinations would be of no known practical value (Hoyle 1966, 275f.), and they are mentioned here only because Hawkins considered them in his study of Stonehenge (Hawkins & White 1966, 169).
44 Actually Δ itself varies slightly (Thom & Thom 1978, 174; 1978b, 9; corrected by Morrison 1980).
45 The times of year at which extremes of the perturbation may occur are discussed by Thom & Thom 1975, 107.
46 It has been stated (Thom 1971, 23; Krupp 1979, 32) that this effect could be detected only at the standstills, but this is not so.
47 Thom 1971, 50.
48 Thom 1971, 81; Heggie 1972, 47.
49 For the same reason it is not possible to assign an accurate date to a supposed lunar orientation on astronomical grounds (Thom & Thom 1975, 113).
50 The conditions under which moonrise and moonset are affected by daylight are discussed by Thom & Thom 1975, 108; and by Moir 1979, 125f.
51 Wood's discussion of this question (Wood 1978, 112) is faulty. I am grateful to Mr T. McCreery for pointing out to me its possible significance. The remarks in the text refer to the case in which the observed limb of the moon rises or sets parallel to a hillslope on the horizon. For the case in which the moon rises or sets over a level horizon, as at Stonehenge, see Moir 1979, 126.
52 For an analogous reason one never observes the moon when the monthly maximum declination occurs precisely at a standstill, but the resulting error is much smaller on average (Thom & Thom 1975, 109; 1978b, 9f.). There is a comparable correction caused by the fact that the monthly maximum declination never quite coincides with a maximum of the perturbation (Morrison 1980).
53 For example Thom 1971, chapter 8.
54 We shall concentrate on Thom's main proposals, but for a number of variants and other methods see Thom 1969b, 24f.; Thom 1971, chapter 8; Thom & Thom 1972b; Thom & Thom 1974, 45f.; Wood & Penny 1975; Thom, Thom & Gorrie 1976, 18; Wood 1978, chapter 7.
55 In what follows we suppose also that A, B, C, lie on a line perpendicular to the line to Z. Further,

the instant when the declination of the moon reaches its maximum is assumed to occur between the moonrises corresponding to B and C, and closer to B.

56 Thom 1971, 101.

57 Heggie 1972, 48. Mr T. McCreery has pointed out to me (private communication) that the error which would result from using a constant value of G could be comparable with the size of the 6-month perturbation.

58 Thom 1971, 100.

59 Reyman 1973, 452. Wood (1978, 184f.) has given a good critique of tidal theories. See also Atkinson 1977.

60 Hawkins 1973, 275.

61 Newton 1974, 5.

62 A nice discussion of this is given by Newton (1974, 18f.).

63 Wood 1978, 70. At a given place, a total solar eclipse occurs once in 360 years on average (Russell *et al.* 1945, 227).

64 Hoyle 1966b, 455.

65 Moir 1979, 125f.

66 Hawkins & White 1966, 176.

67 Newham 1966, 457; Colton & Martin 1967, 478.

68 Thom 1969b, 26f.; 1971, 19; Thom & Thom 1978b, 131.

69 Hawkins 1964, 1259f. A variant is mentioned elsewhere by Hawkins (1968, 59f.).

70 Hoyle 1966b, 454. In his description he includes one marker for each of the two nodes, but one nodal marker is sufficient.

71 Hawkins & White 1966, 183f., where a variant is also described.

72 See, for example, Colton & Martin 1967, 478.

73 Hawkins & White 1966, 184.

74 More precisely, without an *umbral* eclipse occurring. Incidentally this appears to be the essential point underlying a criticism by Colton & Martin (1969). An earlier critique of Hawkins' scheme (Colton & Martin 1967) was partly based on a misunderstanding (Hawkins 1967).

75 Hoyle 1977, chapter 5.

76 For a discussion of possible difficulties involved in acquiring this information observationally, see Thom 1971, 24f.

77 Cf. Aaboe 1974, 35.

78 Atkinson 1974, 130; 1975, 51.

79 MacKie 1977, 228. Nevertheless the Thoms prefer to suppose that some form of writing existed (Thom & Thom 1978b, 181).

80 Sadler 1966, 1120. Our example is different from Sadler's, however.

81 Hawkins & White 1966, 138.

82 Wood 1978, 57.

83 Barber 1973, 34.

84 Declinations of the bright stars for a useful range of dates are tabulated by Hawkins (1968, 65f.). Graphical displays are given by Lockyer (1906, 115f.) and by Barber (1973, 29).

85 Hawkins 1965, 128.

86 Cooke *et al.* 1977, 130. Precisely what is meant by a 'first magnitude star' is not stated in this paper.

87 Somerville 1912, 26.

88 Thom 1967, 101.

89 Smiley 1973, 453.

90 Lockyer 1909, 475. For selection of stars on mythological grounds, see Müller 1936, 59.

91 Thom 1967, 2.

92 See, for example, Newton 1974, 12.

93 Lockyer 1906, 300f. The subsequent discussion in the present text relates to the position of Capella as it was in about 2000 **BC**, viewed from Britain.

94 Thom 1967, 105.

95 See, for example, Somerville 1912, 35f. For determining the approximate date at which the helical rising of a particular bright star occurs, a diagram given by Thom (1967, 105) is useful.

96 Thom 1967, 107.

97 Aaboe 1974, 21f.

Chapter 6: Megalithic orientations

1 Fleming 1975; Burl 1976, 52.

2 Lockyer 1905, 298.

3 Somerville 1923, 194.

4 Thom 1955, 283; 1966, 8; 1967, 94, 97.

5 Lewis 1895, 11.

6 See, for example, Somerville 1912, 45.

7 Thom 1967, 158.

8 Thom 1966, 9, 20; 1971, 52f.

9 Thom & Thom 1971.

10 Thom 1967, 157f.; Müller 1970, 101f.

11 Lockyer 1906, 286.

12 Lockyer 1906, 156.

13 Lockyer 1906, 153.

14 Burl 1976, 110.

15 Lockyer 1909, 359. For a plan of this structure see Thom & Thom 1976, 194.

16 Burl 1976, 110.

17 For example, Ballochroy, Argyll (Thom 1967, 142).

18 For example Cooke *et al.* 1977, 116.

19 Thom 1966, 25; 1967, 145f.

20 Thom 1966, 19.

21 Burl 1976, 229. The site is illustrated by Windle (1912, Fig. 9).

22 See, for example, Burl 1976, 251; Atkinson 1979, 173.

23 MacKie 1977, 92f.

24 For example, Burl 1971, 38.

25 Thom, Thom, Merritt & Merritt 1973, 451.

26 Burl 1979, 154, 214f.

27 Thom 1961b, 295.

28 Lockyer 1906, 274.

29 Thom 1966, 1, 19; 1967, 101.

30 Thom 1967, 129.

31 Thom 1961b, 295.

32 Thom 1967, 99, 151. In fact the centre of the ring lies on this line.

33 Thom 1967, 142.

34 Müller 1970, 104f. See also Lancaster Brown 1976, 228; Burl 1979, 95.

35 Müller 1970, 78f.

36 Somerville 1923, 217f.

37 Patrick 1974.

38 Burl 1979, 137, 158, 219, 255.

39 For example, Lockyer 1906, 137.

40 Lockyer 1906, 173f.

41 Thom 1966, 20. For a list of lines formed by pairs of circles see Thom & Thom 1978b, 28f.

42 Lockyer 1906, 104.
43 Müller 1970, 113.
44 For example at Brogar, Orkney (Lockyer 1906, 131, where he refers to the site as Stenness).
45 See Lockyer 1909, 485.
46 Müller 1970, 30f.
47 Stephan 1916, 218. A photograph will be found in Müller 1936, Fig. 17.
48 Penny & Wood 1973. According to Lockyer (1906, 155) the cursus near Stonehenge was itself orientated to the place where the Pleiades rose.
49 Thom & Thom 1978, 171.
50 Thom 1971, 27.
51 Thom & Foord 1977, 199.
52 Thom 1966, 24, 30, 41. The error in the indication, about 18°, is rather large.
53 Thom & Thom 1971, 157.
54 Thom 1971, 52f.
55 Thom 1967, 98.
56 MacKie 1974, 187.
57 Bailey et al. 1975, 432.
58 Wood & Penny 1975.
59 Thom 1971, 54.
60 See Burl 1976, 196f.
61 Somerville 1912, 47.
62 Thom 1967, 144. See also MacKie (1977, 98) for another possible indicated foresight here.
63 Thom & Thom 1973, 114f.
64 Thom 1967, 133.
65 Thom 1969b, 5.
66 Thom 1966, 55.
67 Müller 1970, 48, 83. See also Müller 1936, 37.
68 Thom, Thom & Thom 1975, 29. One of them was referred to, perhaps inadvisably, as a 'straight track'. A further such track close to Stonehenge is thought to be recent (Atkinson 1979c, S101).
69 Thom 1966, 20f.
70 Thom 1966, 19.
71 Burl 1976, 162.
72 Thom 1967, 98.
73 Thom 1967, 99.
74 Burl 1976, 76.
75 Atkinson 1975, 44.
76 Piggott 1974, 275; for Stonehenge, see Atkinson 1979, 18.
77 This is the case in the Carnac region (Atkinson 1975, 44).
78 Atkinson 1974, 127; 1975, 44, 50; Lamb 1974.
79 Thom 1971, 12.
80 Cf. Burl 1976, 205f.
81 Burl 1976, 207.
82 Stephan 1916, 218.
83 Thom 1966, 2.
84 Thom 1971, 114.
85 Atkinson 1967, 94; Hoyle 1972, 39.
86 Cf. Thom 1955, 285.
87 Thom 1967, 95.
88 Hawkins & White 1966, 125.
89 See Burl 1976, 306.
90 Hawkins 1963, 308; Atkinson 1979b.
91 Atkinson 1966, 214.
92 Newham 1972, 23.
93 Thom & Thom 1974b, 41.
94 Lockyer 1906, 330; Hoyle 1977, 84 (in the case of lunar lines). It has been suggested that the solstitial rising sun just touched the tip of the Heel Stone at Stonehenge (Hawkins 1963, 307; but see Atkinson 1966, 214).
95 Lockyer 1906, 175; Thom 1967, 94. A fire might also be helpful at a lunar foresight (Penny & Wood 1973, 59).
96 MacKie 1974, 174f.
97 Thom, Thom & Thom 1975, 19.
98 Thom, Thom & Thom 1975, 28f.
99 Thom, Thom & Thom 1974, 89.
100 Thom 1966, 25.
101 Thom 1966, 20.
102 Thom & Thom 1977b, 2.
103 MacKie 1977, 101. It is also probably easier to observe the upper limb when horizon foresights are used (Atkinson 1979c, S101).
104 Thom 1971, 13f.
105 Thom & Thom 1971, 155.
106 Thom 1971, 47f. Similar considerations apply to lunar sightlines for zero perturbation (Thom 1969b, 26).
107 Cf. Kendall 1971, 311; Thom & Thom 1978b, 123.
108 Hawkes 1967, 179.
109 Lamb 1974, 218, 223.
110 Heggie 1972, 47.
111 Moir 1979, 127.
112 Thom 1955, 295.
113 Thom 1971, 54.
114 See Burl 1976, 196; Thom & Thom 1978b, 173.
115 For a discussion from the archaeologist's point of view of many of the sites which are of interest in megalithic astronomy, see Atkinson 1975; Hadingham 1975; Burl 1976; MacKie 1977.
116 See, for example, Piggott 1974, 276.
117 Lockyer 1906, 143.
118 Newall 1967, 98.
119 Hawkins 1968, 49.
120 Hawkins 1965, 130.
121 MacKie 1974, 171. Here MacKie gives an interesting checklist of other questions which may be used to test the credibility of a proposed orientation.
122 MacKie 1974, 185f.
123 Atkinson 1966, 215.
124 Lancaster Brown 1976, 187.
125 Thom 1971, 12, etc.
126 See, for example, MacKie 1977, 99.
127 Hawkins & White 1966, 137.
128 Hoyle 1966, 263.
129 Thom 1971, 45.
130 Hoyle 1966, 271; Atkinson 1975, 42.
131 Thom 1966, 8.
132 Somerville 1912, 27.
133 Atkinson 1966, 215.
134 Patrick 1979.
135 Hawkins & White 1966, 145.
136 Thom 1971, 47.
137 Patrick 1979.
138 Thom 1954, 400.
139 Thom 1961b, 293.
140 Barber 1973, 27.
141 For example, Thom 1967, 158; Müller 1970, 104.
142 Thom & Thom 1971, 150. Thom (1967, 25f.; 1971, chapter 3) has given treatments of refraction

which are particularly relevant to megalithic astronomy.

143 Thom 1969b, 3f.; 1971, 29. Thom himself has made significant contributions to our empirical knowledge of this aspect of refraction.

144 Thom 1967, 159.

145 Thom 1971, 33.

146 See, for example, MacKie 1977, 78f.

147 Patrick 1979, S81.

148 Thom 1974b, 51.

149 Thom 1966, 8.

150 Cf. Thom 1971, 113.

151 Thom 1967, 153. However, scientific theories can often wriggle out of criticism. One can always argue that Ballochroy was set up to study refraction! (See Thom 1967, 153; Hadingham 1975, 109.)

152 Thom, Thom & Thom 1975, 19.

153 Thom, Thom & Thom 1975, 29; Thom & Thom 1978b, 2.

154 See Thom 1969b, 21.

Chapter 7: The statistical evidence

1 Quoted by Hawkins & White 1966, 197.

2 Lockyer 1906.

3 Cf. Hawkins 1973, 22.

4 Hawkins & White 1966, 15.

5 Hawkins 1973, 250. In this book we take the opposite point of view.

6 Atkinson 1966, 215.

7 Barber 1972, II 126. For one or two other ideas, see Somerville 1927, 37.

8 Burl 1976, 142, etc.

9 Patrick 1974b, 142.

10 Penny & Wood 1973, 75f. The discussion by Penny & Wood neglects this possibility.

11 Thom 1966, 20.

12 Thom 1971, 66.

13 Thom 1967, 155.

14 Lockyer 1906, 65. Actually the orientation which Lockyer finally settled on was that to a distant Iron Age fort which lies in almost exactly the same direction as the avenue.

15 Trotter 1927, 44.

16 Lockyer (1906, 66) noticed that his axial line passes close to the middle of the gap between two of the sarsens.

17 Thom 1967b, 95.

18 MacKie 1974, 171.

19 Hawkins 1968, 48f.

20 Barber 1973, 36.

21 MacKie 1977, 98f.

22 Hawkins 1974, 158.

23 Patrick 1974b, 16f.

24 Cooke *et al.* 1977.

25 Morgan & Ruggles 1976.

26 For studying large numbers of orientations, the conversion between azimuth and declination may be performed conveniently on a computer. Suitable simple programs are given by Patrick (1974b, Appendix 3). When low accuracy is sufficient, suitable tables may be employed (Thom 1967, 18). For worked examples of the conversion, see Lockyer 1906, 331; Thom 1971, 42.

27 Thom 1955, 288.

28 Thom 1971, 46; 1974, 152.

29 Hawkins & White 1966, 142f.

30 Atkinson 1966, 213f.

31 Freeman & Elmore 1979, S87.

32 If r out of a total of n orientations lie within a certain distance of an astronomically significant direction, and p is the probability that a random line does so, the probability we calculate is

$$P = 1 - \sum_{s=0}^{r-1} \frac{n!}{s!\,(n-s)!}\, p^s (1-p)^{n-s} \quad (1)$$

If n is large and $\lambda = np$ is small, a useful approximation (Poisson) is

$$P \simeq 1 - \sum_{s=0}^{r-1} e^{-\lambda}\, \frac{\lambda^s}{s!} \quad (2)$$

Finally, if λ is not too small but P is small, an approximation based on the Normal distribution is

$$P \simeq \frac{1}{\sqrt{2\pi}}\, \frac{\exp\left(-\tfrac{1}{2}X^2\right)}{X}, \quad (3)$$

where $\quad X = \dfrac{r - \lambda - \tfrac{1}{2}}{\sqrt{\lambda}}$

It is often not necessary to find a rigorous probability level, and one can often decide informally whether the orientations are statistically significant by calculating X: if it is substantially less than about 2, the statistical significance is too low to be of much interest. Note that λ is the number of astronomical orientations which would be expected by chance, and so X is approximately the excess of the actual number over the expected number, divided by the square root of the expected number.

As an example, suppose that 16 out of a sample of 100 orientations lie within a certain distance of some astronomically significant direction, and that the probability that a random orientation would do so is 0.1. Then the probability that at least 16 out of 100 random orientations would do so is $P \simeq 0.040$, by (1). The approximations (2) and (3) yield, respectively, $P \simeq 0.049$ and $P \simeq 0.051$. Thus the excess of the actual number of astronomical orientations (i.e. 16) over the number expected by chance (i.e. $\lambda = 10$) is only marginally significant. Correspondingly $X \simeq 1.74$.

33 Freeman & Elmore 1979.

34 Hawkins 1974, 159.

35 Hawkins 1968, 49f.

36 Patrick 1974b, 48f.

37 The archaeology of Stonehenge is described in Atkinson's absorbing book (1979).

38 Hawkins 1963; Hawkins & White 1966. See first, however, Atkinson 1966.

39 Hawkins 1968. See Hawkins 1967b, 91.

40 Atkinson 1966, 213.

41 Hawkins 1963, 307.

42 Hawkins & White 1966, 136f.

43 Hawkins 1963, 306.

44 Hawkins & White 1966, 144.

45 Hawkins & White 1966, 63.

46 Hawkins & White 1966, 137f.

47 Hawkins 1963, 307.

48 Hawkins & White 1966, 172.

49 See chapter 5, note 43. The lines are listed in Hawkins & White 1966, 143, 169.

50 Atkinson 1966, 214.
51 Hawkins & White 1966, 137.
52 Atkinson found the probability of obtaining at least 23 lines, since the error in one of the lines actually exceeded the limit of 2° which we have been considering. However, the errors quoted by Hawkins & White (1966, 143, 169) are errors in altitude, and the errors in azimuth (which is what is relevant here) are larger. In fact about three of the 24 lines in Stonehenge I are in error by at least 2°.
53 Hawkins 1965b, 394.
54 Hawkins & White 1966, 137.
55 See note 52 above.
56 Hawkins & White 1966, 142; Atkinson 1966, 214.
57 Atkinson 1966, 214.
58 Hawkins & White 1966, 145f.
59 Atkinson 1966, 215.
60 Hawkins 1974, 161.
61 Hawkins 1973, 77.
62 Hawkins & White 1966, 142, 145.
63 Hoyle 1966, 270f.
64 Hoyle 1977, 71f.
65 Consider the extreme case in which all orientations are paired. Then instead of finding the probability of at least 10 successes out of 12, we should calculate the probability of at least 5 successes out of 6. This is about 0.1. Such an effect was pointed out by Newham (1967, 97), who likened the inclusion of paired lines to the statement that a foot-rule was 2 ft long since it measured 1 ft in each direction!
66 Thom, Thom & Thom 1974, 81; Thom & Thom 1978b, 150.
67 Renfrew 1973, 248.
68 The apparent diameter of the sun or moon is about $\frac{1}{2}$°. To determine the corresponding range of azimuth, we multiply by a factor $|\,dA/d\delta\,|$, which depends mainly on latitude and declination. It is tabulated briefly below for a horizon at zero elevation, with obliquity $\varepsilon = 23.9$°.

Conversion factor $\left|\dfrac{dA}{d\delta}\right|$			
		Latitude	
Declination	50°	55°	60°
$\pm(\varepsilon + i)$ (major standstill)	2.1	2.9	7.3
$\pm\varepsilon$ (solstice)	1.8	2.3	3.1
$\pm(\varepsilon - i)$ (minor standstill)	1.7	2.0	2.5
0 (true equinox)	1.6	1.7	2.0

Here we are concerned with a solstitial line at Stonehenge (latitude about 51°), and so we take the conversion factor to be about 1.9. Hence the disc of the sun at the summer solstice rises over a range of azimuth of about 1°. Taking account of sunset and the winter solstice, the total range of azimuth is about 4°, which is approximately one hundredth of the horizon.
69 Thom 1967b, 95.
70 Thom 1967, 3.

71 Thom 1967, 103.
72 Thom 1967, 151.
73 For example, MacKie 1974, 176.
74 Thom 1954, 403.
75 Thom 1967, 102.
76 Thom 1967, 96.
77 Thom 1971, 36f., 41f.
78 Thom 1955, 283.
79 Thom 1966, 26; 1967, 96.
80 Thom 1967, 4.
81 Thom 1954, 396.
82 Thom 1954, 396.
83 Thom 1967, Table 8.1.
84 Thom 1966, Table 2; 1967, Table 8.1.
85 Thom 1967, Table 8.1.
86 Thom 1966, 10.
87 See Thom 1971, 15.
88 Burl 1976, 11.
89 MacKie 1974, 187.
90 Thom 1954, 396.
91 Thom 1967, Table 8.1.
92 Thom 1966, Table 2.
93 Thom 1954, 398.
94 Thom 1955.
95 Thom 1955, 283.
96 Thom 1967, Table 8.1.
97 Thom 1955, 283.
98 Thom 1967, 132.
99 Thom 1967, Table 8.1.
100 Thom 1955, 275.
101 Thom 1966, 24.
102 Thom 1955, 284.
103 Freeman & Elmore 1979, S94f.
104 Thom 1955, 283. Actually, the ranges were 'arbitrarily' extended by 0.2° on either side (Thom 1955, 285), presumably to account roughly for the precision of the orientations. Furthermore the results are affected (though only slightly) when extinction is taken into account (Thom 1966b, 127).
105 Thom 1955, 286.
106 We have used formula (2), note 32, and have added the results from the eight dates.
107 We have assumed a line is equinoctial if the indicated declination lies within 0.5° of the ideal declination, as Thom did in the paper of 1955. The conversion factor (note 68) for latitude 55° was used, and the probability was calculated from (1), note 32.
108 The ranges are taken from Thom 1967. Table 9.1.
109 Thom 1967, 110.
110 Thom 1967, 114.
111 Lockyer 1909, 470.
112 Thom 1967, 116.
113 Thom 1967, 166.
114 Thom 1967, 103.
115 Childe 1955, 294; Thom 1955, 295.
116 Thom 1966b, 127.
117 Thom 1967, 160f.
118 Thom & Thom 1978b, 5.
119 Thom & Thom 1979, 53.
120 Thom 1955, 288.
121 Thom 1967, 165.
122 Thom 1966, 17, 48f.; 1967, 118f.
123 Thom 1967, 165; 1967b, 95f.
124 Müller 1970, 124. A Normal distribution

(which has only one hump), with zero mean and suitably chosen variance, is a perfectly satisfactory fit to the data in Thom 1966, 49, as adjudged by a Kolmogorov-Smirnov test. This suggests that the humps are not statistically significant.

125 Thom 1967, Table 10.1, where there are 14 lines of 'high quality', according to Thom's classification. For an alternative assessment see Ruggles 1981.

126 Such estimates become particularly rough when we consider indications for the major standstill, because the conversion factor (note 68) depends quite sensitively on the latitude. In all these calculations this has been taken as 55°, but for greater precision the actual distribution of latitudes should be taken into account.

127 Kendall 1955.

128 Hawkins 1968, 49.

129 Thom 1967, 125.

130 Thom & Thom 1971, 149f.

131 Thom & Thom 1971, 148f.; 1978b, 110f.; Thom, Thom & Gorrie 1976.

132 Thom & Thom 1971, 159. There is no direct evidence that the stone was ever upright, though Atkinson's opinion (1979, 42) is that it 'must certainly have stood upright originally'. See Atkinson 1975, 43.

133 Thom & Thom 1974b, 41.

134 Freeman 1975.

135 Atkinson 1975, 43f.

136 Thom & Thom 1974b, 43.

137 I am grateful to Professor M. W. Ovenden for stressing this to me.

138 Thom 1971, 76.

139 Thom 1971, 56.

140 Cf. Thom & Thom 1978b, 169.

141 Thom 1971, 50.

142 Patrick 1979.

143 In Thom's notation: S_4S_5, Q, S_1, and S_2S_3.

144 Thom 1971, 47.

145 Note 32, equation (1).

146 E. Hadingham, quoted by Patrick 1975b, 10.

147 Thom & Thom 1973; 1975, which adds to and, in places, corrects the earlier paper. We have excluded the foresight to the northwest (Thom & Thom 1977c) for the following reason. One of the 'nominal declinations' given there seems inconsistent with the values given in the 1975 paper (p. 104). If we included this foresight, with a consistent nominal declination, it would be necessary to increase the maximum allowable deviation of the indicated declinations from the nominal values. This would make the indications at Brogar appear still less significant.

The possibility of natural *solstitial* foresights at Brogar was mentioned by Lewis (1900, 61), though somewhat vaguely. Another sightline in the vicinity is described in Thom & Thom 1978b, 130.

148 Thom & Thom 1975, 104.

149 Thom & Thom 1975, 113f.; 1978b, 136f.

150 Thom & Thom 1978b, 133f.

151 Atkinson 1975, 42f.

152 Thom & Thom 1975, 105.

153 Thom & Thom 1978. For other analyses along similar lines, but subject to similar criticisms, see Thom 1969b, 17f.; Thom & Thom 1979b and 1980 (where the criteria for choosing lines are explicitly relaxed).

154 Thom 1974b, 50; Thom & Thom 1978b, 169f. The possible foresight referred to is at an azimuth of approximately 328° 03'. For a photograph see MacKie 1977b, 105. A site at Knockstaple (Kintyre) is similarly problematical (Moir 1980, 20).

155 Thom 1971, 47. The difficulty of distinguishing between $\varepsilon + i + s - \Delta$ and $\varepsilon + i + \Delta$ is mentioned in Thom & Thom 1978b, 133.

156 Thom 1971, 78.

157 Cf. Thom 1971, 81.

158 Atkinson 1975, 43, 49.

159 Lockyer 1906. Many further examples are listed in the second edition (Lockyer 1909, 481f.), but we consider only those discussed in the first edition. A most interesting critique of Lockyer's work is given by Müller (1936, 29f., 64f.).

160 Lockyer 1906, 127.

161 Hawkins 1968, 65f. Also Lockyer (1906, 113) gives a useful figure which could be used for performing the next calculation.

162 Lockyer 1909, 436.

163 Lewis 1892, 145.

164 Lockyer 1894, viii.

165 Lewis 1886, 471.

166 Barber 1972; 1973. For a summary of some previous work on these sites see Burl 1976, 222. For the orientation of Scottish recumbent-stone circles, see Burl 1974, 73f.

167 Barber 1972, I 12f.

168 Barber 1973, 31.

169 Freeman & Elmore 1979, S90f.

170 See Barber 1973, 26. For information on a larger sample, see O'Nuallain 1975, 95f., 99.

171 Barber 1973, 36f.

172 Burl 1976, 223.

173 Somerville 1923, 200.

174 Lynch 1976, 130.

175 Müller 1970, 104f.

176 Burl 1972, 44. More recently, Burl has suggested that the orientation of the Scottish recumbent-stone circles may be lunar (Burl 1980).

177 Burl 1976, 138. The relation of the stones in the ring at Brogar to the cardinal directions has been considered by Thom & Thom 1978b, 24.

Chapter 8: Evidence from individual sites

1 Patrick 1979.

2 Thom 1967, 97. Strictly, the two aspects are not entirely independent, since one of the lines listed here was later regarded as the indicator of a natural foresight (Thom 1971, 48f.).

3 Thom 1967, 155.

4 D. D. A. Simpson, quoted by MacKie (1974, 178).

5 Thom 1971, 38. According to MacKie (1974, 178) the view from the menhir is clear, but becomes obscured if one views from the observing position corresponding to the evenings before and after the solstice. This still presents a problem, therefore.

6 Thom 1971, 39.

7 MacKie 1974, 180. This crucial fact is disputed by J. Patrick, but variations in refraction may be partly responsible (pers. comm.).

8 Thom 1971, 39; MacKie 1974, 183.
9 Bibby 1974, 191f.
10 MacKie 1974, 181.
11 Thom 1971, 40.
12 The substance of these last two remarks is due to J. Patrick. See also Hadingham 1975, 113.
13 MacKie 1974, 177.
14 The kist would have been a suitable backsight a few hundred years before the menhirs, which is qualitatively consistent with their probable relative ages (MacKie 1974, 177).
15 Thom 1967, 152; Bailey *et al.* 1975, 432.
16 Thom 1954, 403.
17 MacKie 1974, 177.
18 Thom 1967, 97.
19 Thom 1954, 403.
20 Cf. Dibble 1976, 141.
21 MacKie 1974, 177. E. Hadingham has informed me that a cairn is depicted on an old illustration of the site. Indeed, A. Burl has pointed out that the vestiges of the cairn are still visible if the site is viewed from the south.
22 Thom 1966, 25.
23 Wood (1978, 90) has suggested that the cairn was dismantled before the observations began. But see note 21.
24 MacKie 1974, 177; Bailey *et al.* 1975, 432.
25 Thom 1971, 83.
26 Thom 1967, 158.
27 Thom 1971, 95, 103f.
28 Thom 1971, 99f.
29 Thom 1971, 97.
30 Thom 1971, 95.
31 Thom & Thom 1971, 156.
32 Thom & Thom 1972b, 151.
33 Thom & Thom 1972b, 153f.
34 Thom & Thom 1972b, 161f.; 1978b, 180.
35 Thom 1974, 156.
36 Thom & Thom 1972b, 162. The heights of the stones are discussed in Thom & Thom 1978b, 76f.
37 Thom & Thom 1974, 45f.
38 Atkinson 1975, 50.
39 Wood 1978, 116.
40 Thom 1971, 104.
41 Thom 1971, 55.
42 Thom 1971, 68.
43 Thom 1967b, 96.
44 For a review of earlier astronomical theories on Stonehenge, see an article by W. Teasdale quoted by Lancaster Brown (1976, 114). A detailed account of recent theories will be found in Wood 1978, chapter 9.
45 Lockyer 1906, 325f.
46 Lockyer 1906, 62f.
47 See, for example, Trotter 1927, 45.
48 Lockyer 1905b, 392.
49 Somerville 1912, 49.
50 Hawkins & White 1966, 176; Robinson 1970.
51 See Wood 1978, 6; Michell 1977, 18.
52 Hawkins & White 1966, 163, 168. For an interesting assessment of Newham's contribution see Lancaster Brown 1976, 103f. Some of the lines he found are illustrated in Michell 1977, 68.
53 Lockyer 1906, 93. To be precise, Lockyer discusses the lines from the centre to 91 and 93.
54 Thatcher 1976, 145.

55 Hawkins & White 1966, 173. Hoyle (1972, 32) also thought that the calendrical theory was an insufficient explanation of such lines, since they are too accurate for practical purposes. However, he had in mind agricultural purposes, whereas if a calendar was needed to fix the date of some annual rite or festival, then the accuracy of the sight-lines would not have been excessive.
56 Lockyer 1906, 93.
57 Lockyer 1906, 95. He adduced further evidence for this change at other British sites, and also at some in France (Lockyer 1906, 105f., 144, etc.).
58 Hawkins & White 1966, 72.
59 Atkinson 1976, 143f. For a discussion of the archaeological evidence, see Atkinson 1979, 78f.
60 Atkinson 1979, 33. For other geometrical suggestions about the Stations, see Dibble 1976; Hoyle 1977, 38f.
61 Hawkins & White 1966, 143.
62 Hawkins 1974, 161.
63 The effect of this is ignored by Hoyle in his statistical study of orientations defined by the Stations and the Heel Stone (Hoyle 1977, 46f.).
64 Hawkes 1967, 178.
65 This figure has been arrived at in the following way. For each group of parallel sightlines defined by the Stations we select the line which gives the *minimum* deviation. There are three such groups (one parallel to the longest sides of the rectangle, one parallel to the shortest sides, and one consisting of the diagonal 91/93), and 1.8° is the largest of the three figures arrived at in the first selection. In this way we have chosen the smallest deviation which preserves all the essentially distinct sight-lines identified by Hawkins. Therefore the deviation of 1.8°, which is over three times the apparent diameter of the sun or moon, is as favourable as possible to the astronomical theory.
66 This suggestion, accepted by Hoyle (1977, 42f.), was made independently by Newham and by Hawkins (see Atkinson 1966, 215f.). Both were partly anticipated by Charrière (1961), but he was unable to relate his idea to any lunar sightline at Stonehenge. Actually, Stonehenge lies some 75 miles north of the ideal latitude (Atkinson 1976, 143). The Crucuno rectangle, near Carnac, has related properties (Thom & Thom 1978b, 175).
67 MacKie 1977, 124. Hoyle's opinion, however, was that the diagonal was not a deliberate astronomical sightline (Hoyle 1977, 80). Moir (1979, 127) considers that the alignment of the long sides is a coincidence.
68 Thom, Thom & Thom 1975, 26f.
69 Hawkins & White 1966, 124, 143.
70 Hawkins & White 1966, 149f. See also Hoyle 1972, 24.
71 Hawkins & White 1966, 149.
72 Hawkins & White 1966, 143.
73 Cf. Hoyle 1972, 48f. However, Hoyle did think the lines were significant (Hoyle 1977, 92).
74 Hawkins & White 1966, 196.
75 Hawkins 1974, 161f.
76 See Hawkins & White 1966, 195.
77 Newham 1972, 23f.
78 Thom, Thom & Thom 1974, 88f.

79 Burl 1976, 315; MacKie 1977, 125. For a photograph of one of the lunar foresights, see Krupp 1979, 124.
80 Atkinson 1979c, S101.
81 Lockyer 1905b, 391.
82 Atkinson, quoted by MacKie 1977, 127.
83 Thom, Thom & Thom 1975, 19f.
84 Thom, Thom & Thom 1974, 89.
85 Quoted by Hawkins & White 1966, 43f. For other remarks on the siting of Stonehenge see Lancaster Brown (1976, 116), who quotes Wansey, and Hoyle (1977, 76).
86 Thom, Thom & Thom 1974, 86f.
87 Newham 1972, 15f.
88 Newham's own illustration of what would be expected (Newham 1972, 16) is misleading in this respect.
89 Hoyle 1972, 41f.
90 See Hawkins & White 1966, 121.
91 Whitmell 1901. For other estimates see Lockyer 1906, 62; Hadingham 1975, 83.
92 Lockyer & Penrose 1901, 142.
93 Use of more accurate astronomical data yields a revised date of 1840 BC (Trotter 1927, 50). Michell (1977, 23) gives 1820 BC. The value of the azimuth itself has been revised recently (Atkinson 1978, 50).
94 Lockyer 1906, 78. See Atkinson 1979, 193.
95 Cf. Somerville 1927, 39f. This and the subsequent criticism are clearly discussed by Atkinson (1979, 94f.).
96 Trotter 1927, 44.
97 Somerville 1927, 38.
98 Atkinson 1966b.
99 Hawkins 1974, 158.
100 Somerville 1927, 39.
101 Hawkins & White 1966, 176.
102 Atkinson 1966, 215.
103 Hawkins 1963, 308.
104 Hawkins & White 1966, 183f.; Newham 1966, 458.
105 Hawkins 1973, 24.
106 See Stephan 1916, 242.
107 Stephan 1916, 223.
108 Stephan 1916, 228f.
109 Burl 1976, 374f. Such a study may, however, tell us something about number systems in use in megalithic times (Burl 1979, 124f.).
110 Hoyle 1966, 273; 1972, 33.
111 Hoyle 1972, 52; 1977, 59f.
112 Hoyle 1977, chapter 5.
113 Atkinson 1966, 215.
114 Hawkes 1967, 178. For a possible explanation see Hoyle 1977, 102, 108.
115 Newham 1972, 18, 22.
116 Hoyle 1977, chapter 5.
117 Hawkins & White 1966, 182. Actually, Newham's theory of the Aubrey circle does incorporate an alternative explanation (Newham 1972, 20f.).
118 Sadler 1966, 1120; Colton & Martin 1967, 478.
119 Hawkins & White 1966, 185f.
120 Hoyle 1966, 262.
121 Hoyle 1966, 273.
122 Hawkins & White 1966, 15.
123 Hoyle 1972, 51.

124 Hawkins & White 1966, 180.
125 Hawkes 1967, 177.
126 Hawkins & White 1966, 182.
127 Hawkins & White 1966, 185.
128 Müller 1970, 60; Newham 1967, 96; Colton & Martin 1967, 478; Renfrew 1973, 249.
129 Hawkes 1967, 177.
130 Thom 1961, 92.
131 Thom 1967, 157f.
132 Thom 1971, 91f.
133 Thom 1971, 45.
134 Lockyer 1906, 159.
135 Müller 1970, 102.
136 Lockyer 1906, 139.
137 Thom 1967, 100. For the orientation of the Hurlers, see also Lewis 1895, 3.
138 Stephan 1916, 232. Stephan thought it striking that the number of stones in each circle was almost exactly proportional to its diameter. However, the numbers were *estimated* by Lukis on the assumption that stones were on average 12 ft (about 3.7 m) apart! (Lockyer 1906, 135).
139 Lockyer 1906, 174.
140 Burl 1976, 106.
141 Thom 1967, 100, 101.
142 Stephan 1916, 233.
143 Thom 1967, 100; Lockyer 1906, 293.
144 Hawkins 1965, 128.
145 Cooke et al. 1977, 128f. For a history of the Callanish sites, see Ponting & Ponting 1977.
146 Lockyer 1909, 377; Somerville 1912, 28.
147 Hawkins 1965, 128.
148 Thom 1966, 50; 1971, 68, 69.
149 Hawkins 1973, 240.
150 Somerville 1912, 29; Hawkins 1965, 128; Thom 1967, 98. The accuracy of this line has been challenged by Cooke et al. (1977, 128f.).
151 Somerville 1912, 26. Somerville's list was actually incomplete (Müller 1936, 65).
152 Hawkins 1965, 128; Thom 1967, 124, though on p. 98 the date is given as 1760 BC.
153 Somerville 1912, 29.
154 Hawkins 1965, 128.
155 Thom 1967, 124.
156 Somerville 1912, 31; Thom 1967, 123.
157 See Hawkins & White 1966, 165f. For information on the Hyperboreans see Piggott 1968, 79f.
158 Lockyer 1906, 51f. Hawkins mentioned it in connection with both monuments at different times (Hawkins & White 1966, 165f.; Hawkins 1973, 240). Lewis (1892, 152) and MacKie (1977, 227) linked it with Avebury.
159 Hawkins 1965, 130.
160 Cooke et al. 1977, 131; Freeman & Elmore 1979, S93f.
161 Thom 1967, 164.
162 I am grateful to J. A. Cooke for passing on this remark, due originally to J. H. Rogers.
163 Lockyer 1909, 430.
164 Patrick 1974.
165 MacKie 1977, 118.
166 Müller 1970, 5.
167 Müller 1970, 70, 107f.
168 MacKie 1977, 195.
169 Burl 1971, 38; 1972, 37; 1976, 90f.
170 Thom 1971, 48.

171 Thom 1966, 54f.
172 Hadingham 1975, 147 (quoting Browne); Burl 1976, 134 (quoting Le Rouzic); Lewis 1892, 146.
173 Lockyer 1906, 316f.
174 Lockyer 1906, 41, 254, 317; Lewis 1900, 62.
175 Lockyer 1906, 63.
176 Barber 1973, 37.
177 Hawkes 1967, 180.
178 For example Burl 1976, 86.
179 Hoyle 1966, 274.
180 King-Hele 1974, 274.
181 Atkinson 1974, 128; Daniel 1963, 14.
182 See, for example, Müller 1970, 56f.; Hawkins 1974, 166. Most ancient literate societies with any accomplishment in astronomy appear to have concentrated on cyclic phenomena (Aaboe 1974, 22).
183 Hoyle 1966, 262.
184 In a similar vein, Cunnington pointed out that the fact that the bluestones had been brought from far away indicated that the monument could not have been astronomical in a strictly practical sense (see Lockyer 1906, 90).
185 Thom 1967, 105.
186 Somerville 1912, 25.
187 Hawkins & White 1966, 143.
188 Hoyle 1972, 39f.
189 Thom (1971, 114f.), though he expressly stated that it was not an entirely satisfactory explanation. See also Thom & Thom 1978b, 178.
190 Lockyer 1906, 315.
191 Marshack 1972, 826f.
192 Lockyer 1906, 240f.; Somerville 1912, 51.
193 Cf. Renfrew 1973, 16.
194 Müller 1970, 135.
195 Hawkes 1967, 180.
196 Lockyer 1906, 52; MacKie 1974, 189. See also Piggott 1968, 104f.
197 MacKie 1977, 229.
198 Lockyer 1906, 30; Thom 1954, 399. See also Somerville 1912, 49; Hoyle 1966, 276.
199 Burl 1976, 296.
200 Lockyer 1906, 43.
201 Hicks, quoted by Burl 1976, 241.
202 Somerville 1923, 212.
203 Lockyer 1906, 139f.
204 Burl 1976, 79; Hoyle 1977, 17f., where it is illustrated.
205 See Hawkins & White 1966, 155.
206 Maxia & Proverbio 1973.
207 Lockyer 1894, ch. 8f.; Hawkins 1973, 193f.; 1974, 164f.; Krupp 1979, 201f.
208 Eddy 1974; 1977; and 1979, where other astronomically orientated structures in North America are described.
209 Locker 1906, 3f.
210 Lewis 1974, 137.
211 MacKie 1977, 208f.
212 See, for example, Renfrew 1973, Fig. 54; or Aveni 1979, 64. For a general account of archaeoastronomy in Central America, see Aveni 1979b.
213 McCluskey 1977.
214 Maistrov 1974. See also Müller 1936, 8; 1970, 5f.
215 See Müller 1970, 141f.

Chapter 9: The implications

1 Somerville 1927, 35.
2 Thom 1967, 43.
3 MacKie 1977, 95.
4 Thom 1971, 12.
5 Burl 1976, 199. It is further supported by the consistent orientation of Beaker burials in Britain (see Burl 1979, 232).
6 MacKie 1977, 208f.
7 Coe 1966, 173.
8 Thom 1971, 12.
9 Childe 1955, 294.
10 This is not a conclusive argument, for Drs M. G. Edmunds and D. W. Dewhirst have pointed out to me that the mortal remains of James Lick lie in the base of the telescope which he funded, at Lick Observatory in the U.S.A.! (See Berendzen *et al.* 1976, 96.)
11 Thom 1971, 5.
12 Burl 1972, 43.
13 Atkinson 1975, 42.
14 Hawkins 1968, 48.
15 Thom 1954, 400. Each of the first 13 declinations in Thom's table was associated with the appropriate limb, and then a weighted mean was taken. Thom obtains a slightly earlier date in this paper (p. 404), but based on a different analysis of only part of the data.
16 MacKie 1977.
17 Atkinson 1966, 216.
18 MacKie 1974, 170f.
19 Atkinson 1975, 51.
20 MacKie 1977, 4f.
21 Renfrew 1973, ·17. But see MacKie 1977, 20.
22 Atkinson 1975, 52.
23 Atkinson 1975, 51.
24 MacKie 1977, 148.
25 MacKie 1977, 137f.
26 MacKie 1977, 111f.
27 MacKie 1977, 131.
28 Thom & Thom 1975, 113; 1978b, 137.
29 MacKie 1977, 187, 203.
30 Thom & Thom 1978b, 172. MacKie's suggested date for the solstitial site of Kintraw is also much earlier than its astronomical date (cf. MacKie 1977, 81, 224).
31 Atkinson 1975, 45, 51.
32 See, for example, Piggott 1978; Fleming 1978. These reviews were kindly drawn to my attention by Prof. G. E. Daniel.
33 Thom 1967, 133. Similar considerations apply to the sites on Burnmoor, Cumberland (Burl 1976, 96).
34 Roy *et al.* 1963, 66.
35 Thom & Thom 1973, 120.
36 MacKie 1974, 171.
37 Thom 1967, 135; 1971, 114; Thom & Thom 1979, 45.
38 Hawkins & White 1966, 199; Eddy 1974b.
39 Thom 1971, 9.

Bibliography

Note: *where more than one edition of a book is included, the edition to which the notes refer is marked by a dagger* (†).

Aaboe, A. 1974: 'Scientific Astronomy in Antiquity', *Phil. Trans. R. Soc. Lond.* A 276, 21–42.

Angell, I. O. 1976: 'Stone Circles: Megalithic Mathematics or Neolithic Nonsense?', *Math. Gaz.* 60, 189–93.

1977: 'Are Stone Circles Circles?', *Science and Archaeol.* no. 19, 16–19.

1978: 'Megalithic Mathematics, Ancient Almanacs or Neolithic Nonsense', *Bull. Inst. Math. Applic.* 14, 253–8.

& Barber, J. W. 1977: 'An Algorithm for Fitting Circles and Ellipses to Megalithic Stone Rings', *Science and Archaeol.* no. 20, 11–16.

Atkinson, R. J. C. 1966: 'Moonshine on Stonehenge', *Antiquity* 40, 212–16.

1966b: 'Decoder Misled?', *Nature* 210, 1302.

1967: in 'Hoyle on Stonehenge: Some Comments', *Antiquity* 41, 92–5.

1974: 'Neolithic Science and Technology', *Phil. Trans. R. Soc. Lond.* A 276, 123–31.

1975: 'Megalithic Astronomy – A Prehistorian's Comments', *J. Hist. Astron.* 6, 42–52.

1976: 'The Stonehenge Stations', *J. Hist. Astron.* 7, 142–4.

1977: 'Interpreting Stonehenge', *Nature* 265, 11.

1978: 'Some New Measurements on Stonehenge', *Nature* 275, 50–2.

1979: *Stonehenge*, Penguin paperback, Harmondsworth.

1979b: (addendum to Moir 1979), *Antiquity* 53, 129.

1979c: 'The Thoms' New Book', *J. Hist. Astron.* 10, S99–102.

Aveni, A. F. 1979: in K. Brecher & M. Feirtag (eds.), *Astronomy of the Ancients*, Cambridge (Mass.) and London.

1979b: 'Astronomy in Ancient Mesoamerica', in Krupp 1979.

Bailey, M. E., Cooke, J. A., Few, R. W., Morgan, J. G. & Ruggles, C. L. N. 1975: 'Survey of Three Megalithic Sites in Argyllshire', *Nature* 253, 431–3.

Baity, E. C. 1973: 'Archaeoastronomy and Ethnoastronomy So Far', *Curr. Anthrop.* 14, 389–449.

Barber, J. W. 1972: *The Stone Circles of Cork and Kerry: A Study*, M.A. Thesis, National University of Ireland, University College, Cork.

1973: 'The Orientation of the Recumbent-Stone Circles of the South-West of Ireland', *J. Kerry Archaeol. Hist. Soc.*, no. 6, 26–39.

Behrend, M. 1976: in 'Discussion of Dr Freeman's Paper', *J. R. Stat. Soc.* A 139, 44.

Berendzen, R., Hart, R. & Seeley, D. 1976: *Man Discovers the Galaxies*, New York.

Bibby, J. S. 1974: 'Petrofabric Analysis', *Phil. Trans. R. Soc. Lond.* A 276, 191–4.

Broadbent, S. R. 1955: 'Quantum Hypotheses', *Biometrika* 42, 45–57.

1955b: in 'Discussion on Professor Thom's Paper', *J. R. Stat. Soc.* A 118, 292–3.

1956: 'Examination of a Quantum Hypothesis Based on a Single Set of Data', *Biometrika* 43, 32–44.

Burl, H. A. W. 1971: 'Two "Scottish" Stone Circles in Northumberland', *Archaeol. Ael.* 49, 37–51.

1972: 'Stone Circles and Ring-Cairns', *Scot. Archaeol. Forum* 4, 31–47.

1974: 'The Recumbent Stone Circles of North-East Scotland', *Proc. Soc. Ant. Scot.* 102, 56–81.

1976: *The Stone Circles of the British Isles*, New Haven and London.

1979: *Prehistoric Avebury*, New Haven and London.

1980: 'Science or Symbolism – Problems of Archaeo-astronomy' *Antiquity*, 54, 191–200.

& Freeman, P. R. 1977: 'Local Units of Measurement in Prehistoric Britain', *Antiquity* 51, 152–4.

Chanter, J. F. & Worth, R. H. 1906: 'The Rude Stone Monuments of Exmoor and its Borders. Part II', *Rep. Trans. Devon Ass. Advmt. Sci.* 38, 538–52.

Charrière, G. 1961: 'Stonehenge: Rythmes Architecturaux et Orientation', *Bull. Soc. Préhist. Franç.* 58, 276–9.

Childe, V. G. 1955: in 'Discussion on Professor Thom's Paper', *J. R. Stat. Soc.* A 118, 293–4.

Coe, M. D. 1980: *The Maya*, 2nd edn, London and New York; also Penguin paperback, Harmondsworth 1971.†

Colton, R. & Martin, R. L. 1967: 'Eclipse Cycles and Eclipses at Stonehenge', *Nature* 213, 476–8.

1969: 'Eclipse Prediction at Stonehenge', *Nature* 221, 1011–12.

Cooke, J. A., Few, R. W., Morgan, J. G. & Ruggles, C. L. N. 1977: 'Indicated Declinations at the Callanish Megalithic Sites', *J. Hist. Astron.* 8, 113–33.

Cowan, T. M. 1970: 'Megalithic Rings: Their Design Construction', *Science* 168, no. 3929, 321–5.

Crawford, G. I. 1976: in 'Discussion of Dr Freeman's Paper', *J. R. Stat. Soc.* A 139, 41–2.

Daniel, G. E. 1963: *The Megalith Builders of Western Europe*, 2nd edn, London.

Devoir, A. 1909: 'Urzeitliche Astronomie in Westeuropa', *Mannus* 1, 71–82.

Dibble, W. E. 1976: 'A Possible Pythagorean Triangle at Stonehenge', *J. Hist. Astron.* 7, 141–2.

Dick, O. L. 1972: *Aubrey's Brief Lives* Penguin paperback, Harmondsworth†; also Secker & Warburg, London 1949.

Eddy, J. A. 1974: 'Astronomical Alignment of the Big Horn Medicine Wheel', *Science* 184, 1035–43.

1974b: 'Popular Astro-Archaeology', *J. Hist. Astron.* 5, 66.

1977: 'Medicine Wheels and Plains Indian Astronomy', *Tech. Rev.* (MIT) 80, 18–31.

1979: 'Archaeo-Astronomy of North America', in Krupp 1979.

Fleming, A. 1975: 'Megalithic Astronomy: A Prehistorian's View', *Nature* 255, 575.

1978: (Review of MacKie 1977b) *Antiquity* 52, 158–9.

Freeman, P. R. 1975: 'Carnac Probabilities Corrected', *J. Hist. Astron.* 6, 219.

1976: 'A Bayesian Analysis of the Megalithic Yard', *J. R. Stat. Soc.* A 139, 20–35.

1977: 'Thom's Survey of the Avebury Ring', *J. Hist. Astron.* 8, 134–5.

Freeman, P. R. & Elmore, W. 1979: 'A Test for the Significance of Astronomical Alignments', *J. Hist. Astron.* 10, S86–96.

Freer, R. & Quinio, J.-L. 1977: 'The Kerlescan Alignments', *J. Hist. Astron.* 8, 52–4.

Gingerich, O. 1977: 'The Basic Astronomy of Stonehenge', *Tech. Rev.* (MIT) 80, 64–73.

Hadingham, E. 1975: *Circles and Standing Stones*, London and New York.

Hammersley, J. M. 1955: in 'Discussion on Professor Thom's Paper' *J. R. Stat. Soc.* A 118, 291–2.

    & Morton, K. W. 1954: 'Poor Man's Monte Carlo', *J. R. Stat. Soc.* B 16, 23–38.

Hammerton, M. 1971: 'The Megalithic Fathom: A Suggestion', *Antiquity* 45, 302.

Hawkes, J. 1967: 'God in the Machine', *Antiquity* 41, 174–80.

Hawkins, G. S. 1963: 'Stonehenge Decoded', *Nature* 200, 306–8.

1964: 'Stonehenge: A Neolithic Computer', *Nature* 202, 1258–61.

1965: 'Callanish, a Scottish Stonehenge', *Science* 147, 127–30.

1965b: 'Sun, Moon, Men, and Stones', *Amer. Sci.* 53, 391–408.

1967: 'Stonehenge 56 Year Cycle', *Nature* 215, 604–5.

1967b: in 'Hoyle on Stonehenge: Some Comments', *Antiquity* 41, 91–2.

1968: 'Astro-Archaeology', *Vistas Astron.* 10, 45–88.

1973: *Beyond Stonehenge*, London.

1974: 'Astronomical Alinements in Britain, Egypt and Peru', *Phil. Trans. R. Soc. Lond.* A 276, 157–67.

    & White, J. B. 1966: *Stonehenge Decoded*, London (New York 1965); also Fontana paperback, London 1970.†

Heggie, D. C. 1972: 'Megalithic Lunar Observatories: An Astronomer's View', *Antiquity* 46, 43–8.

Hogg, A. H. A. 1968: (review of Thom 1967) *Archaeol. Camb.* 117, 207–10.

1974: in 'Contributions to the Discussion on Ancient Astronomy: The Unwritten Evidence', *Phil. Trans. R. Soc. Lond.* A 276, 267.

Hoyle, F. 1966: 'Speculations on Stonehenge', *Antiquity* 40, 262–76.

1966b: 'Stonehenge – An Eclipse Predictor', *Nature* 211, 454–6.

1972: *From Stonehenge to Modern Cosmology*, San Francisco.

1977: *On Stonehenge*, San Francisco and London.

Kendall, D. G. 1971: (review of Thom 1971) *Antiquity* 45, 310–13.

1974: 'Hunting Quanta', *Phil. Trans. R. Soc. Lond.* A 276, 231–66.

1976: in 'Discussion of Dr Freeman's Paper', *J. R. Stat. Soc.* A 139, 37–9.

1977: 'Hunting Quanta' in *Proc. Symp. to Honour J. Neyman*, Warsaw.

Kendall, M. G. 1955: in 'Discussion on Professor Thom's Paper', *J. R. Stat. Soc.* A 118, 291.

Kent, J. 1976: in 'Discussion of Dr Freeman's Paper', *J. R. Stat. Soc.* A 139, 39–40.

King-Hele, D. G. 1974: in 'Concluding Remarks', *Phil. Trans. R. Soc. Lond.* A 276, 273–5.

Krupp, E. C. (ed.) 1979: *In Search of Ancient Astronomies*, London (New York 1977).

Lamb, H. H. 1974: 'Climate, Vegetation and Forest Limits in Early Civilized Times', *Phil. Trans. R. Soc. Lond.* A 276, 195–230.

Lancaster Brown, P. 1976: *Megaliths, Myths and Men*, Poole, Dorset.

Lewis, A. L. 1886: 'On Three Stone Circles in Cumberland, with Some Further Observations on the Relation of Stone Circles to Adjacent Hills and Outlying Stones', *J. Anthrop. Inst.* 15, 471–81.

1892: 'Stone Circles of Britain', *Archaeol. J.* 49, 136–54.

1895: 'Prehistoric Remains in Cornwall', *J. Anthrop. Inst.* 25, 2–16.

1900: 'The Stone Circles of Scotland', *J. R. Anthrop. Inst.* 30, 56–73.

Lewis, D. 1974: 'Voyaging Stars: Aspects of Polynesian and Micronesian Astronomy', *Phil. Trans. R. Soc. Lond.* A 276, 133–48.

Lockyer, J. N. 1894: *The Dawn of Astronomy*, London.

1905: 'Notes on Stonehenge. I.-Conditions and Traditions', *Nature* 71, 297–300.

1905b: 'Notes on Stonehenge. IV.-The Earliest Circles (continued)', *Nature* 71, 391–3.

1906: *Stonehenge and Other British Stone Monuments Astronomically Considered*, London.

1909: *Stonehenge*, 2nd edn, London.

    & Penrose, F. C. 1901: 'An Attempt to Ascertain the Date of the Original Construction of Stonehenge from its Orientation', *Proc. R. Soc. Lond.* 69, 137–47.

Lynch, A. 1976: *The Stone Alignments of (Counties) Cork and Kerry*, M. A. Thesis, National University of Ireland, University College, Cork.

Lysaght, A. M. 1974: 'Joseph Banks at Skara Brae and Stennis, Orkney, 1772', *Notes Rec. R. Soc. Lond.* 28, 221–34.

McCluskey, S. C. 1977: 'The Astronomy of the Hopi Indians', *J. Hist. Astron.* 8, 174–95.

MacKie, E. W. 1974: 'Archaeological Tests on Supposed Prehistoric Astronomical Sites in Scotland', *Phil. Trans. R. Soc. Lond.* A 276, 169–94.

1977: *Science and Society in Prehistoric Britain*, London and New York.

1977b: *The Megalith Builders*, Oxford.

Maistrov, L. E. 1974: in 'Contributions to the Discussion on Ancient Astronomy: The Unwritten Evidence', *Phil. Trans. R. Soc. Lond.* A 276, 267–8.

Marshack, A. 1972: 'Upper Palaeolithic Notation and Symbol', *Science* 178, 817–28.

Maxia, C. & Proverbio, E. 1972: 'Astroarchaeology and Megalithic Civilizations', *Scientia* 107, 1–5.

1973: 'Orientamenti Astronomici di Monumenti Nuragici', *Ist. Lomb. (Rend. Sc.)* A 107, 298–311.

Michell, J. 1977: *A Little History of Astroarchaeology*, London (published as *Secrets of the Stones*, New York 1977).

Moir, G. 1979: 'Hoyle on Stonehenge', *Antiquity* 53, 124–9.

1980: 'A Review of Megalithic Lunar Lines', *Northern Archaeol.* 1, 14–22.

& Ruggles, C. L. N. & Norris, R. 1980: 'Megalithic Science and Some Scottish Site Plans', *Antiquity* 54, 37–43.

Morgan, J. G. & Ruggles, C. L. N. 1976: 'Indications at the Cefn Gwernffrwd Site', *Archaeol. Camb.* 125, 162–5.

Morrison, L. V. 1980: 'On the Analysis of Megalithic Lunar Sightlines in Scotland', *J. Hist. Astron.*, 11, **S.** 65-77.

Müller, R. 1936: *Himmelskundliche Ortung auf nordisch-germanischem Boden*, Leipzig.

1970: *Der Himmel über dem Menschen der Steinzeit*, Berlin.

Newall, R. A. 1967: in 'Hoyle on Stonehenge: Some Comments', *Antiquity* 41, 98.

Newham, C. A. 1966: 'Stonehenge – A Neolithic "Observatory"', *Nature* 211, 456–8.

1967: in 'Hoyle on Stonehenge: Some Comments', *Antiquity* 41, 96–7.

1972: *The Astronomical Significance of Stonehenge*, Leeds.

Newton, R. R. 1974: 'Introduction to Some Basic Astronomical Concepts', *Phil. Trans. R. Soc. Lond.* A 276, 5–20.

O'Nuallain, S. 1975: 'The Stone Circle Complex of Cork and Kerry', *J. R. Soc. Antiquaries Ireland* 105, 83–131.

Patrick, J. D. 1974: 'Midwinter Sunrise at Newgrange', *Nature* 249, 517–19.

1974b: *Investigation into the Astronomical and Geometrical Characteristics of the Passage-Grave Cemeteries at the Boyne Valley, Carrowkeel and Loughcrew*, M. Sc. thesis, University of Dublin.

1975: 'A Critical Assessment of Megalithic Science', a paper read at a conference on *Ceremonial, Science and Society in Prehistoric Britain*, University of Glasgow, unpublished.

1975b: 'Megalithic Exegesis: A Comment', *Irish Archaeol. Res. Forum* 2, 9–14.

1979: 'A Reassessment of the Lunar Observatory Hypothesis for the Kilmartin Stones', *J. Hist. Astron.* 10, S78–85.

1979b: *An Information Measure Comparative Analysis of Megalithic Geometries*, Ph. D. thesis, Monash University.

& Butler, C. J. 1974: 'On the Interpretation of the Carnac Menhirs and Alignments by A. and A. S. Thom', *Irish Archaeol. Res. Forum* 1, 29–39.

& Wallace, C. S. 1979: 'An Information Theory Test for Thom's Megalithic Geometry', unpublished manuscript.

Penny, A. & Wood, J. E. 1973: 'The Dorset Cursus Complex – A Neolithic Astronomical Observatory?', *Archaeol. J.* 130, 44–76.

1974: 'Astronomical Alinements Associated with the Dorset Cursus', *Phil. Trans. R. Soc. Lond.* A 276, 268–70.

Piggott, S. 1968: *The Druids*, London and New York; also Penguin paperback, Harmondsworth 1974.†

1974: in 'Concluding Remarks', *Phil. Trans. R. Soc. Lond.* A 276, 275–6.

1978: (Review of MacKie 1977), *Antiquity* 52, 62–3.

Ponting, G. & Ponting, M. 1977: *The Standing Stones of Callanish*, printed at Stornoway.

Porteous, H. L. 1973: 'Megalithic Yard or Megalithic Myth?', *J. Hist. Astron.* 4, 22–4.

Renfrew, C. 1973: *Before Civilization*, London and New York; also Penguin paperback, Harmondsworth 1976.†

Reyman, J. E. 1973: in 'Comments' on Thom, Thom, Merritt & Merritt 1973, *Curr. Anthrop.* 14, 452.

Robinson, J. H. 1970: 'Sunrise and Moonrise at Stonehenge', *Nature* 225, 1236–7.

Roy, A. E., McGrail, N. & Carmichael, R. 1963: 'A New Survey of the Tormore Circles', *Trans. Glasgow Archaeol. Soc.* N. S. 15, 59–67.

Ruggles, C. L. N. 1981: 'A Critical Examination of the Alleged' Megalithic Lunar Observatories', in Ruggles, C. L. N. & Whittle, A. W. R. (eds.), *Megalithic Astronomy and Society*, Brit. Archaeol. Rep., Oxford.

Russell, H. N., Dugan, R. S. & Stewart, J. Q. 1945: *Astronomy*, rev. edn, vol. 1, Boston.

Sadler, D. H. 1966: 'Prediction of Eclipses', *Nature* 211, 1119–21.

Smiley, C. H. 1973: in 'Comments' on Thom, Thom, Merritt & Merritt 1973, *Curr. Anthrop.* 14, 453.

Smith, I. F. 1974: 'The Neolithic', in C. Renfrew (ed.), *British Prehistory*, London.

Somerville, T. B. 1912: 'Prehistoric Monuments in the Outer Hebrides, and Their Astronomical Significance', *J. R. Anthrop. Inst.* 42, 23–52.

1923: 'Instances of Orientation in Prehistoric Monuments of the British Isles', *Archaeologia* 73, 193–224.

1927: 'Orientation', *Antiquity* 1, 31–41.

Stephan, P. 1916: 'Vorgeschichtliche Sternkunde und Zeiteinteilung', *Mannus* 7, 213–48.

Thatcher, A. R. 1976: 'The Station Stones at Stonehenge', *Antiquity* 50, 144–5.

Thom, A. 1954: 'The Solar Observatories of Megalithic Man', *J. Brit. Astron. Ass.* 64, 396–404.

1955: 'A Statistical Examination of the Megalithic Sites in Britain', *J. R. Stat. Soc.* A 118, 275–95.

1961: 'The Geometry of Megalithic Man', *Mathl. Gaz.* 45, 83–93.

1961b: 'The Egg Shaped Standing Stone Rings of Britain', *Archives Int. d'Hist. Sci.* 14, 291–303.

1962: 'The Megalithic Unit of Length', *J. R. Stat. Soc.* A 125, 243–51.

1964: 'The Larger Units of Length of Megalithic Man', *J. R. Stat. Soc.* A 127, 527–33.

1966: 'Megalithic Astronomy: Indications in Standing Stones', *Vistas Astron.* 7, 1–57.

1966b: 'Megaliths and Mathematics', *Antiquity* 40, 121–8.

1967: *Megalithic Sites in Britain*, Oxford.

1967b: in 'Hoyle on Stonehenge: Some Comments', *Antiquity* 41, 95–6.

1968: 'The Metrology and Geometry of Cup and Ring Marks', *Systematics* 6, 173–89.

1969: 'The Geometry of Cup-and-Ring Marks', *Trans. Anc. Monuments Soc.* n.s. 16, 77–87.

1969b: 'The Lunar Observatories of Megalithic Man', *Vistas Astron.* 11, 1–29.

1971: *Megalithic Lunar Observatories*, Oxford.

1974: 'Astronomical Significance of Prehistoric Monuments in Western Europe', *Phil. Trans. R. Soc. Lond.* A 276, 149–56.

1974b: 'A Megalithic Lunar Observatory in Islay', *J. Hist. Astron.* 5, 50–1.

1977: 'Megalithic Astronomy', a paper read on 6th September 1977, *R. Inst. Brit. Architects.*

1978: 'The Distances Between Stones in Stone Rows', *J. R. Stat. Soc.* A 141, 253–7.

Thom, A. & Merritt, R. L. 1978: 'Some Megalithic Sites in Shetland', *J. Hist. Astron.* 9, 54–60.

Thom, A. & Thom, A. S. 1971: 'The Astronomical Significance of the Large Carnac Menhirs', *J. Hist. Astron.* 2, 147–60.

1972: 'The Carnac Alignments', *J. Hist. Astron.* 3, 11–26.

1972b: 'The Uses of the Alignments at Le Ménec Carnac', *J. Hist. Astron.* 3, 151–64.

1973: 'A Megalithic Lunar Observatory in Orkney: The Ring of Brogar and its Cairns', *J. Hist. Astron.* 4, 111–23.

1973b: 'The Kerlescan Cromlechs', *J. Hist. Astron.* 4, 168–73.

1974: 'The Kermario Alignments', *J. Hist. Astron.* 5, 30–47.

1974b: 'Reply by A. Thom and A. S. Thom', *Irish Archaeol. Res. Forum* 1, 40–4.

1975: 'Further Work on the Brogar Lunar Observatory', *J. Hist. Astron.* 6, 100–14.

1977: 'The Megalithic Yard', *Measurement and Control* 10, 488–92.

1977b: 'Megalithic Astronomy', *J. Navigation* 30, 1–14.

1977c: 'A Fourth Lunar Foresight for the Brogar Ring', *J. Hist. Astron.* 8, 54–5.

1978: 'A Reconsideration of the Lunar Sites in Britain', *J. Hist. Astron.* 9, 170–9.

1978b: *Megalithic Remains in Britain and Brittany*, Oxford.

1979: 'Rings and Menhirs: Geometry and Astronomy in the Neolithic Age', in Krupp 1979.

1979b: 'The Standing Stones in Argyllshire', *Glasgow Archaeol. J.* 6, 5–10.

1980: 'A New Study of All Megalithic Lunar Lines', *J. Hist. Astron.*, 11, S. 78-89.

& Thom, A. S. 1976: 'Avebury (2): The West Kennet Avenue', *J. Hist. Astron.* 7, 193–7.

Thom, A., Thom, A. S. & Foord, T. R. 1976: 'Avebury (1): A New Assessment of the Geometry and Metrology of the Ring', *J. Hist. Astron.* 7, 183–92.

Thom, A., Thom, A. S. & Gorrie, J. M. 1976: 'The Two Megalithic Lunar Observatories at Carnac', *J. Hist. Astron.* 7, 11–26.

Thom, A., Thom, A. S., Merritt, R. L. & Merritt, A. L. 1973: 'The Astronomical Significance of the Crucuno Stone Rectangle', *Curr. Anthrop.* 14, 450–1.

Thom, A., Thom, A. S. & Thom, A. S. 1974: 'Stonehenge', *J. Hist. Astron.* 5, 71–90.

1975: 'Stonehenge as a Possible Lunar Observatory', *J. Hist. Astron.* 6, 19–30.

Thom, A. S. & Foord, T. R. 1977: 'The Island of Eday', *J. Hist. Astron.* 8, 198–9.

Thompson, J. W. 1976: in 'Discussion of Dr Freeman's Paper', *J. R. Stat. Soc.* A 139, 35–6.

Trotter, A. P. 1927: 'Stonehenge as an Astronomical Instrument', *Antiquity* 1, 42–53.

Whitmell, C. T. 1901: 'The Date of Stonehenge', *Nature* 65, 128–9.

Windle, B. C. A. 1912: 'On Certain Megalithic Remains Immediately Surrounding Lough Gur, County Limerick', *Proc. R. Irish Acad.* 30, 283–306.

Wood, J. E. 1978: *Sun, Moon and Standing Stones*, Oxford.

& Penny, A. 1975: 'A Megalithic Observatory on Dartmoor', *Nature* 257, 205–7.

Index

New county and regional names are given in brackets after old county names (where these differ) or the names of islands. **Boldface** numerals refer to principal entries and *italic* numerals to illustrations and their captions.